PRAISE FOR HERBAL DIPLOMATS

"Herbal Diplomats provides the reader with a fascinating and very readable historical overview of the contributions and role of women in the healing arts, foundational to modern nursing. Dr. Libster weaves a tapestry of competencies and care in a trilogy presentation of nurses from the Shakers, the Latter-day Saints, and the Sisters of Charity from Emmitsburg, Maryland. The outcome is a captivating treatment of the development of nursing, changes in the prevailing domestic system of healthcare, and emergence of a dominant medical culture involving physicians of various orientations. The result defined a turning point in medical freedom and self-care, resulting in "not only the prevention of disease but of the prolongation of life."

— BETTY ANN MCNEIL, D.C., ARCHIVIST
Daughters of Charity Archives | Emmitsburg, Maryland (USA)

"Dr. Libster 's work is an important contribution to an area of study in the history of nursing and health care in the United States. This is a work that has patiently waited 150 years to have its story told. Medical and nursing care of the nineteenth century commonly employed the use of herbal medicines. Dr. Libster offers a fine overview of that tradition. She skillfully integrates the history of the tradition of herbal medicine of the mid and late nineteenth century with the history of nursing identity and practice of the time. Then she offers the stories of three specific religious groups who each developed a unique tradition of nursing practice: the Shaker Infirmary and Community Nurses, the pioneer nurses and midwives of the Church of Jesus Christ of Latter-day Saints (Mormons), and the Sisters of Charity and early American Catholic hospitals. Though current members of any of the three groups may recognize Dr. Libster's orientation as an "observer," rather than member, she shows considerable sensitivity and facility in explaining the history of these three groups. She tells their stories in the context of the time regarding medical practice and nursing practice."

— ELAINE SORENSEN MARSHALL, R.N., PH.D.
Dean and Professor | College of Nursing | Brigham Young University

"Histories of medical practice written during the 19th century focus primarily on the activities of male physicians and overlook the critical roles played by women as healers and caregivers. In Herbal Diplomats, Martha Libster re-evaluates the contributions made by women to healthcare by looking at three distinct groups of nurses/care-givers. Using the journals and receipt books left by Shakers, the Church of Jesus Christ of Latter-day Saints, and the Sisters of Charity, Libster is able to highlight the prominence of women's nursing activities in the health and healing of their families and communities over a dependence on academic medicine. Her insightful blending of women's traditional domestic roles with their understanding of botanicals helps to show how these women were able to provide a system of medical care they could use at home, how they shared their knowledge with other women in their communities, and how they informed the developing practices of the larger healthcare system."

— SHARON DUANE KOOMLER
Curator of Education and Collections | Shaker Museum and Library | Old Chatham, NY

Also By Martha Libster

Demonstrating Care: The Art of Integrative Nursing

The Integrative Herb Guide for Nurses (Book and CD-Rom with videos)

Sister Matilda Coskery's Advices Concerning the Sick:
A Healing Heritage of Holistic Nursing Care
(coming in Summer 2005)

For additional information and courses about nurse - herbalism:
www.GoldenAppleHealingArts.com
www.NursesHerbal.net

Herbal Diplomats

The Contribution of Early American Nurses (1830–1860) to Nineteenth-Century Health Care Reform and the Botanical Medical Movement

Martha M. Libster, Ph.D., R.N.

Golden Apple Publications

Editor: Linda DeMasi Indexer: Medea Minnich
Book design and Illustrations: Mark Gelotte, www.maeric.com

Printed in the United States of America by Thomson Shore.

Publisher's Cataloging in Publication Data
Libster, Martha M, 1960-
Herbal Diplomats: The Contribution of Early American Nurses (1830–1860) to Nineteenth-Century Health Care Reform and the Botanical Medical Movement / Martha M. Libster, Ph.D, R.N.
xiv, 386 p.:ill., p. cm.
Includes bibliographical references and index
ISBN 0-9755018-0-1
1. Medicine, Botanic–United States–History.
2. Nursing–United States–History 3. Women–United States –History I. Title: Herbal Diplomats

---

The historical information regarding the therapeutic use of botanicals included in Herbal Diplomats is not intended to be a substitute for the services of a health care professional nor is it meant to authorize or endorse the use of herbs by the public or health professionals unskilled in the use of botanical therapies. Neither the author nor the publisher is responsible for any consequences incurred by those employing the historical remedies reported in this text. Herb knowledge is constantly changing. Different opinions by experts, continued research and clinical results, individual circumstances and possible error in preparing this publication require the reader to use their judgment and current information when making decisions which in anyway might be construed as related to information contained in this book.

For my parents, who started me on the quest . . .
and for my beloved Harold, without whom
I could never have claimed the treasure.

CONTENTS

Acknowledgements

This book would not have been possible without the support and vision of many people. While the responsibility for the accuracy of the work rests solely with me, I would like to thank the following people and institutions for their incredible support, patience, enthusiasm, and guidance: Professor Anne Digby, my rudder across the pond, who always believed that I would find the herbal "needle in the haystack;" Olga Church and Mary Chamberlain, for their understanding and careful review of this work; and Helen Sweet and Harriet Irvine, who gave me support during my research. This book would also not have been possible without the early cheerleading of Marlaine Smith and Denny Webster, who believed me when I told them there was a story I wanted to tell and encouraged me with heartfelt blessings. I especially thank Suzanne Thurman, Elaine Sorensen Marshall, and Sister Betty Ann McNeil, who reviewed the chapters related to nurses with careful attention to detail and without the benefit of reading the whole story.

The following people and their organizations were ever so helpful in offering me access to archives, sharing ideas, and pulling together historical resources: Starlyn D'Angelo, Jerry V. Grant, and Sharon Koomler, Old Chatham Shaker Village; Renee Fox, Canterbury Village; Michael Volmar, Fruitlands Museum; Mary Jo Groppe Shaker Historical Society and Museum, Shaker Heights, Ohio; Tina Agren and Michael Graham, Sabbathday Lake Shaker Village; Christian Goodwillie, Hancock Shaker Village; the staff at Western Reserve Historical Society, Cleveland, Ohio; Jean Solensky, Winterthur Museum and Library; Ronald Watt, Jay Burrup, Jeff Johnson, and other staff, LDS Church Library, Salt Lake City, Utah; Edith Menna, Daughters of the Utah Pioneers staff, Salt Lake City, Utah, and Fillmore, Utah; Janelle, Utah Historical Society; Stan Larson and staff, Marriott Library, University of Utah; Kathy Connick and staff, Lloyd Library, Cincinnati, Ohio; Ellen Shea, Sarah Hutcheon, and staff, Schlesinger Library,

Radcliffe Institute for Advanced Study, Cambridge, Massachusetts; Anne Shepherd, Cincinnati Historical Society; Billie Broaddus, Cincinnati Medical Heritage Center; the staff at University of Colorado Denison Library; the staff of the Wellcome Library, London, England; Ed Hood, Christy White, Daphne Stevens, and staff, Sturbridge Village, Massachusetts; Jack Eckert, Joan Thomas, and staff, Countway Library of Medicine, Harvard University, Boston, Massachusetts; the staff at the American Antiquarian Society, Worcester, Massachusetts; Rich Behles, University of Maryland Medical Center Archives; Sr. Betty Ann McNeil D.C., Bonnie Weatherly, and staff, Daughters of Charity Archives, Emmitsburg, Maryland; Father John Schipp and staff, Old Cathedral Library, Vincennes, Indiana; the staff at the Vincentian Studies Institute, DePaul University, Chicago, Illinois; Sister Margaret Ahl, Archivist, Daughters of Charity Albany Province, Albany, NY; Sister Genevieve Keusenkothen, Archivist Marillac Provincial House Daughters of Charity.

I also would like to acknowledge the input of the following scholars: Mary Ann Haagen, Steven Foster, James Duke, Lowell Levin, Carol Cornwall-Madsen, David Whittaker, Laurel Ulrich, Peter Benes, Marge Bruchac, Margaret Moss, Reverend Al Ledoux, and Reverend Edward Udovic, C.M.

My friends and family have been a tremendous support through many years of research and writing. Without them I would not have finished the task at hand.

Thank you from the bottom of my heart to Deb, who was always there with the inspiration for a vision whenever I needed it; Michael, who helped me find my own process; Fradelle, for her infusions of victory; JoAnn, Priscilla, Lori, and all of my friends, who are the reason I got through it all day by day; my family, for wondering and caring when it really counted; my patients, without whom I would have lost my sense of humanity and my purpose; and last but not least, I must acknowledge the plants, for their constant support of my own health and for their beauty that continuosly inspires me.

FORWARD

This is a very timely historical study because, like so much present-day discussion, it focuses on what complementary medicine can offer. The author's research into the forgotten achievements of female community nurses and their skilled use of indigenous botanical remedies also alerts us to the important roles assumed by women as caregivers in the past. Recognized as nurses by their communities, these strong women assumed a role as cultural diplomats or mediators in bringing their caring skills from the private sphere of the home into a more public arena.

Discovering the healing therapies such individuals used has been a considerable research achievement. The author has provided detailed case studies of three fascinating groups of early botanical nurses who worked in the northern United States within the Shaker community, the Church of Jesus Christ of Latter-day Saints, and the Catholic Sisters of Charity. She shows how the forgotten story of these mid-nineteenth-century nurses provides a valuable historical extension to the conventional interpretation that American nursing began with nursing organization during the Civil War or the introduction of the Nightingale model reforms into hospital training schools.

Reading this absorbing book opens up new historical vistas. The narrative should fascinate those readers who are broadly interested in women's cultural history, as well as those whose interest is more specifically in nursing history or in complementary medicine.

— Anne Digby
Research Professor in History,
Oxford Brookes University, UK.

FORWARD

Author Martha Libster, nurse, herbalist and historian, meticulously traces the origins of nursing in America and weaves the advent of nursing with the Botanical Medical Movement and the unfolding of western allopathic or 'modern' medicine. Though the emphasis of Martha Libster's well researched book is on nursing and nurses, *Herbal Diplomats* is far more than a historical documentation of nursing in America. It is also a history of American herbalism as practiced by the early settlers and medical practitioners of this country and the unfolding of modern western allopathic medicine. Most importantly, *Herbal Diplomats* brings to the forefront a number of important questions about the role of nurses in modern health care and questions some of the practices of modern medicine. Though her emphasis is on the role that nurses play in our health care system, *Herbal Diplomats* really addresses the entire health care system, its strengths and faults . The author has provided us with a brilliantly documented, thoughtful and thought provoking book on our modern medical system as it has unfolded in the last two centuries and how it might better serve the needs of the American public by incorporating a "tiered system of health care that embraces an integrative approach to health care." Martha Libster is in the finest sense a 'bridge walker', a person who, as she aptly describes in *Herbal Diplomats* "acts as a bridge between the 'modern' western model of medical training" and the traditional practice of community healers and herbalists.

— Rosemary Gladstar
Herbalist and Teacher
Author of *Gladstar's Family Herbal*
Founder of Sage Mountain Retreat
Center & Native Plant Preserve

CHAPTER 1

INTRODUCTION: HARVESTING A HISTORY OF WOMEN HEALERS

On February 22, 1856, Martha Spence Heywood (1812–1873), a Utah pioneer, wrote in her journal[1] about caring for her precious children during serious illnesses of measles and canker. Her son, Nealy, took sick first, for which she gave him saffron and sage tea. She bathed him with saleratus[2] water to "bring out" the measles, for which she also continued administering the tea. Martha stayed by her child day and night, a practice known as "watching." As Nealy got better, Martha's daughter, Sarepta, came down with the rash but no canker. Martha consulted an elder in her church about Sarepta. The elder rendered the opinion that Sarepta's canker was not visible because it was in her stomach and the rash had "turned in." As Martha watched her daughter struggle with the illness, she observed that the "chief difficulty lay in her breathing and not in the canker."

Martha went to Sister Bentley for lobelia, an herb known by the Utah pioneers to help breathing. However when she got the lobelia, she must have received a bit of important advice from Sister Bentley too, because she wrote that it was not "wise" to give her daughter the lobelia because she had given the canker medicine "that had blue vitriol in it." Sister Bentley seemed to know that blue vitriol and lobelia were not to be given at the same time, so Martha chose to give her daughter castor oil instead. She also anointed Sarepta with oil consecrated by her church's elders. After a few days, Martha gave Sarepta doses of lobelia tincture. She knew that in order for the herb to help her daughter's breathing it must "operate." With lobelia, this meant that when a therapeutic or an operating dose was reached, the person taking the tincture should vomit. Unfortunately, the lobelia did not "operate" in Sarepta, even after several hours.

Martha then gave Sarepta rhubarb to "work off" the lobelia. The lobelia operated, and with it Sarepta passed some phlegm. In caring for Sarepta, Martha discovered hard phlegm stuck to her daughter's mouth, which convinced her that Sarepta's difficulty was in her chest. As was often customary when caring for a family member with lung disease, Martha then put onions under Sarepta', arms, and with the assistance of her neighbor, Mrs. Bigler, she put Sarepta's feet into water. After administering these remedies, Sarepta took a turn for the better, and she seemed to breathe easier. Louisa Barber came to watch the little girl at night, so after days of watching and caring for her sick children, Martha could finally go to bed, where she fell into a heavy slumber.

It was not unusual in early and mid-nineteenth-century America for women to care for their families or another's family in this way. In the early and mid-nineteenth century, health care was not synonymous with professional medical care, as it is today in the United States. Before the development of American schools of medicine and nursing and the emergence of pharmaceutical companies, American women were the ones who doctored and nursed their families and produced their own healing remedies in their homes. It was considered good citizenry to be one's own "doctor." The title of "doctor" did not hold the same meaning as it does in the twenty-first century. Americans used the term to refer to a community healer, even if that healer did not have a formal, university-based education. They also used the term *doctor* to refer to a university-educated man who held a diploma in medicine. In the mid-nineteenth century, diplomaed physicians were, for the most part, educated in Britain, usually in Edinburgh or London. University-trained physicians were called "Regulars." During the decades leading up to the Civil War, there were few Regulars, especially in rural areas. Americans often cared for themselves or were cared for by female family members or community caregivers.

Many Americans in the early and mid-nineteenth century rejected the notion that university-educated physicians, especially

British-educated physicians, were better healers because of their education. Most of the healers of the period did not have a university education. They were self-taught and mentored by those with experience and a knowledge of healing. The mentoring that healers received was in many cases no less formal than the university programs of the day. Women were excluded from university medical schools during the early and mid-nineteenth century, however, they participated fully in community healing networks that included health education and the promotion of self-care practices. Knowing how to care for one's family during an illness was important to American women, such as Martha Spence Heywood. Many nineteenth-century women kept receipt books in which they archived their favorite healing remedies as well as culinary recipes. Americans were also fond of self-help books. American-written self-help books, called "advice" books, flourished in the mid-nineteenth century.

Women had stores of remedies in their own homes that were mostly botanical in nature. The family kitchen and distillery became the "laboratory" of every goodwife where remedies were produced and perfected. Numerous remedies might be used during a single illness. The word "medicine" in the mid-nineteenth century was used much more broadly than in present American culture. In present-day vernacular, the word "medicine" is often associated with the numerous oral remedies usually supplied in pill form from a drug manufacturer through its vendors, community pharmacies. In the mid-nineteenth century, prior to the boom in the pharmaceutical industry, the word "medicine" meant much more to American citizens and community healers.

Medicines were most often botanical in nature and were applied in many forms, including topical and environmental. Topical applications included salves, poultices, infused oils, plasters, and compresses. Environmental applications included baths, inhalations, and steams. In addition to pills or tablets, oral applications of botanicals included teas, tinctures, liquid alcohol extracts, syrups, soups, juices, and wines, to name a few. Throughout history, the words "botanical" and "herb" have been used to describe plant-based remedies. The words "botanical," "herb," and "plant" will be used interchangeably throughout this book. The word "therapies" is used in this book instead of the word "medicine" because it is more inclusive of the full range of remedies used by people in the mid-nineteenth century.

Reforming Health Care

The use of botanical or herbal therapies was an important part of the healing culture of the period. Americans were encouraged by local healers and even presidents, most notably Thomas Jefferson, to care for themselves with locally grown herbs rather than rely on more expensive chemical and herbal remedies imported from Britain. In the nineteenth century, the United States had achieved political independence from Britain but was still dependent culturally. Americans of European descent were often more familiar with, and still using, European remedies. They were not so quick to discard their British healing recipes, their self-care books, such as Buchan's *Domestic Medicine*[3] or their herbals.[4] A time-old tradition of European self-care took on new meaning in the nineteenth-century political climate of President Andrew Jackson's democracy when the "common man" was revered and the cures of diplomaed physicians had become suspect.

Americans were becoming increasingly concerned about the adverse effects of the Regular physicians' common cures of bloodletting and oral doses of calomel, a medicine formulated from mercury. "Reform" was a key word for the period, and health care reform was just as socially prominent as religious, political, and economic reforms. At the center of the reform movements in health care was the question of whether or not a health care provider needed to be diplomaed, that is, given a license, certificate, or diploma of any kind from her or his state of residence or from an educational institution. The public and health care providers, such as the Thomsonians, questioned the skills of the university-diplomaed physicians of the period. As the structure for American government was being laid, Americans were concerned that the contribution of the "common" citizen, her or his wisdom, ability, and experience, be valued and protected. The right of the common citizen, that is, one without a higher education at a British university, to provide health care and advice needed to be defended.

This book describes a time in history when Americans celebrated freedom and democracy by experimenting with their newly formed democratic nation. Men and women considered health and the expression of medical freedom the foundation of all other freedoms—religious, political, and economic. Medical freedom included the ability to choose how to heal, who could practice the healing arts, and which substances and techniques were used in healing. The ability to choose health care modalities or to use selected practitioners based upon one's personal health beliefs was viewed by most Americans during the period 1830- 1860 as one of the most important social issues of the day.

American health care from 1830 to 1860 can be characterized as a period of reform, exploration, sectarianism, and conflict between medical sects. This thirty-year period before the Civil War was the peak of a period in health care history referred to as the "Botanical Medical Movement." The Botanical Medical Movement provided the most organized challenge of health care sects to the medical orthodoxy of the Regulars in American history. It was during this period that the curative powers of nature, in particular, herbal remedies, were embraced in a new way by American citizens and healers alike. It was also a period when interest in native medicinal herbs was growing and when Americans shared healing practices, recipes, and health information.

Leaders of the Botanical Medical Movement and other health care reform movements were very active politically. They often wrote and spoke on the subject of medical freedom and democracy. There are numerous references in the historical literature regarding the political concerns of the health sects and reformers.[5] The following chapters provide examples of how the democratic principles of President Andrew Jackson, the seventh U.S. president, who served two terms in office from 1829 to 1837, and Thomas Jefferson, the third U.S. president, who served from 1801 to1809, were often referred to by health care reform leaders of the Jacksonian period as "foundational" to the development of the health of the citizens of the United States.

In addition, it is probable that the Lewis and Clark expedition and Jefferson's strong support of the exploration of American resources, including botanical resources, were influential in stimulating the public's and community healers' desire for the use of *American* botanical therapies as an expression of medical freedom and American identity. Jefferson was a botanist and sponsored the exploration of Lewis and Clark during his term in office. The Lewis and Clark expedition began in 1803, after the United States bought the Louisiana territory, approximately 820,000 square miles, from France. While the main purpose of the expedition was to mark a trade route from the Mississippi River to the Pacific Ocean, Lewis and Clark were also charged with establishing relationships with Indian tribes and with the scientific exploration of North American flora and fauna.

History of Women

Historical texts on mid-nineteenth-century medicine and pharmacy, for the most part, depict the stories of white male physicians, both Regular and Botanic, who provided health care in what has been referred to by nineteenth-century historians as the "public sphere." Those histories, which include extensive data regarding the Botanical Medical Movement, provide a significant part of the social framework for the description of health care in the nineteenth century. The historical works of scholars Alex Berman,[6] John Haller,[7] and Michael Flannery[8] on the Botanical Medical Movement provide an account of the history of the botanical medicine practices of the period and are included here with excerpts from original manuscripts of medical leaders of the movement, such as Samuel Thomson[9] and Wooster Beach.[10] Medical and botanical histories of the period make no mention, however, of the role of women healers, including nurses and midwives, during the Botanical Medical Movement. There has been little study of the role of healing women and their influence on the health reforms of the period and no study of their role in the success of the Botanical Medical Movement's challenge to orthodoxy.

In the mid-nineteenth century, women and men worked, for the most part, in separate spheres, men in the "public" sphere and women in the "domestic." In general, mid-nineteenth-century

American women valued domesticity.[11] Their focus was the improvement of home, family, and community, and they sought to bring about cultural change, and even political change, through their work in and out of the home. The issue of domain and the relationship between the public and domestic spheres has been a "central concern of women's history,"[12] particularly among nineteenth-century historians. Nineteenth-century women have been described in terms of the dichotomous concept of existing in a separate "sphere" from men. They have been shown to be mistresses of the home or domestic sphere. Nineteenth-century women's literature affirms that feminine qualities were considered by many, both men and women, a "source of personal strength and pride and a fount of public regeneration."[13] The separation of nineteenth-century women from the more public male sphere provided a basis for the strengthening and expression of what was a distinctly female culture.[14] The concept of "separate spheres" or "women's sphere" has been challenged as being restrictive, dualistic, and oppressive, and it has been suggested that a more liberating one, "women's culture,"[15] be adopted in describing nineteenth-century women. Both concepts of nineteenth-century women's sphere and women's culture will be explored throughout this book. Ultimately, it will be shown that the women nurses of the period existed primarily in the borderland, or a third "sphere," somewhere between the domestic and public sphere, where they generated and maintained a cultural power as community health care leaders.

One of the main values of the women of the period, even into the late nineteenth century, was the "feminization of culture." Women leaders in the nineteenth century are often referred to in contemporary literature as "cultural feminists."[16] The term *feminist,* however, was not utilized in the mid-nineteenth century. "Women's leader" or "women's rights leader" was the title used. The feminization of culture, as the propagation of the public sphere with women's values, was the ideal of many nineteenth-century women and women leaders. Women sought greater cultural transformation rather than political change, the focus of men and the public sphere. They sought social change through cultural and personal change. Mid-nineteenth-century women were powerful change agents and were often indirect in their approach in seeking to achieve this cultural transformation. Nineteenth-century women believed that using their personal power to submit to male dominance in the public sphere would indirectly bring greater stability to their own families and their young democratic nation. Women leaders of the mid-nineteenth century believed that their attention and devotion to the development of domestic culture would potentially save the lives and souls of Americans. Leaders, such as Margaret Fuller and Mary Gove Nichols, educated and inspired women to move toward change in all areas of life, from social reforms, to diet, to health care.

Women leaders of the mid-nineteenth century often focused on the importance of honoring the differences between women and men. They held a vision that women's feminine values, which included the qualities of cooperation and nonviolence, for instance, were not only worthy of the private domestic sphere but if brought into the public sphere could transform society. Underlying the feminization of culture of the period was a "matriarchal vision: the idea of a society of strong women guided by essentially female concerns and values."[17] Fuller expressed the goals of the feminization of culture when she wrote that there should be "the reinstatement of a 'plant-like gentleness', a harmonic, peaceful rule, an end to violence in all areas, including such violence against self as the use of alcohol and drugs and the slaughter of animals for food,"[18] which would most likely have included an end to male Regulars' use of harsh chemical drugs. It is not surprising, given the value of "plant-like gentleness" as one of the valued expressions of the feminization of culture of women of the period, that botanical therapies, often perceived as gentler remedies, played a dominant role in the health care culture throughout the nineteenth century. This book describes how the actions of mid-nineteenth-century women nurses contributed to the cultural transformation of the period, specifically in regard to health care and botanical therapies.

While women had certainly used healing plants prior to this period, this use of plants in the mid-nineteenth century became associated with health care reform. Health care reform movements, including the Botanical Medical Movement, were an expression of the changing philosophies and beliefs of nineteenth-century women about health and their desires to change American society for the better by taking responsibility for their own health as well as for that of their families. It is well documented that women's health issues were at the center of the Botanical Medical Movement. For example, in Samuel Thomson's journal dedicated to women, the *Boston Thomsonian Manual and Lady's Companion,* he pleaded with women to take back their health care, especially gynecological care from the male physicians, who were beginning to dominate midwifery practice. This book attempts to demonstrate how mid-nineteenth-century women, in particular, nurses, contributed to the changes in the health care of a developing nation by actively participating in the Botanical Medical Movement as one expression of their matriarchal vision of healing.

Essentially Nurses

Who were the mid-nineteenth-century women nurses, and what are their histories? Nineteenth-century women, given the state of medical practice and the role of women in society, are often viewed from, what I believe, an essentialist perspective. Often I am asked if all women of the period were not just "essentially nurses." This book, most especially the vignettes of the unique women in the three case studies in chapters 5–7, provides numerous examples of the differences between the general caring culture or network of the women of the mid-nineteenth century and professional community caregivers known by the specific title "nurse." Thus not all American women were nurses. In mid-nineteenth-century literature, the word "doctor" is generally used to refer to males. In general, a woman doctor, who at the time of the mid-nineteenth century was not allowed access to formal education, is referred to as a "doctress" or a "woman doctor." The word "nurse" is consistently used to refer to a community-identified woman caregiver. Although the actual professional boundaries were quite blurred in the mid-nineteenth century in comparison with contemporary standards and practice, the historical nursing records do allow for greater definition of professional roles.

A nonessentialist perspective of the meaning of being "women" in the mid-nineteenth century is used here as opposed to an essentialist view. The essentialist view of women in history implies that the identity of women, in this case the nurses of the period, is independent of their social context. Similar to trait theory, the essentialist view implies a preassigning of a stereotypically derived concept of women in nurturing and caregiving roles, based upon current professional nursing definitions. A nonessentialist or "positional" perspective, however, allows for identifying women within a constantly changing historical and social context.[19] This nonessentialist approach to history, used here, can allow the story of the women to be viewed as fully as possible.

Histories of nursing contain little to no mention of who the American "nurses" were of the period 1830–1860s, let alone to what extent they used botanical therapies or were involved in health care reform, such as the Botanical Medical Movement. The stories of nurses and healing amongst mid-nineteenth-century women presented here are the result of my historical research. With my interest in nursing, women's history, and the history of healing therapies such as herbalism, I was beset with some questions that I believed, having served for over twenty years in the healing arts, might be important to understanding the present state of American health care and the future of it as well. What was the contribution of women nurses to health care culture and reforms during the period of the Botanical Medical Movement? How did women learn about botanical use and other healing, caring, and comforting practices they used? Did they learn from each other, as did Martha Heywood, or was information about botanicals and healing shared in more formal ways that might have been preserved and, therefore, able to be discovered and studied? Who were the nurses, and how did they use botanical therapies?

A Needle in the Haystack of History

While the botanical contributions of male public figures of the period have been researched and published, the contributions of women nurses to the field of botanical therapies in America, and more specifically to the outcomes of the Botanical Medical Movement, have not been addressed. John Tosh wrote about the underrepresentation of women in history in general, maintaining that mainstream history does not offer a universal history but a "blinkered account of half of the human race."[20] This appears to be the case in terms of the history of American women nurses' use of botanical therapies. The history written about the Botanical Medical Movement, which focuses on male public figures, might very well leave a reader thinking that women nurses were nonexistent. A review of general American histories of medicine also might leave one believing that there were no women leaders in health care during the mid-nineteenth century at all. However, a review of women's histories, such as by Abram,[21] Verbrugge,[22] and Silver-Isenstadt,[23] reveals that there were indeed numerous women health care leaders in the mid-nineteenth century. They were nurses, physicians, healers, and community women.

There is also no mention of the role of women nurses in the mid-nineteenth century in the histories of the Botanical Medical Movement, save a sentence or two about the widow Benton, Samuel Thomson's childhood mentor in herbalism.[24] Women in general and nurses in particular are virtually invisible in mid-nineteenth-century health care historical literature. American ethnographic and folkloric studies, however, have lent some insight into the role of early women healers. Sharon Sharp wrote in 1986 that "Women have played vital roles as the primary keepers and carriers of complex systems of knowledge regarding folk medicine, and intergenerational networking between women has served as the primary mechanism for the transmission of rich and varied heritages in the healing arts."[25] Her research shows that herbalism was not the exclusive domain of women, but that the knowledge of herbal remedies, and the transmission of that knowledge, usually rests with women, and that women's contributions have been virtually neglected historically.

One historian wrote the following about the dearth of history about early American nurses: "Most glimpses of the work of midwives and nurses come from passing references to their activities in the surviving letters and diaries of their patients, a limited and skewed sampling at best."[26] The only role for women identified in the literature on the Botanical Medical Movement was as recipients and purchasers of botanical products and services from male botanical entrepreneurs such as Samuel Thomson. Upon first examination of the existing literature on the Botanical Medical Movement and nineteenth-century medicine, it seemed that my quest for the historical evidence of the botanical work of women nurses of the period was to be a search for the proverbial "needle in the haystack."

Very little has been written about the history of *early* American nursing. Many historians equate the emergence of American nursing with the late nineteenth century. While it is common knowledge among colonial historians that women nursed their families and communities, and that some who performed these acts were autonomous professionals who were paid,[27] nursing histories often directly or indirectly identify the beginning of American nursing with the organization of nurses for service during the Civil War and, more often, the introduction of the Nightingale model in American hospital training schools of the late nineteenth century.[28] Because of this trend, there is a significant gap between the histories of colonial women healers, who autonomously used botanical therapies extensively in their caregiving practices, and late-nineteenth-century nurses, whose identity became intertwined with medicine by focusing on hospital work, relying more on technology, and subsequently using botanicals less in practice. The stories presented here are of some of the nurses from this gap in nursing history, that of mid-nineteenth-century America, the period 1830–1860.

Definitive answers to the questions "Who is a nurse?" and "What is nursing?" have historically eluded nursing scholars, even to the present day.[29] In today's culture, the word "medicine" is often used as an inclusive term referring to nursing and other healing arts. For historical clarity, "medicine" will be used in this book only when referring to the actual practice of medicine, as can best be determined by the historical records used. Examining history can be a means of defining professional as well as individual identity. One nurse historian wrote: "The study of history represents the potential for the discovery of unity and continuity in one's identity. Beyond the search for truth it can offer hope and reassurance. Further, the possession of an intelligent appreciation of the emergence and evolution of an identified group is fundamental to that group's status as a profession."[30] It is hoped that the histories presented here can add to the definition of nursing identity.

Nursing today is often thought of by many in terms of that which is taught in university-based nursing schools and those tasks, most often hospital based, licensed by state boards of nursing. University education for nurses and state boards of nursing did not exist in the mid-nineteenth century. The identity of a nurse in the mid-nineteenth century was not defined by a legal or an educational system, but by her relationship with the community she served. Therefore, the definition of nurse adopted for this historical research is a woman identified by her community as an expert in caring for the sick, pregnant, or infirm. Midwives are included in the use of the word "nurse." The word "midwife" is also used here to describe a specific nursing specialty, that of caring for pregnant women and their infants.

While nineteenth-century women such as Martha Spence Heywood nursed themselves and their families, there were women healers, called "nurses," as will be described here, whose caring and comforting abilities went well beyond those of the average goodwife. In addition, as will be shown here, nurses were often the ones who taught community women their healing skills. The nurses were also the experts who were called upon in healing crises to help and guide when women's basic self-care practices were not sufficient.

American nursing literature contains brief references to nursing prior to the 1860s. Well-known texts by nursing history scholars such as Reverby,[31] Ashley,[32] and Melosh[33] have focused primarily on the years after the introduction of Florence Nightingale's work to the United States, most particularly after nursing education and practice became "institutionalized" (i.e., organized in the public sphere, as in hospitals) in 1873. Current American nursing textbooks, core curriculum, and licensing examinations do not include content on botanical therapies. This was not always the case. American nursing textbooks until the 1950s, such as the popular texts of Bertha Harmer and Virginia Henderson,[34] included herbal "*materia medica*."[35] For example, the topical application of herbs such as cayenne (*Capsicum frutescens*) and mustard (*Brassica spp.*)[36] was described in the textbooks as being used for the herbs' counterirritant effect, to warm and stimulate circulation in a particular part of the body.[37] Two published diaries, one of a colonial midwife, *A Midwife's Tale: The Life of Martha Ballard,* by Laurel Ulrich, and one of a mid-nineteenth-century midwife *Mormon Midwife: The 1846–1888 Diaries of Patty Bartlett Sessions,* edited by Donna Smart, also contain evidence of early American midwives' use of botanical therapies.

Historical texts of nineteenth-century medicine and pharmacy, such as the works of Vogel and Rosenberg,[38] Kett,[39] and Starr[40] make some reference to the use of herbs by colonial nurses or midwives. Starr includes a brief reference to early American nursing in his statement that "Before the 1870s, trained nurses were virtually unknown in America."[41] The historical records presented here demonstrate that a more accurate statement might be that "Hospital-trained or physician-trained nurses were virtually unknown before the 1870s." The history of early nursing education of the mid-nineteenth-century is another example of the importance of the attendance to the perspective of the domestic and public spheres. Historians who focus their study on the public sphere and male leadership of that sphere often miss the important social, cultural, and historical content found in the domestic sphere, in which there are predominantly women and leaders who are more informal and whose activities are often best identified within a community context. It is not uncommon that many popular American histories and historical archives include only prominent male figures. The early American history of health care is found in the work of women community healers. The history of women healers, often rural women, even community-recognized expert "nurses," is often considered "too common" to collect, yet it is significant to the history of American health care. Rural women often leave fewer records than urban women. Thus often aggregate histories, such as those presented here, must be provided.

I speculate that nurses have been perceived as more "common" everyday healers perhaps because their leadership and authority, like that of midwife Martha Ballard of Maine, was demonstrated within their patients' homes and the community. Mid-nineteenth-century women, most often by choice, did not participate formally and publicly in the political arenas in which men and university-educated physicians navigated freely. Women leaders in many ways blended into the cultural fabric of community as they performed their duties. The choice of domain for their work should not diminish their potential for recognition as health care experts, nor should it preclude historians from attempting to examine their stories.

Nursing practice has historically been defined within the context of the nurse-patient relationship. Therefore, it is hypothesized that what American patients were doing with herbs in their self-care practices is potentially important in ultimately being able to understand the botanical contribution of nurses. Popular self-care/advice books of the period and the domestic medicine literature prevalently used by nineteenth-century patients were found in numerous history of medicine collections explored during this research. These books, discussed extensively in chapter 4, are included to enrich one's understanding of the broader context of nurses' interaction with botanical therapies.

The thoroughness and validity of a body of historical work may be called into question when women are not represented. Adding the "voice" of women nurses to the existing body of knowledge regarding the history of botanical therapies in the nineteenth century can only strengthen and deepen one's understanding of the history of American health care and, therefore, inform present-day practice and perhaps even future American health policy and practice decisions. As mentioned, the purpose of this historical research was to follow the "threads" of questions to the "needles" of historical evidence buried in haystacks of time. I began with the question, "Were there American nurses during the Botanical Medical Movement, and, if so, what were they doing with herbs?" Chapters 2–4 of the book "sew" together my findings of general supporting history into a foundation for the recognition of the botanical work of mid-nineteenth-century nurses in the stories presented about three groups of fascinating American women in chapters 5–7. I believe that these histories support what other historians have found: that the use of botanical therapies is historically associated with American women's nursing work.[42] These histories provide specific evidence that there were professional women nurses during the mid-nineteenth century who did have expertise in herbalism and who contributed greatly to the success of the Botanical Medical Movement.

Three Groups of Women Nurses

This is a history of the use of botanical therapies by women nurses whose community service included promoting health and caring for and comforting the sick in antebellum America, the period 1830–1860, the peak years of the Botanical Medical Movement. Chapters 1–3 provide the general historical background of what health care was like in mid-nineteenth-century America. Chapter 2 describes the broader context of health care during the period of which nursing was a part. Special attention is paid to the influence of Jacksonian democracy and the numerous health care reform movements of the period, in particular, a specific sect known as "Thomsonianism," named after its charismatic leader, Samuel Thomson, that excelled during the Botanical Medical Movement. Chapter 3 details the mid-nineteenth-century patient's role in health care, with attention to patient self-care practices and the use of advice books. The focus of chapter 4 is on defining the mid-nineteenth-century nurse and her role in health care during this period.

Chapters 5–7 include three specific examples, or descriptive case studies, of communities of American women nurses and their use of botanical therapies during the peak period of the Botanical Medical Movement. The final chapters of this book include a summary of the significance of the contribution of the three groups of nurses to the health reform of the period, herbalism, the history of nursing and women healers, and potentially to present-day nursing and health care.

The three nursing communities researched are the Shaker infirmary nurses, the pioneer nurses and midwives of the Church of Jesus Christ of Latter-day Saints (LDS), and the Sisters of Charity (SOC) hospital nurses. The histories of each of the three groups were produced by piecing together community records, nurses' instruction manuscripts, recipe books (referred to as "receipt books" in the nineteenth century), letters, and archival records, which include individual journals and diaries of those in the communities as well as those who worked with or were related to the nurses. The three histories are compared and contrasted in chapter 8 so that patterns or trends in behavior that can add to one's understanding of professional nursing and the use of botanical therapies by women of the period are illuminated.

While individual nurses are highlighted throughout the book, the focus of the nursing histories is not on individual women nurses per se. The stories of individual women nurses are used to provide a more complete understanding of the nurses as a group. Because it appears that nurses of the period typically did not record their activities, this collection of smaller historical threads of individual nurses' accounts is woven together from group archives and community records of mid-nineteenth-century nurses and their botanical work to form the fabric of a larger historical tapestry. Historians have been likened to weavers whose "craft is to produce a strong fabric of interpretation out of the warp of sequence and the woof of contemporaneity."[43] I use the word "tapestry" to describe this women's history because the historical data of the women nurses as a whole are rich in color, complex in design, and beautiful, much like many of the tapestries one might see hanging on the wall of a museum.

This historical tapestry takes its shape and design from the collective stories of women nurses' botanical use rather than from the story of a single woman. The richness of the tapestry became evident to me early on in my research in the sheer volume of historical information that was uncovered. There was no needle in the haystack. Rather, I had found an entire sewing room. It was clear that the sum total of the stories of mid-nineteenth-century women nurses and their use of botanicals would exceed the confines of one book. Therefore, presented here are the histories of European-American (Caucasian) nurses living in the northern United States, from the eastern seaboard to Utah.

The main reason for choosing European-American nurses in the North is that in my research for a previous text on herbalism in nursing practice, I had read in some histories of the Botanical Medical

Movement that the Shakers, a religious sect found in numerous villages in some New England states and New York State, were identified as leaders in herbal production in the nineteenth century. I hypothesized that exploring the health care of the Shaker communities might potentially lead me to a group of women nurses that knew about herbs. In addition, in my work as a clinical herbalist, I had, over the years, a number of interactions with members of the Church of Jesus Christ of Latter-day Saints, who were producers of herbal products. I thought that there might be a history of botanical use in the community. While my initial contacts, historians and archivists in both of these communities, were quite skeptical about finding evidence of women nurses, botanical therapies use, or, more importantly, both, my initial archival visits to Salt Lake City, Utah, and to the Shaker archives at Case Western Reserve in Cleveland, Ohio, proved fruitful. Original manuscripts from both communities during the period 1830–1860 revealed that there were identified nurses in the communities whom I suspected, and ultimately confirmed, had botanical knowledge.

I also had previous knowledge from general nursing history that the SOC group included the first American nurses in hospitals in the 1820s. This group was chosen as the third group for my research, for two reasons. First, unlike the other two groups, I had no evidence that it possessed botanical knowledge and thought that the group of nurses might provide a contrast to the other groups. Second, I did a preliminary search of the nursing literature on early American Catholic nurses[44] and discovered that the SOC had extensive archives in a number of locations, specifically in Emmitsburg, Maryland. Religious affiliation was not a predetermined criteria for this research. It was an emergent result of my desire to study groups of nurses that have historical significance. Both herbalism and nursing have been connected to religious practice and spirituality, as can be seen historically in records of Christian communities from the time of Jesus' birth, when he received gifts of valuable myrrh and frankincense, to the healing works of Hildegard of Bingen, in which botanicals played a significant role. In retrospect, I was not surprised that I should find nurses or the practice of herbalism in the historical records of the three American religious communities. There are similarities and differences between the cultures of the three communities, therefore, each culture is explored separately.

Cultural Diplomacy on the Home Front

A health care culture is founded upon a community's health and spiritual beliefs, experiences, practices, remedies, and education. It is exemplified in a community's self-care practices and in the caring and curing work of community healers. How people heal and care for themselves and each other in times of illness, as well as how they promote health and longevity, changes over time with scientific experience, education, and changing health beliefs. Women nurses, as the histories of the period recorded here appear to confirm, were cultural *diplomats* in their healing and self-care practices. This book tells the story of that diplomacy — the ability to listen to both "sides" of the health care reform issues — the ideas and cures of the Regulars and the Botanic physicians and the remedies and self-care suggestions of other healers and health care reformers to create and utilize the ideas of all in an integrated, caring regime of remedies and therapeutic interventions.

The word "diplomat," as it is used today, refers to a person who engages in diplomacy. Diplomacy has two meanings: "The art and practice of conducting negotiations between nations" and "the skill in handling affairs without arousing hostility: tact."[45] In the vernacular, many understand diplomacy as a function of the realm of international relations. Therefore, diplomatic negotiations are usually thought of as dealing with political agendas, and diplomacy "between nations" infers the dialog occurring between countries. As I studied their work, it became clear that the words "diplomacy" and "diplomat" described the service of nineteenth-century women nurses if I broadened the definition and allowed for a slightly different meaning when applied to the culture of the period with its public and domestic spheres. As historian Nancy Cott points out, histories need to identify how women of the nineteenth century were being defined "in or out of the language of citizenship."[46]

The term *diplomacy*, as it is used here, describes the actions of women nurses in the mid-nineteenth century in terms of their citizenship, culture, and political domestic sphere. The terms *diplomacy* and *diplomat* have not necessarily been applied to the activities of women in the early and mid-nineteenth century. When the histories of health care, at the time a very political subject, and the histories of women nurse-herbalists are examined alongside the histories of the Regulars and Botanics of the public sphere, it becomes apparent that women were indeed performing, directly or indirectly, consciously or unconsciously, diplomatic acts. They tactfully and skillfully mediated and then taught the application of the healing arts, including herbalism, from an integrated perspective of including the knowledge and experience of many health care sects, such as the Regulars and the Botanics, and the healing traditions from their countries of origin and those learned from American Indians utilized often in domestic care, the care and comforting of the sick, and the promotion of health in their communities.

Before the Civil War began in 1860, women occupied their own political sphere from that of men. Historians, such as Paula Baker, state that the political participation of the nineteenth-century woman took place "in the context of the home."[47] Women's political activity typically centered on issues that concerned the public good, such as health care reform. As will be discussed throughout this book, women who participated in political life were actually expressing their citizenry neither in the realm of male electoral politics nor in the home. They managed to create and navigate a middle realm that has been referred to historically as the "borderland,"[48] a place where women's community service and political demands did not violate the canons of domesticity that many American men and women of the period valued as the "cult of domesticity" or "true womanhood."

Because women's reason for entrée into the borderland was community service and the development of American culture, I suggest that the histories told here are an expression of a specific form of diplomacy, that of cultural diplomacy. Cultural diplomacy today, defined as "the exchange of ideas, information, art, and other aspects of culture among nations and their peoples in order to foster mutual understanding,"[49] is an aspect of American foreign policy.

In this instance, the different health care sects are representative of different "nations," with different beliefs, practices, and social structures. Nineteenth-century women and nurses, as will be described, in practicing a form of integrative care that drew upon the health cultures of different sects, provided an opportunity for the exchange of health beliefs and practices in their women's societies, homes, and community services that was less than common in the public sphere of medical men. Cultural diplomacy in general and herbal diplomacy in particular were the foundations for the contribution of women nurses to the Botanical Medical Movement.

Historians record the healing practices of various cultures, the healing work of community leaders in the healing arts and the self-care practices and health beliefs of community members who strive for greater health and well-being, and the remedies used and the therapeutics applied in the care and comfort of the ill. Much of the early American history of healing, in particular, women's domestic healing practices, is similar to other cultures' healing traditions, embedded in a rich oral tradition. Some women, such as Martha Heywood, wrote of their health practices in their personal journals and diaries, but many did not. Making and applying remedies in the care of the sick was a common occurrence and often not considered noteworthy. Some women did record the remedies they used in their recipe books, passing on their healing remedies as they did their favorite culinary recipes. It was in the home that the healing remedies and the sickroom expertise of women nurses were developed. Any attempt to shed light on the story of American women healers of the early and mid-nineteenth century must include the exploration of the domestic work of women, which encompassed the work of women in the borderland.

The Global Tapestry of Herbalism

Botanical therapies are used by people of all cultures. Their use has continued to evolve with the emergence of modern technology. In the 1980s, members of the World Health Organization (WHO) Traditional Medicine Programme estimated that "80 percent of the more than 4,000 million inhabitants of the world rely chiefly on traditional medicines for their primary healthcare needs, and it can safely be presumed that a major part of traditional therapy involves the use of plant extracts or their active principles."[50] Botanicals have provided the substance for numerous pharmaceutical drugs and ultimately the blueprint for the manufacture of synthetic copies for hundreds of other drugs. At one time, up to 25 percent of all prescription drugs dispensed in the United States were derived directly or indirectly from plants, fungi, or bacteria.[51] In addition to prescription drugs, large numbers of herbal products are purchased by the American public for use in self-care practices. In 1997, sales of botanical dietary supplements in the United States totaled an estimated $5.1 billion, a 380 percent increase from 1990.[52] Often these supplements are manufactured and sold in capsule or tablet form in much the same way that prescription drugs are marketed. It seems that the patients for whom nurses care are more often than not using botanical therapies in their own health and healing practices.

While herbalism may have lapsed in importance since the 1950s, many American nurses are becoming increasingly interested in the clinical and historical evidence in using botanical therapies to heal the sick and promote wellness. That interest is beginning to generate a desire for studies about how nurses learn about botanical therapies and use them in clinical practice. For example, a 1999 study by McFarlin, Gibson, O'Rear, and Harman[53] investigated the preparation of nurse-midwives in the use of herbs to stimulate labor and found that while 64 percent of the nurse-midwifery education programs included instruction in the use of herbs to stimulate labor, 69 percent of the certified nurse-midwives who used herbs to stimulate labor reported learning about using them from other midwives, 4 percent reported learning from formal research publications, and none reported learning from formal education programs. The practice of women nurses networking and sharing botanical information today is also a recurrent theme in the history of women and botanical therapies presented here.

As early as the 1970s, Dr. Madeleine Leininger, an American nurse-theorist, emphasized the important role of the nurse in identifying and responding to the cultural similarities and differences in caring for the needs of patients. As a transcultural nursing scholar, Leininger identified the importance of professional nurses understanding "folk" healing practices in their countries of origin as well as the "professional" nursing concepts[54] learned in their nursing education programs. In helping nurses integrate traditional or folk health beliefs and practices, such as the use of herbs, it is important that the historical evidence, not only of the botanical therapies but also of the historical relationship of the profession with healing traditions, such as the use of herbs, be included in practice, theory, education, and research. The history of the relationship of mid-nineteenth-century European-American nurses with American Indians and the possible sharing of healing traditions is also explored throughout this book.

The Roots of American Nursing

Like the roots of many healing plants, the histories associated with human endeavor run very deep. The history of American women nurses runs very deep as well. As I began working on the stories of the women presented here, I began to get a real sense of the depth of the histories of the women of the period. I found myself comparing my historical research of the women nurses to an experience I had a number of years ago when I was the coordinator of a medicinal herb farm. A very tall man came to help the farm crew with the fall harvest. He asked me for his assignment, and I showed him the horseradish patch and told him that I wanted him to harvest the roots. He asked how far to dig, and not really thinking, I said, "Just follow the roots." When I came back to check on him a few hours later, the over-six-foot-tall man was not to be found. As I walked toward the spot where I had left him, I could see a large trench. Soil was flying out of the ditch. I looked into the trench and there was the man, over his head in the earth. He looked up and said, "Well, you told me to follow the roots . . . you can't believe how long these things are!" The process of collecting history is similar to a horseradish root harvest. The more one digs, the more one may find. The roots of the history of women healers run deep, just like the horseradish roots. In order to answer any historical question, one has to pick a point in time, as in picking up the first thread in creating a tapestry, and begin to tell the story. For this history, the first thread is the "root" of the nurses of the Botanical Medical Movement, the period 1830–1860. This book represents the product of the first harvest.

HARVESTING HISTORY—STAGE I

GATHERING IN

Three stages are involved in an herb harvest: gathering in the herbs from selected fields and meadows, sifting and sorting the herbs to separate out the usable plants, and processing the herbs into various remedies. Three stages also were involved in preparing this history and uncovering the stories of women nurses' contribution to the Botanical Medical Movement. In this book, I have organized the history into the aforementioned three stages.

The next three chapters, 2–4, represent the "gathering in" of the general social and health care history of the mid-nineteenth century, the women nurses in particular, and the state of botanical therapies at the time. Chapter 2, "Mid-Nineteenth-Century American Health Care" describes the health care "system" and the health care sects of the period, primarily the Botanical Medical Movement. Chapter 3, "The Mid-Nineteenth-Century Patient: Herbs, Advice Books, and Medical Freedom," provides the reader with the historical background of American health care of the period as it relates to the citizen as the patient. This chapter describes the importance of medical freedom and self-care to the patient of the mid-nineteenth century that resulted in the success of numerous health-related advice books, including instruction in botanical self-care.

Chapter 4, "The Mid-Nineteenth-Century Nurse: Home, Herbs, and Women's Healing Networks," describes the culture of American nineteenth-century women and the highly valued realm of domestic art and science from which the community-recognized "nurse" emerged. The history of women's healing networks is discussed in detail, with a special emphasis on the recording of botanical remedies in recipe/receipt books, which are often one of the best sources for information about women's history, including the way women heal themselves and others.

Chapter 2

Mid-Nineteenth-Century American Health Care

> Nature has a college of her own—in it I have studied... The voice of nature breathed within my soul. I sought the woods, the fields, the forests of my native land; from verdant banks I gathered healing herbs. . . . Thus my diploma is seen in the success which heaven hath thrown around me.[1]
>
> — A. I. Coffin, M.D, *A Botanic Guide to Health and the Natural Pathology of Disease*

The nineteenth century in America was a time of questioning how one lived. It was a time of experimentation, the 1837 depression, "new" philosophies such as Swedenborgianism and transcendentalism, and hundreds of experimental colonies or communes, such as the Oneida Community in New York State and Alcott's Fruitlands in Massachusetts. It was a time of challenges to the leading religions of the day and the creation of spiritual movements such as the free love movement of Thomas and Mary Nichols. Some physicians had women patients concerned that too much education would make them ill, and some women responded by learning their own anatomy from educational programs, such as the Ladies Physiological Institute, and turning to women "doctors," such as Harriot Hunt and Mrs. Elizabeth Mott. The abolitionist movement was intensifying, people were embracing health care reform and hygienic doctrines, and numerous healers with a wide range of philosophies and treatments were publicizing their successes with current medical challenges, such as the infectious disease cholera.

One of the most common diseases during the nineteenth century was cholera, with nationwide epidemics in 1832, the period 1849–1854, and 1866. Yellow fever was comparable to cholera in its impact, and it appeared every year between 1800 and 1879.[2] Other common diseases were malaria (ague), dysentery, diarrhea, pneumonia, influenza, and tuberculosis (consumption). People of the nineteenth century faced a number of potential health challenges.

> The country was young and poor, with a considerable amount of illness. Polluted water supplies, unsanitary means of sewage disposal, unhygienic methods of food preparation and transportation, and the lack of any control over mosquitoes, flies, and other insect vectors exposed many people to illness. Among the rural and poor urban inhabitants, malnutrition, poor housing, and exposure to weather grossly intensified the harsh effects of the more general factors. Illness was thus a major part of the lives of Americans, and major epidemics as well as the persistent endemic diseases were characteristic of the period.[3]

This chapter examines the health care "system" of mid-nineteenth-century American Regular physicians and the type of medicine they practiced, called "heroics." It also reviews the nature of nineteenth-century health care reform and its relationship to the values associated with Jacksonian democracy, the opposition that emerged within the ranks of the Regulars to a medical monopoly, and, finally, the health care contribution of the Empirics of the period, in particular, the Thomsonians and their opposition to the Regulars.

The Health Care System of the Regulars

Mainstream orthodox physicians known in nineteenth-century society as the "Regulars," were university-educated men who followed the teachings and medical theories of other university-educated medical men, such as Benjamin Rush, an eighteenth-century physician who signed the Declaration of Independence adopted in 1776 and a professor at the University of Pennsylvania Medical School. Rush "helped indoctrinate hundreds of students in a highly dogmatic generalized approach to medicine, one which assumed that there was only one disease and, therefore, that only a single basic treatment was ever necessary."[4] Regulars' treatment was usually a strenuous regime of some combination of purging, usually with oral doses of mercury, known as calomel, and bloodletting. Bleeding and calomel were considered universal remedies.[5]

American Regular doctors of the early to mid-nineteenth century were still influenced by the monistic theory of illness that had been in evidence for centuries. Illness was believed to be the result of a single underlying condition caused by an imbalance in the four humors (blood, phlegm, and black and yellow bile) that affected a person's entire body. Major medical theory included the belief that disease could be completely understood in terms of the gross pathological symptoms exhibited by the patient. Fever is one example. It was believed that any therapeutic intervention that produced a change in the patient's symptoms, such as decreased fever, was acting on the disease and was, therefore, effective.

In the eighteenth century, many patients and doctors alike believed that illness came from God as a punishment for sin, and that being brought to the brink of death by harsh treatments was the best medicine. Even into the nineteenth century, Americans' responses to illness, especially epidemics such as cholera, had been linked among Christian Americans to a health belief that the illness was punishment for a sin.[6] It is, therefore, understandable that in their search for atonement for sin, Christian Americans would be willing to endure the sometimes horrifying adverse effects of a therapy.

To the mid-nineteenth-century American Regular physician, one's professional affiliation was very important. "Medical practitioners could not convincingly invoke any particular claim to scientific respectability. . . but they could lay claim to the authority of credentials."[7] The question for the Regulars was whether or not their license would come from their state medical society or their medical schools, both of which were growing in numbers. Medical societies had received the power to license from the states, but there was a conflict. Most states made diplomas equivalent to licenses, which exempted medical school graduates from the state licensing requirements. Medical societies wanted all new physicians to pay for licenses from them, and the schools claimed that their diplomas were adequate.

The diplomaed physicians were gradually attempting to gain public support and confidence by advancing their work as the only acceptable, safe, and reliable doctoring in the United States. They sought to pattern themselves after their British colleagues in hopes of gaining the same level of social prestige as physicians in Britain held. The purpose of their professionalizing activity was to distinguish themselves from surgeons and apothecaries as well as the numerous other community healers. Their goal was to be a society of "gentlemen who declined to work with their hands and only observed, speculated, and prescribed."[8]

This did not work in America as it had in Britain. In the eighteenth century, very few American physicians worked full-time in their profession. Many did as Benjamin Rush suggested: they became farmers not only to be better able to support their families but also to earn the trust of their patients by working with their hands. Rush taught his students that farming would help them prevent their "cherishing even for a moment an impious wish for the prevalence of sickness in your neighborhood."[9] Physicians were also continuing the eighteenth-century trend of separating themselves from religion. Many ministers had been the physicians of colonial communities, working with their wives as nurses alongside them. The dual role of clergy-physician diminished in the nineteenth century, especially as technology in medicine advanced.

The separation of religion or spiritual matters from the practice of medicine was a symptom of a greater cultural change that was occurring, the separation of science and nature and the elimination of nature from medicine. Nature represented chaos, ambiguity, and even death, with death being a part of the course of a natural life. With increasing industrialization and invention, it was thought that people had the potential to progressively learn to dominate a perceived "natural" course of events in a given situation, and even to dominate nature itself. Nineteenth-century Americans, men in particular, were quickly moving away from the agrarian way of life encouraged by early leaders such as Jefferson to begin to seek rewards from industry. Mid-nineteenth-century American society was moving away from the farm and the forests and into the cities. Many Americans were turning from "New World," pioneer colonial life intimately connected with the earth and nature in the hopes of gaining the greater comforts and progress that technology and industry offered.

During the Enlightenment period in the eighteenth century, in both Britain and in the United States, physicians achieved a greater understanding of anatomy and physiology, and there was widespread belief that "science and technology, as Francis Bacon had taught, would enhance man's control over nature and social progress, [and] prosperity and the conquest of disease would follow."[10] Health beliefs and practices became linked to technologically based scientific development. Medicine's emerging role in society was to gain control over nature and, therefore, to control human nature as well. What had begun as a movement among religious (e.g., Puritan, Calvinist) clerics to control nature and "take dominion over the earth"[11] now spread to the physician, who believed that with new technology and science, physicians could also "take dominion over the earth." There is evidence that the physician became more successful than the religious man. During the Enlightenment, "more people were being born in the presence of a medical attendant, [and] more were dying with the ministrations of a physician rather than a priest."[12]

The concept of domination over nature was not new, but during the Enlightenment, this concept moved from being just a religious one to being a foundational part of American industrialized culture, including medical culture. The cultural connection between humans and nature was altered. Nature, traditionally viewed as feminine mother-teacher, hence "Mother Nature" was beginning to be imaged as a submissive body. Nature, or the natural, was quickly being devalued by a culture that increasingly prized scientific progress and that was becoming equated with industrialization and technology. One author summarized that "the new mechanical order and its associated values of power and control would mandate the death of nature."[13]

There was a potential conflict, however, for the physician who held fast to the hopes and ideals of the Enlightenment, that science and technology would produce the answers to overcoming disease and perhaps even death. Many of the remedies used in medicine in the nineteenth century were "natural"; they were plant "simples,"[14] later to be referred to as "crude" medicines by pharmaceutical laboratory scientists. What would become of the old traditions of using Mother Nature's herbs for medicine? The orthodox answer once again lay in the control of nature. "Nature, tamed and subdued, could be transformed into a garden to provide both material and spiritual food to enhance the comfort and soothe the anxieties of men distraught by the demands of the urban world and the stresses of the marketplace."[15] Control of nature and control of natural medicines would become part of the drive for "modern" medicine.

Heroic Medicine

Mid-nineteenth-century physicians turned to medicines that would effect a powerful, heroic action. They taught their patients that "powerful agents were powerful remedies."[16] Three kinds of drugs were used routinely: emetics, which produced vomiting, and cathartics (such as mercury, or calomel) or purgatives, which acted as extremely powerful laxatives. "These drugs should not be confused with twentieth-century medicines; their effect was much more drastic and immediate."[17] In addition to calomel and bloodletting, "blistering" was used, a treatment involving the application of cantharides to irritate the skin and raise a blister.

It was late in the eighteenth century that calomel first gained great popularity in America when Benjamin Rush used doses of ten grains of calomel and ten of jalap (another powerful purgative) in treating patients during the 1793 Philadelphia yellow fever epidemic. Some of the adverse effects of the use of calomel included excessive salivation, soreness and swelling of the gums and tongue, ulcers, a metallic odor, and,rotting jawbones. A number of other emetics and purgatives were used to replace calomel. Some were minerals and deadly poisons, and others were powerful botanicals, such as cayenne pepper (*Capsicum frutescens*). Cayenne pepper emetics were commonly referred to as "pepper pukes." All produced consistent and demonstrable changes in the patient's symptoms. One of the most popular was tartar emetic, which was tartrate of antimony and another was the purgative niter, or saltpeter, which also affected the heartbeat. Jalap (the root of *Ipomoea jalapa*), another common botanical purgative, was so harsh that it was often mixed with other chemical drugs to reduce its dangers. Its harshness can best be judged by the fact that it was mixed with calomel to make it more palatable. (For more information see Color Insert H.)

Tonics were supposed to build up the body through improved appetite and digestion. One of the most popular tonics was arsenic, which was used in Fowler's solution or other compounds. *Cinchona spp.* bark (also commonly known as "Peruvian bark") and quinine were popular too, especially in the treatment of malaria. Crude opium was also used at this time. Cinchona and opium were replaced in the second half of the century by morphine, an opium alkaloid.

Early nineteenth-century physicians were typically paid for the remedies they provided but not for their services. It was not uncommon, given their belief in the value of heroics, to honor the request of patients who wanted to see the results of the remedies for which they had paid. Patients and their physicians wanted to see dramatic results, and often "big doses"[18] of a medicine such as calomel or multiple rounds of bloodletting were involved in the treatment of the ill. Many Regulars believed that gentler medicines were warranted for those who were mildly ill but were actually "cruel"[19] if used in the care of those who were very sick. Eventually, many Americans became completely convinced of the importance of demonstrative, rigorous therapies. Two medical historians wrote: "Laymen could, indeed, be even more importunate in their demands for an aggressive therapy than the physicians attending them thought appropriate."[20]

Health Reform and Jacksonian Democracy

By the mid-nineteenth century, Americans became discouraged over the poor outcomes of the Regulars' heroic treatments. Health care reform movements had become common. People, especially women health care reform leaders, voiced their opposition to the heroic treatments of the Regulars that were increasingly opposed as being too "violent." Many began to question the foundation of heroic therapies, the belief that illness was punishment for sin and needed to be remedied by strong medicine. Marie Louise Shew, author of the 1844 book, *Water Cure for Ladies*, wrote: "It is unwise, irrational, and unphilosophical to regard illness as the *infliction* of Divine Providence."[21]

With the continued threat of deadly infectious diseases, many nineteenth-century Americans believed strongly that health care reform was vital to the emergence of a stronger, healthier nation. Mary Gove Nichols and her husband, Thomas Nichols, preached that health care reform was the "pivot" of all other social reforms. In their words, "So long as people are diseased, nothing can be done for them."[22] The Nichols's contribution was that "the 'personal' is 'political'" and that the "individual body and the social body more than mirror one another—that the two are inextricably bound."[23] Popular health care reform lecturers such as the Nichols, Sylvester Graham, and William Alcott taught that health care reform was a moral imperative.[24] There were two main foci of the work of leading health care reformers. One was a more general attention to the hygienic and lifestyle practices of Americans, such as whether or not drinking coffee was healthy and how many times a week a person could engage in sexual activity and maintain health. The other was a specific challenge to the educated medical orthodoxy and its attempt at what was perceived as "medical monopoly."

Any attempt at monopoly, medical or otherwise, was perceived as a threat to the success of the new nation by many mid-nineteenth-century Americans. They valued the opportunity of a fair chance for all American citizens. The most prominent qualities of society of the period were equality and competition.[25] Eighteenth- and nineteenth-century Americans questioned any activity that even remotely resembled government restraints on the people, such as the establishment of licensure laws by any group. These nineteenth-century societal ideologies reflect the values and beliefs associated with what has come to be known historically as "Jacksonian democracy."

In 1829, Andrew Jackson was elected the seventh president of the United States on the platform of representing the "common man." His presidency was built upon the values of Jeffersonian democracy, states' rights, and representation of all classes of Americans, including the "working man." Jacksonian Americans supported the containment of the "party of privilege," an upper-middle, class sect of large-scale industrial and commercial capitalists that was the beneficiary of the "Hamiltonian program of subsidy, protection, and monopoly."[26] Under the Jackson administration, business entrepreneurs increased exponentially to challenge the business elite group of the time, such as the bankers.[27] The very image of Jackson as president was a challenge to the established pattern in Washington that one had to be part of an "aristocratic clique" to be president. Jacksonian democracy represented the rise of the power of the farmers and landowners of middle-class America.[28]

In addition to valuing the "common man," the values of Jacksonian democracy included self-care and the belief that people's individual contributions would benefit the social good of the nation. Valuing self-care also meant valuing reliance upon American skills and goods and a cultural separation from England that had been an ideal since the Jefferson administration. In addition, Jacksonian values included the belief that the government that governed least governed best.[29] The political ideals of Thomas Jefferson in the early part of the century, that of simple government and an agrarian economy, were powerful influences on the Jacksonian democracy.

During the Jacksonian democracy, the Regulars, seeking licensure and professional establishment, were defeated time and again. Given the values of the Jacksonians, who retained political power, it is not difficult to understand why this would be the case. The Regulars were often educated in Britain and, therefore, held a practice (skills or "goods") that could be perceived by "common" Americans as representative of Britain. They were university-educated, which meant that they were not "common men" but elitist, because one needed, at this time, to be quite wealthy to study medicine in Britain. From the perspective of the Jacksonians and many health care reformers, the British-educated elitists, who were trying to establish licensing laws that set them apart as the only ones capable of safely practicing medicine in the United States, were seeking a monopoly and a curtailment of the health care freedoms that Americans valued often above all other freedoms.

Many Americans, including Thomas Jefferson, were very skeptical about the state of the medical services being offered. Regular physicians of the mid-nineteenth century did not have the trust of the public and, therefore, did not have the strength as an organized profession to achieve monopoly or control of American health care. Many health care reform leaders, which included Regulars, were supporters of Jacksonian democracy. The concepts of self-care were applied to health teaching. For example, *Domestic Medicine or Poor Man's Friend in the Hours of Affliction, Pain, and Sickness,* written in 1830 by John Gunn, M.D., was dedicated to "His Excellency Andrew Jackson" and the work "divested of foreign terms and obscure technicalities attempted to render it intelligible to all." Dr. Gunn opposed medical monopoly. He wrote: "Morally and physically speaking, every man ought to be his own physician, so far as circumstances render it possible; and even in case of great difficulty, and when it is essential to employ a regular physician, a partial knowledge of the science of medicine would not only enable a man to guard against imposition and imposture, but to make a judicious and safe selection."[30]

Health care reform leaders taught, and many nineteenth-century Americans believed, that state medical societies were indeed elitist and were attempting to establish a medical monopoly on health care through the enactment of licensing laws. The major activity of American medical societies became licensing and establishing fees and a code of ethics for members. The revenue accrued by licensing boards was an important source of income to the societies. Licensing "was useful to the profession in providing income to the societies, adding greater formality to the apprenticeship system, and giving prestige to physicians who served on the boards."[31] Exclusivity was the major objective of medical societies.

The origin of licensing is frequently traced to medieval Europe's guild system, where a guild was empowered by the state to exercise a monopoly over the practice of its craft, to control admission to it, and to determine any membership fees to be charged. Historians may disagree about whether or not the intent of the first American medical societies and the American Medical Association established in 1847 was to monopolize medicine and health care. What seems apparent, however, is that there were influential health care reformers and Regulars, as well as many American citizens, who believed that the leadership of the Regulars was elitist, and that the Regulars were indeed vying for economic and political control of medicine and health care.

As mentioned previously, there were few American medical schools in the early years of the new nation, so physicians were educated in Britain, primarily in Edinburgh and Oxford. British-educated Regular physicians had attempted to import the British Royal College of Physicians' model of physician-dominated of health care. The Royal College model was hierarchical with its own members differentiated as either licentiates or esteemed fellows. Because there were few full-time American physicians in the late eighteenth century, the hierarchical structure promoted by medical societies was only accepted when the leaders made the decision that any medical school graduate who passed examination and had a good reputation in practice could be accepted as a fellow of the society.

The continued modifications to the model meant that medical societies were basically unsuccessful in importing the hierarchical British medical system and its attendant authority.[32] The public, health care reformers, and many Regulars opposed licensing laws and medical society dominance as a medical monopoly. Elected officials opposed medical monopoly as well. While legislatures were generally willing to grant medical societies their own licensing powers, they were unwilling to create laws that would have seriously curtailed the healing practices of those who were skilled but unlicensed. The penalties for unlicensed practice in the mid-nineteenth century were generally nonexistent or insignificant, and midwives, apothecaries, and Botanics were some of those exempted from licensing requirements. There was a period in the early part of the nineteenth century when licensed Regular physicians had achieved an aspect of medical monopoly in that they obtained the sole right to sue for uncollected fees in court; however, the law was repealed shortly thereafter.

Regular physicians soon realized that established licensing laws were totally unenforceable, thus they began to have second thoughts about retaining the laws. In the mid-nineteenth century, physicians in Chicago became opposed to the enactment of any new medical licensing laws, because they believed that their enactment would only "increase public sympathy for unlicensed physicians."[33] Once state medical societies lost interest in a licensing system, organizations of unlicensed practitioners were able to obtain repeal of the licensing laws in every state but New Jersey.[34]

In general, mid-nineteenth-century Americans supported independence, social reforms, and what they perceived as progress in technology. The steamboat and the telegraph had been invented, and many other inventions were appearing on the public scene. Scientific invention meant progress, and progress meant that the life of American citizens would ultimately be more civilized and comfortable.[35] But the Industrial Revolution and technology had not yet been wedded to medicine and health care. Americans wanted and valued "scientific," industrialized progress, but they also valued their simple, agrarian roots and the importance of the "common man."

Opposition within the Ranks of the Regulars

Historian Joseph Kett stated that the Jacksonian sentiment of the day was not the only reason for the opposition to the medical establishment and licensure. "The collapse of licensing in the 1830s cannot be explained simply by reference to a Jacksonian mentality scornful of institutional restraints. The causes of this deterioration were partly ideological, but to a significant extent they arose also from contradictions within the medical institutions themselves."[36] For example, homeopaths were classified as "Regular physicians." They were university educated and very popular in American society;

however, homeopaths used remedies in very small doses and opposed the orthodox medical practice of the day that usually included large dosings of drugs such as calomel. Non-homeopathic Regulars, such as Oliver Wendell Holmes, believed that allowing the continued acceptance of homeopaths in medical societies would cause problems for the orthodox Regulars. By 1870, the American Medical Association excluded homeopaths from state medical societies.

Throughout the mid-nineteenth century, the changes occurring in health care culture epitomized the underlying changes in antebellum American culture. The public and practitioners alike had to make decisions about the acceptance or rejection of health beliefs that would influence behavioral changes. There was no universal agreement about the appropriate course or definition of scientific progress within the various health care sects. However, the heterogeneity of mid-nineteenth-century American health care was ultimately supplanted by an emerging culture of institutionalized health care education, medical dominance, licensure, and diplomas.

While the value of heroic therapies was upheld by the majority of physicians, some physicians, as well as health reformers, argued that physicians should wait on the therapeutic effects of nature whenever they were not confident in their therapies. Earlier, President Thomas Jefferson stated the following in a letter to Dr. Casper Wister in 1807:

> The disorders of the animal body, and the symptoms indicating them, are as various as the elements of which the body is composed. The combinations, too, of these symptoms are so infinitely diversified, that many associations of them appear too rarely to establish a definite disease; and to an unknown disease, there cannot be a known remedy. Here then, the judicious, the moral, the humane physician should stop. Having been so often a witness to the salutary efforts which nature makes to re-establish the disordered functions, he should rather trust to their action, than hazard the interruption of that, and a greater derangement of the system, by conjectural experiments on a machine so

> complicated and so unknown as the human body, and a subject so sacred as human life. . . . I would wish the young practitioner, especially, to have deeply impressed on his mind, the real limits of his art, and that when the state of the patient gets beyond these, his office is to be a watchful, but quiet spectator of the operations of nature.[37]

Early in the nineteenth century, few physicians had taken his advice. But by the 1830s, many Regulars began to change. "Criticism of traditional therapeutics had become a cliché in sophisticated medical circles; physicians of any pretension spoke of self-limited diseases, of skepticism in regard to the physician's ability to intervene and change the course of most diseases, of respect for the healing powers of nature."[38] Many believed in the self-limiting nature of most ailments. They taught that the physician's duty was to aid the process of natural recovery. Rest, a strengthening diet, or a mild cathartic was all that was needed to aid nature in most cases of illness. The Regulars were influenced by the health promotion and disease prevention philosophies of health care reformers and perhaps by changes in the sociopolitical climate. They were also influenced by the strong presence and social acceptance of numerous other health care providers.

The Empirics

The medical profession is a culture with its own set of norms, values, and beliefs and its own language that can set it apart from the "common man." In nineteenth-century culture, the title "doctor" or "physician" was not protected for any one particular group of practitioners. A Regular, however, considered any non university-educated physician a "mere Empiric," someone who "had no philosophy of cure save that of hit or miss."[39] A "quack" was an Empiric with no theoretical grounding, who often "exaggerated his abilities" to help and heal.[40] Quackery has a culture of its own. The word "quack" has historically been used vernacularly as a pejorative term describing a disreputable healer. It is a term whose use has grown with the commercialization of health care. The public's rejection of doctors' orders and of embracing self-care practices is considered part of the realm of quackery too, self-quackery. "The self-dosing habit . . . was crucial to the viability of quackery. . . Quackery was that branch of medicine which boldly promoted itself through the spoken and printed word . . . to so captivate the mind of the public."[41] Both Empirics and Regulars took advantage of the financial benefits and social fascination with the "fashion of health care,"[42] that is, quackery. They wrote advice books and made their own remedies to sell to an eager public.

By a Regular's definition, a university-educated healer of good breeding was not a "quack." Empirics, while not university educated, were not necessarily uneducated or ignorant about health and healing. For example, many nineteenth-century empirics were quite knowledgeable and highly apprenticed in the use of botanical therapies.[43] These empirics were called "Botanics," "Botanic physicians," "root doctors," "herb doctors," or "Indian doctors." Their practice was entirely limited to the use of herbs, which they sometimes claimed they learned from the Indians. The empirics argued that their therapies were superior to that of well-educated Regular physicians, who often had no life experience in healing diseases. During the Jacksonian period, the knowledge and experience of those with healing training through familial or experiential routes were often highly valued by the public.

Industrialization and urbanization challenged the Jeffersonian and Jacksonian ideals of an agrarian economy during the early and mid-nineteenth century. Industry produced a greater need for factory workers, so men and women left their homes in the country to find work in the cities, while immigrants in large numbers arrived in American East Coast cities. Educated Regular physicians congregated in larger cities almost exclusively during this time,[44] because the populations of the urban areas were large enough to support their practices. Empirics and other practitioners who lacked university training, including midwives, bonesetters, apothecaries, and nurses, practiced in all communities but were found primarily outside of the larger urban areas. Many were itinerants. The demographic distribution of practitioners with their representative cultures most likely influenced the populations these practitioners served. Americans in urban areas might have been more influenced in their health beliefs and decisions by Regulars and those in the rural areas by Empirics. Two of the groups researched for this book, the Shakers and the Latter-day Saints, resided in rural America in the mid-nineteenth century, and one group, the Sisters of Charity, lived in Emmitsburg, Maryland, which because of its close proximity to the city of Baltimore may differ in its health care practices and in the use of herbs than in the two rural groups.

Thomsonians — Leading the Empirics

In the mid-nineteenth century, botanical therapies were at the center of the heated debate between the Regulars and the Empirics. An entire sect of Empirics emerged with its botanical remedies in the 1830s to challenge the growing power and the heroic practices of the Regulars. The sect was led by a New Hampshire farmer, Samuel Thomson. Samuel Thomson (1769–1843) was of Scottish descent.

The Thomsons were a poor rural family that depended on the skill of an herb and a root healer who was named by Thomson "the old lady Benton." Mrs. Benton applied herbs topically to her patients and gave them hot herbal beverages to drink to produce sweating. Thomson wrote: "By her attention to the family, and the benefits they received from her skill, we became very much attached to her; and when she used to go out and collect roots and herbs, she would take me with her, and learn me their names, with what they were good for."[45] Thomson wrote about the care of his mother in the home of Mrs. Benton and about being "cured" himself of the "canker rash" by the widow Benton, who used "such medicine as our country afforded."[46] As a child, Thomson helped community members find the herbs they needed in the wild. When he turned sixteen, his parents considered sending him to live with Dr. Fuller, of Westmoreland (a former county in England), who was called a "root doctor."[47] But Thomson was not allowed to go, because he did not have enough education, and because he was needed to fulfill his duties on his family's farm.

Thomson resigned himself to work on the farm until one day,

at age nineteen, he accidentally cut his ankle to the bone. "My father sent for a Doctor Cole, of Jericho, who ordered sweet apple-tree bark to be boiled, and the wound to be washed with it, which caused great pain, and made it much worse, so that in eight days my strength was almost exhausted . . . the doctor said he could do no more for me. . . . I told him [his father] if he could find some comfrey root, I would try a plaster made of that and turpentine."[48] He had the comfrey plaster applied to his ankle, opposite the wound, and his father kept the wound open with string. Thomson did not eat and barely slept for weeks. Regular physicians suggested that the leg be cut off, but his father took him to a surgeon, Dr. Kitteridge.

Thomson described his interaction with Kitteridge. "He took off the dressing with great care and handled me very tenderly. . . . Kitteridge had extraordinary skill in surgery. . . His system of practice was peculiarly his own, and all the medicines he used were prepared by himself, from the roots and herbs of our own country. He was a very eccentric character, and uncouth in his manners; but he possessed a good heart, and a benevolent disposition. He was governed in his practice by that great plan which is dictated by nature."[49] This description demonstrates that Thomson was not uncompromisingly against the practice of Regulars. It also demonstrates his personal understanding of the healing art as being more than technique or therapeutics. He acknowledges the caring he received from Dr. Kitteridge along with the remedies. Thomson did recover from the injury, but even with the help of the comfrey plaster and Dr. Kitteridge's salve and surgical skill, he writes that he recovered only after the "good nursing and constant care"[50] of his mother and friends.

Thomson was very influenced in his negative opinion of the Regulars by his experience of watching his loved ones succumb to the Regulars' "experiments." He wrote of his wife's travail during childbirth.

> Her fits continued and grew worse; there were six doctors attending her that day, and a seventh was sent for; but she grew worse under their care; for one would give her medicine, and another said that he did wrong; another would bleed her, and the other would say he

> had done wrong; and so on through the whole. I heard one of them say that his experience in this case was worth fifty dollars. I found that they were trying their practice by experiments; and was so dissatisfied with their conduct, that at night I told them what I thought; and that I had heard them accusing each other of doing wrong; but I was convinced that they had all told the truth, for they had all done wrong. They all gave her over to die, and I dismissed them, having seen enough of their conduct to convince me that they were doing more hurt than good. After they were gone, I sent for Dr. Watts and Dr. Fuller, who were called root doctors. They attended her through the night, and in the morning about the same hour that they began, the fits left her.[51]

Thomson saw a problem with the medical practices of the Regulars and decided that he could change it. He took on the medical "system" of the Regulars in the 1820s through the 1840s, ultimately with the support of many Americans who were discouraged by what they perceived as the empty promises of the Regulars. Those who followed Thomson's leadership and his botanical healing practices were called "Thomsonians."

Thomsonians were the most prominent of the botanical medicine sects of the mid-nineteenth century. Fervent acceptance by Americans of botanicism was not only a reaction to the disgust they felt for the heroics therapies of the Regular physicians, botanicism also represented the integration of a belief in rational medicine with trusted, natural remedies. Botanicism was for many nineteenth-century Americans, Empirics and Regulars, the best of both worlds. It combined the directive, concise approach of biomedicine (e.g., "Here is what you do") and the often gentler remedies of herbalism, although the question of gentler medicine was often a matter of degree. Samuel Thomson's botanical program was one of the first prescriptive, organized systems of botanical therapies in America. His botanical system of health care was patented,[52] mass-produced, and put into the hands of the public, which was ready for reform and leadership. He was a passionate leader against what he perceived as a growing American medical monopoly. Thomson felt that his work was his mission and his duty. "I shall endeavor to instruct them [parents] all in my power, by giving a plain and clear view of the experience I have had, that they may benefit by it. If they do not, the fault will not be mine, for I shall have done my duty. I am certain of the fact that there is medicine enough in this country, within the reach of everyone, to cure all the disease incident to it, if timely and properly administered."[53] This statement demonstrates a kinship with the self-help ideology of Jacksonianism and the philosophies of Thomas Jefferson.

There was almost a religious zeal with which Thomson pursued his duty. He and his followers also saw their work as being political in its opposition to the American medical monopoly. His work, as well as that of other Thomsonians, such as Elias Smith and Alva Curtis, and the Eclectic physician, Wooster Beach, was part of the thrust for medical freedom typical of the Jacksonian era.[54] Thomson proclaimed that every man could be his own doctor, that every man had the right to choose his physician, and that every physician had the right to determine his own practice. His system of medicine focused on steams and botanical therapies. The purpose of the treatments was to restore vital heat to the interior and exterior of the body. This he achieved through the use of physical heat, such as in steaming the body and drinking hot teas and in using warming herbs such as cayenne pepper (*Capsicum frutescens*) in the form of "pukes." (For more information see Color Insert H)

Thomsonian historian John Haller records that the seventy botanical remedies in the Thomson system, or *materia medica*, "included a combination of American Indian, immigrant, folk, and domestic remedies whose origins were blurred but stood the test of his own practice and experimentation."[55] Thomson is renowned for his use of lobelia (*Lobelia inflata*) (For more information see Color Insert A), and is often pictured holding a sprig of the plant in his hand. Thomson personally experienced the emetic effects of lobelia since early childhood. He even claimed throughout his life to have "discovered" the plant. According to Haller's research of early American botanical records, *Lobelia inflata*, a plant native to North

America, may have been known but not used as medicine necessarily the way Thomson used it. But Thomson's claims to intellectual property could still be called into question. It seems highly unlikely that indigenous Americans and highly informed immigrant herbal healers such as Mrs. Benton would not have used the plant on occasion when an emetic or a "puke" was warranted. American botanist C. S. Rafinesque wrote the following about *Lobelia inflata*:

> The herbalist, Samuel Thompson [*sic*], claims in his guide of health to have discovered the properties of this plant towards 1790; but the Indians knew some of them; it was one of their puke weeds, used by them to clear the stomach and head in their great councils. Its medical properties have since been confirmed and elucidated by Doctors Cutler, Dorsey, Thatcher, Bigelow, Barton, Bradstreet, Randall, Eberle, &c. It is now extensively used, although many physicians consider it as a deleterious narcotic, uncertain and dangerous in practice: while Thompson [*sic*] denies it, and considers it as harmless, depending almost all together upon it in his new and singular practice of medicine, borrowed chiefly from the steaming and puking practice of the Indian tribes.[56]

Thomson's use of lobelia was often controversial with the Regulars. Some considered lobelia a deadly poison. In 1809, Thomson was put on trial for poisoning one of his patients with lobelia, however, he was acquitted.

Thomson had seven major remedies as part of his course of medicine. He numbered them 1–7 and only released the lists of the ingredients to those who had purchased the "rights" to use his patented system for self and family by paying twenty dollars. His number 1 remedy was the "emetic herb" lobelia, used internally or externally according to three different recipes. His number 2 herb, cayenne, was taken in powder form in hot water or tea.[57]

Thomson was extremely successful in introducing his system

of botanical medicine to the American public, despite the fact that the therapeutic investment in using his course of botanical therapies involved hours of time on the part of the practitioner and patient, sometimes up to half a day, for which the patient was charged $2.50 to $3. But it would seem that Thomsonians did not choose their therapies for the cash return. "The calomizer [Regular heroic doctor] may visit 20 or 30 patients [per day], and makes ten times as much as the Botanic."[58] Haller wrote that there were 167 authorized agents listed in the *Thomsonian Recorder* by 1833, and in Ohio alone, it was estimated that Thomson's herbal medicines were used by almost half of the population.[59]

The Thomsonian Botanic system was found to be highly successful during the epidemics of the 1830s and 1840s. A Regular physician, John Dawson admitted in 1841 before a state medical convention that "in a local epidemic of 'fever', the Thomsonians had affected cures, while the Regulars had been unsuccessful."[60] The pressure that the Thomsonians and other medical sects, such as the water cure and homeopathic physicians, placed upon the Regulars and their heroic practices achieved its goal. Increasing numbers of Regulars grew skeptical of their ability to affect cures with their heroics, and by mid century, the practice of the Regulars was becoming milder and less intrusive. As mentioned earlier, some Regulars even began to talk about the healing power of nature and of the natural tendency of the body to heal itself. For example, Dr. Jacob Bigelow's essay on self-limited diseases, read before the Massachusetts Medical Society in 1835,[61] encouraged many Regulars to rethink their practice.

Despite Thomson's success with the public, his own students and colleagues left him to start their own groups, usually because of their disagreement with him over his staunch (Jacksonian) opposition to opening clinics and offering formalized education to practitioners. For example, in 1838, Alva Curtis created the Independent Thomsonian Botanic Society, which would exist into the twentieth century. The Thomsonians, given their requirements for public and practitioner adherence to patent law and Thomson's directives, were themselves, for all intents and purposes, diplomaed. They were no different from the Regulars in their desire for public recognition, medical power, and control, even if their purpose was to protect the American people from the monopolistic designs of the Regulars.

Within forty years, the Thomsonians would be replaced by botanical physicians called "Eclectics." They were led by Wooster Beach and were even more successful in gaining public support in some ways than the Thomsonians. They were diplomaed and did not oppose the institutionalization of education for Botanic physicians. Beach, who began his rival movement in 1829, still accepted the Regulars' heroic practice of using aggressive therapeutics; however, he and the "Beachites," as early Eclectics were called, practiced the "doctrine of substitution." They claimed to substitute less "lethal" remedies, often botanical, to accomplish the same ends of making a profound impression on a patient's symptoms. For example, the Eclectics used poke root (*Phytolacca decandra*) instead of calomel to stimulate biliary secretion and iris root to produce the salivation and gum involvement that they believed was a positive effect of calomel.[62] Their intent was to create similar changes in a patient's symptoms without producing the adverse effects of the medicines of the Regulars. The differences between the Regulars' and the Eclectics' treatment outcomes were for the most part indistinguishable, especially from the perspective of the Thomsonians, who did not consider Beach a true Botanic, since he recommended bloodletting and was a Regular physician who held membership in the New York Medical Society. Beach did claim to have botanical training in that he began his medical studies as an apprentice to Dr. Jacob Tidd, "a German who had spent time with the American Indian learning their uses of barks and herbs."[63]

Eclectics strongly supported the patenting and manufacture of herbal drugs. Herbal drugs that ultimately became the foundation for the wedding of scientific technology and nature in the field of botanical therapies. The Eclectics developed close professional and economic ties with apothecaries or pharmacists, who were considered doctors in the early 1800s and whose professional development included but was certainly not limited to the development of the American (botanical and chemical) dispensatories or pharmacopoeia used by practitioners. They ultimately developed tests for the adulteration of herbal products and for the identification of phytochemicals. Medicine was becoming as industrialized as many other parts of American culture.

The scientific medical industry grew stronger as the American health care system eventually became more centralized around the practice of the Regulars. Historian William Rothstein concludes: "Medical historians have often argued that scientific medicine constituted the triumph of Regular medicine over homeopathic and Eclectic [e.g., botanical] medicine. . . . Scientific medicine was not a triumph for any sect; it was the death of all sects."[64] A new medical science had emerged with one voice. That which Samuel Thomson had opposed at the top of his voice had indeed occurred, and American medicine and health care were increasingly defined by the American Medical Association (AMA), which began in 1847. In his presidential address of 1901, Charles Reed, president of the AMA, said the following:

> Practice has changed. The depletions, the gross medications [of the Regulars], the absurd attenuations [of the homeopaths], the ridiculous antimineralism [of the Eclectics] have given way to a refined pharmacy, and to a more rational therapy. Sacrificial surgery has yielded to the spirit of conservatism. . . . I proclaim, events proclaim, the existence of a new school of medicine. It is as distinct from the schools of fifty years ago as is the Christian dispensation from its Pagan antecedents. It is the product of convergent influences, of diverse antecedents.[65]

An American pharmacist wrote in the late nineteenth century: "Many plants of which the Eclectics alone first availed themselves have ended up becoming the common property of the entire medical profession."[66] Over time, physicians and pharmacists integrated botanical therapies into their new paradigm of rational science to the point where botanicals often were no longer used as natural or crude medicines. The medicine in vogue was a simple oral tablet or a tiny portion of powder, often tasteless and easy to take. Rational medical science had begun to achieve its goal of dominating nature, as exemplified in learning how to package nature's medicinal secrets and give patients the benefits of herbal remedies without the discomfort of having to experience the bitter tastes of herbs or the inconvenience of messy herbal remedies such as poultices. The botanical medicine industry, the production of oral remedies in particular, along with the invention of chemical drugs, was fast becoming the mark of objective, rational, "scientific" medicine of American industrial society.

BOTANICAL COLOR INSERTS

Descriptions of major medicinal herbs and plants used in early American nursing (1830–1860)

Lobelia inflata

LOBELIA

Lobelia (*Lobelia inflata*) is a plant native to the United States. *King's American Dispensatory* records, "Few drugs are more favored among Eclectic physicians than lobelia, and certainly none others have so interesting a history."[1] *Lobelia inflata* was used by the Cherokee, Crow, and Iroquois Indians in healing and religious practices.[2] Because of its extensive use as an emetic, lobelia was commonly referred to as "emetic weed," "puke weed," or "vomit weed." It also has been used extensively in the care of adults and children with asthma and, therefore, has been known by its common name "asthma weed." The main active principle in lobelia is an alkaloid called lobeline. Lobeline is the constituent known to be an emetic.[3] Lobelia seeds have been shown through chemical analysis to contain high amounts of lobeline, thus supporting the empiric observations of Shaker nurses and physicians that the seeds had greater power to operate as an emetic. The emetic action of lobelia is usually accompanied by perspiration, muscle relaxation, and mental acuity. It also has been used internally for constipation, headache, indigestion, cardiac conditions such as angina, and respiratory complaints such as chronic pneumonia or bronchitis. It has been used externally for skin problems such as eczema and poison ivy and also has been used in sprains and for rheumatic pain.[4] Lobelia is referred to in one Shaker receipt book as an "Anti Scrofula plant which destroys the effects of Mercury, and checks the progress of consumption, Scurvy, King's Evil, Cancers, the Sprew and Dow worm in children."[5] Historically, lobelia was endowed with near panacea-like actions, not unlike antibiotics when they were first discovered a century later. If lobelia did antidote mercury, as Sister Sarah noted, and most likely the Thomsonians believed as well, it would explain the attempts by some to discredit its use.[6]

Aralia nudicaulis

SARSAPARILLA

Sarsaparilla *(Aralia nudicaulis)* has been used traditionally by American Indian tribes such as the Abnaki and Cherokee, as well as the Shakers, for strengthening the blood.[7] Some sources reported the American *Aralia* "sarsaparilla" as being "equally efficacious, if not superior" to smilax.[8] C. S. Rafinesque, a botanist, wrote in 1828 of *Aralia*: "All the Spikenards or Aralias are popular medical plants throughout the United States: they made part of the Materia Medica of the native tribes, and are extensively used by country practitioners. . . . An infusion or a decoction of the same, are efficient substitutes for those of Sarsaparilla (and more powerful) in all diseases of the blood, syphilitic complaints, chronical rheumatism, local pains, cardialgy, bellyache, &c."[9] However, Linnaeus Smilax, M.D., for whom the smilax plant was named, did not agree. He wrote: "But it has not the most distant resemblance to the genuine article, nor is it in any way allied to it, having more the appearance of chopped straw, and, medicinally, about as much virtue. A decoction of this trash, together with other deleterious ingredients, constitutes the compound of that *monster quackery* that now disgraces our metropolis under the assumed name of Sarsaparilla; to which neither the herb, nor the nostrums made from it, have the slightest claim."[10]

Ferula foetida
Daucus carota

- C -

ASAFOETIDA

Asafoetida (*Ferula foetida*) is indigenous to Persia and Tibet and has been commonly used at least since the seventeenth century. The plant is in the Apiaceae or carrot family and has a hairy root like a parsnip. The smell and taste of asafoetida resemble the plants in the Allium family (e.g., onion, garlic). The plant part most commonly imported and used by Americans in the nineteenth century was the gum resin obtained by cutting into the top of the root. The milky juice from the root hardens, is scraped off, and then is set to harden once again. Sliced potatoes were occasionally found to adulterate asafoetida gum resin. The oil and the bitter resin are the active principles in asafoetida. Asafoetida is an antispasmodic and a stimulant, an expectorant, an emmenagogue, and a vermifuge. It has been used by people (particularly women) with nervous irritation, depression, headache, gastrointestinal problems such as flatulence, bronchial cough, menstrual problems, and to increase lactation.[11] It was common into the early twentieth century for children to wear asafoetida in bags around their necks to ward off disease (most likely related to the odor).

- D -

WILD CARROT

The wild carrot referred to in Atkin's story may have been *Daucus carota*, commonly known as "Queen Anne's lace." This plant is in the carrot family, Apiaceae, and the tops look like a garden carrot. The flowers are commonly infused when in full bloom by the Delaware,[12] Mohegan, and Oklahoma[13] Indians for people with diabetes. The root is decocted and used as a blood medicine by the Iroquois[14] Indians. There is some mention of the root being used as a "dermatological aid" (but not necessarily a wound-healing agent), by the Cherokee and Iroquois[15] Indians.

Humulus lupulus

HOPS

The strobiles, or pineconelike flowers of hops (*Humulus lupulus*) were very important to women of the early nineteenth century. Harvesting hops strobiles, the main ingredient used in preserving and flavoring beer, was a large source of income for many European-American women, from the New York area in particular. Hops was grown commercially in New York beginning in 1808. By 1839, New York produced one third of the United States hops crop, and by 1859 it produced seven-eighths of the market.[25] Hops was big business.

Women were considered "an important and skilled labor force, and their wages were the major expense in the hop business."[26] Both local rural women and urban women went to the hops fields in August to pick the crops. They needed no tools, just the ability to work long hours in the hot sun. Farm women supported the migrant hops pickers by sewing comfortable bedding and preparing quality meals. "Because pickers chose employers by the quality of the food and their productivity depended upon it, women's ability to plan, process, and prepare food was crucial."[27] In the late nineteenth century, European-American women hops pickers were replaced with unemployed urban males and then machinery.

Nineteenth-century nurses and physicians also knew the therapeutic benefits of hops. Hops is best known for its hypnotic effects. Hops-stuffed pillows and tea were used to promote sleep. While the mechanism of action for the sleep-inducing effects of hops is basically unknown, the clinical effect is undisputed.[28] Traditionally, hops also was used topically as a compress or poultice for swelling, inflammation, wounds, nerve pain, rheumatism, pneumonia, and abdominal spasms and discomfort.[29]

A constituent in hops, 8-prenylnaringenin, has been shown to have greater phytoestrogenic activity than genistein and daidzein, two well-known isoflavonoid phytoestrogens found in soy (*Glycine max*) and red clover (*Trifolium pratense*), for example.[30] Women who handpick hops have been known to develop menstrual irregularities. Could there be physical or medical reasons why so many (married) women of the early nineteenth century wanted to handpick hops in the hot August sun? The women may have known from interaction with their social networks that hops picking had therapeutic value, that it was one way to delay pregnancy for a period of time. During the nineteenth century, many women were diagnosed by male physicians as suffering from hysteria and related nervous disorders. Women also may have entered into hops picking for the sedative effect picking the strobiles had on the nervous system.

Papaver somniferum

POPPY

Poppy is an annual with a large white or scarlet flower head with four petals and a hairy stem that is 2 to 5 feet long. The leaves are alternate and 4 to 8 inches in length and 2 to 3 inches wide. The flower capsules that remain after the petals fall away contain the juice from which opium is formed. It also contains numerous seeds that are eaten or pressed for oil used in cooking or burning. The medicinal properties of poppy, such as narcotic and sedative properties, are derived from the alkaloids in the plant which are found primarily in the capsule juice and to a much lesser degree in the rest of the plant. The seeds, however, contain no opium alkaloids.[31]

The juice is harvested from the capsule by cutting the capsule in a specific way. The capsule is cut on a hot afternoon so that the juice dries rapidly. The opium is then collected in poppy leaves and formed into cakes. Opium taken in appropriate doses is narcotic and pain relieving, is sedative in some circumstances, and has historically been used as an antispasmodic, febrifuge, and diaphoretic. Large doses are poisonous. Opium has been used as medicine at least since the times of the ancient Greeks, 370 B.C. It was taken orally and applied externally.

Poppy-derived opium was used to relieve discomfort associated with inflammatory disease, rheumatic neuralgia, and gout. Various recipes for tincture of opium, known as "laudanum," were used orally in the nineteenth century for pain relief. Poppy syrup was given to children and adults for such complaints as pain, calming the nervous system, cough, dysentery, and diarrhea. The crushed capsules have been combined with chamomile flowers and applied topically as a poultice for pain.[32]

Rosa gallica

ROSE

A thorough description of the numerous ways rose (rosa gallica) petals have been used therapeutically throughout history could fill an entire book. A few of those uses are mentioned here. First, rose petals are edible and the rose water made from them is often used in the culinary arts. Therapeutically, rose petals are antimicrobial, anti-inflammatory, tonic, and astringent, and are used both internally and externally. A decoction of red rose, combined with white wine was used for headache and pain in the eyes, ears, and throat. Rose fragrance is hypnotic[33] and is often used to calm the nerves.

Rose has historically been used for the skin. Powdered dried rose petals are applied topically in diaper rash and rose water is used by women to soften and tone the skin. Rose water and ointment have traditionally been used to relieve heat and inflammation of the head, forehead, and temples. Rose water has been used in washing sores on the skin.[34] Rose is a good example in herbalism of how numerous remedies are created from a single plant or part of a plant.

Capsicum frutescens

CAYENNE

Cayenne (*Capsicum frutescens, or annuum*) is a member of the Solanaceae plant family. The word "cayenne" is from the Greek word "to bite," alluding to the pungent properties contained in the pepper and the seeds. There are several species of capsicum, all varying in their degrees of pungency. The earliest evidence of the use of cayenne pepper in the human diet is from excavations in Mexico that show that cayenne was being cultivated as early as 7,000 years ago[16] and continues to be eaten today with almost every meal. The pepper is eaten as a vegetable when either green or red, in the raw, dried, pickled, or cooked state. It is used all over the world to add a pungent, spicy flavor to many foods. Varieties of chili provide a wide range of heat, from the hot, spicy types to the cool, sweet green of the bell pepper. Pungency is determined by a taste test and is usually expressed in Scoville (heat) units or British thermal units (BTUs).[17]

In Western herbalism, cayenne is known as a warm, powerful stimulant and is often used to increase circulation. "Cayenne has been used in folk remedies for asthma, dyspepsia, low back pain, sore throats, pneumonia, rheumatism, and skin sores. It has been used for treating cancer and tumors and is regarded as an aphrodisiac, a stimulant to the central nervous system, a digestive aide, and a tonic with the ability to induce sweating, dispel intestinal gas, and promote cessation of hemorrhage through astringent action."[18] Cayenne has a history of use in reducing chronic renal congestion by increasing capillary activity and reducing irritation. It affects the bladder and rectum similarly in cases of bladder spasms, diarrhea, constipation, and hemorrhoids. It has been used to treat low-grade fevers where there is dryness and constriction of the tissues with dry tongue and diminished salivary secretion. Cayenne also has been used internally for flatulence, angina pectoris, low body heat, depressed vitality, "sluggish" body reactions, and tired and painful muscles. Externally, cayenne infusion and tincture have been used as a gargle for a sore throat and as a compress for skin ulcers, chilblains, or toothache.[19]

Cayenne grows easily in the southwest area of the United States. Many indigenous Americans have used it as food, such as in stews and soups, and as a condiment. The Cherokee Indians take the plant medicine internally for colds and for the treatment of colic or apply poultices to the soles of the feet in gangrene or nervous or low fevers.[20] Hispanic Americans drink a mild tea made from red "chili" (the Aztec name for cayenne pepper) to "warm the bones" during colder winter months. Chili caribe, a mild red chili, is used to increase circulation, and the chili powder is even put into shoes to warm the feet. Salves are made from cayenne to put on the chest to loosen mucous.[21]

"Cayenne is used as a powerful local stimulant with no narcotic effect. It is applied topically as a liniment or a poultice to cause a counterirritant effect, the reddening of the skin by increasing the local circulation. It causes dilation of the vessels that, in turn, increases the supply of blood to the area of the body. Cayenne tincture and the extract of capsaicin, a plant constituent, are used in topical counterirritant preparations to treat arthritis, rheumatism, neuralgia, low back pain, and mild frostbite."[22] Cayenne is foundational to American herbalism. In 1939, Jethro Kloss, the author of a classic American herbal text, *Back to Eden*, wrote: "The key to success in medicine is stimulation, and capsicum is the great stimulant. There are many languid people who need something to make the fire of life burn more brightly. Capsicum, not whiskey, is the thing to do it."[23] He clarifies cayenne's stimulating action in that it is different from other medicinal substances. "It seems almost incapable of abuse, for however great the excitement produced by it, this stimulant prevents the excitement subsiding so suddenly as to induce any great derangement of the equilibrium of the circulation. It produces the most powerful impression on the surface, yet never draws a blister; on the stomach, yet never weakens its tone. It is so diffusive in its character that it never produces any local lesion, or induces permanent inflammation. . . . Capsicum has a wonderful place in inflammation. We have often been told that it would burn the lining of the stomach, and our medical, as well as lay friends, have at times shown fear at its use. We assure the student that the fear of capsicum is unfounded. We have used it freely for over a quarter of a century, and therefore feel that our experience is worth more than the opinions of those who know nothing about it experimentally."[24]

Kloss's writings demonstrate the ongoing tension between the experienced herbalists and the medical doctors (into the twentieth century) who are unknowledgeable and inexperienced in the use of botanical therapies. The people and practitioners who used the "old ways," such as the use of cayenne, had a set of health beliefs substantiated by observable evidence from experience in successfully using the botanical therapy many times. Many Americans and Latter-day Saints used Thomsonianism and other botanical therapies because the remedies were known, effective, and trusted.

Chapter 3

The Mid-Nineteenth-Century Patient: Herbs, Advice Books, and Medical Freedom

> I know of no safe depository of the ultimate powers of the society but the people themselves: and if we think them not enlightened enough to exercise their control with a wholesome discretion, the remedy is not to take it from them, but to inform their discretion by education. [1]
>
> —Thomas Jefferson, letter to William C. Jarvis, in *The Writings of Thomas Jefferson*

This chapter focuses on the history of the mid-nineteenth-century American patient, her or his health beliefs, self-care and health-seeking behaviors, and medicines. American health care culture during the period 1830–1860 had become centered on the belief in "being one's own doctor" and on the pursuit of medical freedom through education to improve one's health through self-care. This chapter begins with a historical example of the experience of a nineteenth-century patient. It then continues with an overview of the self-care advice books of the period, which were very popular with patients who desired freedom from reliance upon doctors. Herbals also are included in the exploration of the advice books of the period. The chapter concludes with a brief exploration of the medicines available to the nineteenth-century patient, in particular, the contribution of the patent medicine industry.

One way to begin to identify and define the role of the mid-nineteenth-century nurse is to construct the social context from which the "nurse" can emerge. Because the identity and the role of the nurse are defined in terms of the relationship with her patients, describing the patient as part of the social context can be used to assist in the process of revealing the historical identity of the nurse. The following is a synopsis of the diary accounts of one such nineteenth-century patient, Homer Merriam, of the Merriam family from Massachusetts, publishers of the now-famous American dictionaries.

In 1862, Homer Merriam wrote of his life, beginning with his birth in 1813 to his elder years in California in 1908.[2] In his autobiography, Merriam vividly describes his health beliefs and the variety of opportunities and choices in health care that he faced in his quest for health. Many of Merriam's health beliefs and experiences are fairly typical of the mid-nineteenth-century American health care culture. Merriam begins his life story with the heading "bad reading." He describes his health belief that his excessive love of reading novels or the "most exciting scenes of history" weakened his memory and mental digestion, secluded him from society, gave him "false views of life," and "tended to pervert by lack of exercise the strengthening of his body."[3] In 1835, at age twenty-two, he sold his library and went to work for his brothers, which also "afforded little exercise." He found himself "feeling badly, with symptoms which I did not then but do now understand to denote dyspepsia, jaundice, etc."[4]

Merriam began his quest for better health by changing the climate in which he lived and moving to Cincinnati, Ohio. His doctors had told him to go to the country for his health, so he moved in with a Quaker family on their farm. His diet consisted of "mush and hasty pudding" during that time. He described visiting some friends in Indiana during which time he went to consult a physician "accounted as skillful." "He [the doctor] said I seemed to have no disease, but that he never knew a person able to be about with a pulse so slow as mine, which gave only about thirty beats in a minute. He advised me to return East and remain there until I felt well, and I decided to do this, though it was with much reluctance that I gave up the West."[5] He tried to go back East on horseback, thinking that the ride would be better for his health, but ultimately he returned by stage coach in the company of a friend.

When he returned East, he lived with his mother, worked a little, "rode his brother's horse, and took medicine." He was "largely dosed" by Dr. Woodward of the Insane Hospital of Worcester without "good effects" and then was advised to go on a fishing voyage, which he did. When he returned, still in 1835, he went to Saratoga, New York (now called "Saratoga Springs" because of its healing mineral springs), and saw a physician, Dr. Weeks, whom he described as "seeming to understand my case better than any physician I had before consulted, was very sanguine that in a few months I should gain good health."[6] He remained in Saratoga for a few weeks and then went to work for his brothers in Massachusetts, testing his health. He recorded: "But on leaving Saratoga and the daily free use of the Congress water, I seemed at once to run down, my tongue becoming thickly coated, my insatiable appetite returning (this had been one of the strong symptoms of my ill health)."[7] He subsequently returned to Saratoga, this time to remain for a number of seasons during which time he married his physician's daughter.

He was ultimately pronounced "cured" in Saratoga, but after leaving there he once again felt "run down." In what he called "a sort of desperation," he decided to take the advice of an acquaintance with similar symptoms who had been helped by an Indian doctress. He went to Norwich, Massachusetts and lived in the home of the Indian doctress for four months. He describes the doctress as being eighty years old with a reputation in the county that was quite good, in that she had "cured or helped a good many sick people." He wrote that the doctress had a son in his fifties who gathered roots and herbs for her and prepared them as medicine, and that the doctress had a "good knowledge" and "good degree of skill" in the use of herbs. He "improved very decidedly in health, taking pretty freely of various preparations of roots and herbs . . . and did not run down again as I had done after leaving Saratoga, but continued in comfortable health."[8] He wrote that he was at least able to "attend to business" for twenty-four years after the healing with the Indian doctress. He seemed to have found a new level of wellness.

However, during his life he would suffer "nervous headaches," often every day. He wrote of seeking to cure himself by spending "seven or eight weeks in a water cure establishment" in Brattleboro, Vermont, consulting physicians, and going to the mountains in the summer with his family. In 1852, he describes a "radical change" in his life, in that he left the family business to improve his health by moving to a farm. It was not until 1893, in his eighties, long after the death of his first wife from breast cancer and his remarriage, that Homer Merriam wrote for the first time, "I have good health and vigor for my age."[9]

After 1900, his autobiography also contains accounts of his family being attended to by a variety of practitioners, such as a "lady physician," a "homeopath," an "allopathic physician," and a number of private-duty "nurses." While there is no reference in his writings to the social and political issues of medical freedom, which were present during the nineteenth century, he does clearly demonstrate the self-direction, power, and freedom of the nineteenth-century patient, who often was inclined to try various healing modalities and do whatever it took to achieve better health.

A Turning Point in Medical Freedom

American health care culture was at a major turning point in history in the mid-nineteenth century. Society was in conflict between sustaining and improving the "system" of domestic health care, which had existed in the United States for centuries, and allowing the emergence of a dominant medical culture. At the center of the changes occurring during the period we also find not only Regular physicians, Botanics, and legislators, but as in any democracy, we also find the people—the American patients.

Through participation in health care reform, many mid-nineteenth-century Americans found a personal way to experience and express their desire for freedom. As mentioned in chapter 2, self-care practices and "being one's own doctor" were synonymous with medical freedom. In colonial America, the health care of both rich and poor Americans was carried out in the home, most often by women. But home life was swiftly changing. Americans saw the effects of the changes in what was once an agrarian society quickly becoming an industrialized, urban-focused nation. Husbands went to work in the cities, leaving women to take up the majority of the work in sustaining the home. The American health care reform movement of the nineteenth century can be seen, at least in part, as a response to the pains of industrialization. As health care had always been a part of the domestic work, the expanding role of domestic health care services paralleled the expansion of women's domestic work.

With changes in the domestic scene came changes in health beliefs and practices. Americans, often discouraged with the unsuccessful activities of the Regulars, believed that they had individual accountability and control over their health, whereas in previous generations, people practiced quiet resignation to the will of God. "People were beginning to reject the notion that illness was a result of the infliction of a Divine Providence. Health reform advocates, both secular and Regular, shared the belief in the prevention of disease through understanding the laws of physiology and hygiene."[10] American patients, under the tutelage of health care reformers, came to believe that health care reform was the vehicle for self-improvement and, therefore, ultimately for the betterment of society, individual by individual. "Health reform constituted part of a larger cultural response to the pressures and strains of a modernizing nation."[11]

How a community heals is a vital part of that culture. Health care has been defined as a "total social resource."[12] Health beliefs are not only an expression of a particular culture, but they can be the foundation for greater social change. Nineteenth-century Americans, in particular, women, believed that they had the power to create a fresh culture by embracing the new health beliefs and strategies of knowledgeable health care reformers. The focus of mid-nineteenth-century health care reform was the promotion of social progress through individual accountability for one's health. Health care reformers taught that improvement of the individual was a means to the larger cultural change of social regeneration. They offered the possibility not only of prevention of disease but of the prolongation of life.

Health care reform beliefs and philosophies and the leaders associated with them were often at the center of nineteenth-century society. It was a period in which numerous health sects flourished, with each sect expressing its views and promoting its health strategies under the protection of the U.S. Constitution, often in a tremendous spirit of competition. Health care reformers, such as Samuel Thomson and Sylvester Graham,[13] not only promoted a message of health promotion through individual responsibility, but they also called upon Americans to demand that health and medical care be democratic, and that no one sect of health practitioners be favored over another. In addition, a popular nineteenth-century belief was that science was to be democratic, and that "Insofar as medicine was valid and useful, it ought also to be plain and simple."[14] People and many practitioners believed that the public should have complete access to health-related knowledge. Other social leaders, such as Reverend John Wesley (1703–1791) of Britain, set the stage in the late eighteenth century for mid-nineteenth-century reform when he observed the following:

> As theories increased, simple medicines were more and more disregarded and disused. . . . In the room of these, abundance of new ones were introduced, by reasoning, speculative men; and those more and more difficult to be applied, as being more remote from common observation . . . till at length physic became an abstruse [*sic*] science; quite out of the reach of ordinary men.[15]

Health care reformers who publicly condemned the work of the Regulars were soon joined by the many Americans who were growing skeptical of the claims of university-educated physicians. "Many Americans who already had a rationalist, activist orientation to disease refused to accept physicians as authoritative. They believed that common sense and native intelligence could deal as effectively with most problems of health and illness."[16] By mid century, criticism of orthodox medical practice had reached astonishing proportions; Regulars had good reason to be on the defensive. The practice, or "so-called *science* of medicine, has been little else than one of experiment, observed Mrs. Marie Louise Shew in a scathing indictment. Standard medical therapeutics, she claimed, had hitherto been characterized by 'uncertainty' and 'chance'. Little progress had been made in alleviating the sufferings of mankind."[17]

But the Regulars continued to gain professional strength by marginalizing other health sects (such as the homeopaths, Botanic physicians, midwives, and self-educated doctor-healers) and diminishing the importance of self-care and domestic care by defining their ways of providing health care as the only "real" care. Slowly and surely the Regulars built their professional image as learned professionals, set apart as providing advanced healing skills, techniques, and modalities. They sought to monopolize medical and health care practice when they "constituted only a fraction of the total number of medical advisors."[18] It would not be too long before medical care was to become synonymous with health care in the minds of the American public. Self-care would be subjugated by it.

Self-Care and Cultural Authority

Greater urbanization and the industrialization of society, especially toward the end of the nineteenth century, brought with it a greater willingness on the part of American citizens—especially in the towns—to accept and pay for the services of physicians.[19] At first, domestic medicine did not differ much from the medicine practice by the early physicians. "Elite physicians and ordinary housewives shared a medical paradigm and used similar cures."[20] A good housewife in colonial times created recipes for healing through imitation and education from numerous sources. In pioneer times, health care and medical information and resources were shared in the interest of family and community survival. Self-care was practical and simple, and the tools people used most often included the natural, accessible remedies that one could grow outside of one's back door, such as healing plants.

Later American patients, in particular the women who were now running the homes single-handedly while their spouses joined industrial workforces, began to participate in the commodification of health and medical care. They embraced the lifestyle and diet-based health care reforms of various health care leaders in their daily hygienic and self-care practices. They purchased supplies and accompanying instructional materials. They also had Regulars and other healers visit their families in their homes to provide care. People's self-care practices, also called "domestic medicine," were changing as a result of the influence of the numerous health care sects' community health education and promotion programs being conducted through newspapers, books, journals, and public lectures and by word of mouth.

The American medical profession continued to grow, as did the population of the United States. By 1830, the medical profession had become crowded with applicants and had created more than twenty medical schools, whereas in 1800, less than six were in existence. At the end of the mid-nineteenth century, there were still too many physicians and too many medical schools given the population and the effective demand. And given the Jacksonian health care reformers' success in controlling the medical monopoly, the popularity of the health care reform message, and the public's increasing interest in self-care, it is no wonder that there was a boom in the self-care advice book market during this period. While not the first time in history that a nation had been interested in the topic of self-care, the nineteenth-century advice book and self-care movement constituted the first "wide-scale health-reform movement in American history."[21]

Self-care, taking care of oneself and one's family, was an expression of the pioneer spirit that was part of American character. Thomas Jefferson brought with him to his presidency his personal strong belief in the importance of health promotion and self-care. In a letter to his favorite nephew and student, he wrote: "Health is the first requisite after morality."[22] Thomas Jefferson himself attributed his remarkable health to his self-care practices of eating a primarily vegetarian diet, living temperately, and taking daily morning cold-water footbaths.[23]

In the nineteenth century, self-care was an expression of individual liberty and responsibility for health, so one was best able to contribute to building a great democracy. While Samuel Thomson stressed the importance of opposing the medical monopoly of the university-educated physician, other medical freedom activists and self-care advisors were working with the public to create a new health care culture that valued health promotion and disease prevention. Americans believed that their personal responsibility for hygiene and a healthy lifestyle affected the health of their families and society as well as their own personal health. Health care reformers taught self-care techniques that the public could apply within its own homes, making it easy for the adoption of such practices. And while Americans may have been hungry for independence from Regulars and heroic medicines, they would not have accepted health care practices that did not "work."

Nineteenth-century American cultural values regarding health included the freedom to explore all health options and to discover what "worked." During this period, the Regulars, as well as leaders from other health care sects, strove to obtain authority and recognition of their recommendations for what would "work" to relieve suffering. They competed for cultural authority,[24] the ultimate acceptance of their beliefs, thoughts, and values, their definition of reality in terms of what constituted appropriate, safe, and effective health care. While some Regulars clearly demonstrated through their lectures, writings, and practice that they claimed no monopoly on healing, many believed that they had a duty to educate the public about the science of medicine and to drive out "quacks."

Just as some Regulars, as will be discussed later in this chapter, wrote their advice books to help their fellow citizens "be their own doctors," others wrote in an attempt to define the "real" practice of medicine and to expose all other health philosophies, beliefs, and practices as "quackery." These Regulars claimed that because they had the knowledge and wisdom needed to be good physicians, their civic duty was to protect the public from "quacks." But health care reformers and other practitioners claimed that it was the Regulars themselves who were the real "quacks," and that the public could protect itself. They pleaded for continued freedom of choice in health care and their right to voice opinions contrary to the orthodoxy. Health education was one way that both "sides" deemed it necessary to help the public identify "quacks."

Retrospectively, some may equate the changes in health care that occurred during the mid-nineteenth century with reform leaders such as Samuel Thomson; however, the changes occurred as much as a result of a change in ideology, beliefs, and values and a change in cultural "objects" (i.e., the introduction of advice books, botanical protocols), as well as a change in social actors (i.e., social authority figures). As mentioned previously, Americans viewed health care reform as a way to save the nation. Health reform of the mid-nineteenth century took on some of the characteristics of a religion with an organized set of attitudes, beliefs, and practices with health care reform leaders as spiritual guides. Although medicine, since the time of Francis Bacon, had seemingly achieved a separation from religion, it could not claim to have achieved a separation from cultural beliefs and practices. And it was these beliefs and practices that the American public challenged. Successful sect leaders such as Graham and Thomson could not have succeeded without the cultural authority granted to them by the American people.

Cultural authority is differentiated from social authority. Social authority is about the authority of an individual. A physician attempting to exert authority over patients, nurses, and other practitioners is an example of the expression of social authority. Cultural authority emerges from the realm of meanings and ideas and is defined by Starr as "the probability that particular definitions of reality and judgments of meaning and value will prevail as valid and true."[25] One example of cultural authority is the Regulars' attempt to fashion society's definition of health care to include the services of physicians as gatekeepers of quality health care.

Nineteenth-century Americans challenged both the social and cultural authority of the Regulars. Rejecting a form of cultural authority, such as the health beliefs of Regular physicians, was a logical result of strongly held democratic views. The beliefs of mid-nineteenth-century Americans about medical freedom and the way people valued commonsense self-care practices were seemingly more powerful than any fears that might have emerged from listening to the claims of the Regulars. Many people rejected the Regulars' claims that they were more knowledgeable about health and medicine, and that their care was inherently safer. They also rejected the claim of the Regulars that self-care and following the advice of books, reformers, and other practitioners were potentially harmful.

The concept of self-care was implicit in the health care reformers' theory of coping with sickness. For many nineteenth-century health care reformers, disease was the balancing effort of nature to overcome or cast out of the body some impurity or poison that interfered with a healthy life. Since the natural condition of a person was good health, to keep well he or she needed only to avoid unwise practices, such as eating the wrong foods and losing control of his or her "passions." It was believed that a person rarely needed to pay for the help of a Regular and did not need heroic medicines such as calomel, blistering, and bleeding. A mid-nineteenth-century cultural belief was that a person's knowledge of his or her own physical nature would make him or her free. It was in the midst of this tremendous shift to the democratic health care culture of the common person that the boom in self-care advice books, that often included herbal remedies, emerged anew.

The Literary Legend of the Advice Movement

Regulars, Botanics, other health practitioners, and writers of the mid-nineteenth century all participated in the health advice book movement. The growth of literacy and industry and the waning of traditional structures of apprenticeship and household training made it both practical and necessary to offer in print form the kinds of practical instruction that in an earlier era might have been transmitted orally. Literacy was highly valued during the period. Census records demonstrate that by 1840, 83 percent of the total population of the U.S. Census was made up of free whites and of those whites over age twenty, 96 percent were literate.[26] While records indicate that 2 percent of the population was free blacks and 15 percent "colored slaves," no literacy records were available for these groups. In general, northern states, such as Massachusetts, with as few as one or no slaves reported for its population, had literacy rates for free whites over age twenty as high as 99 percent. The success of the Botanics and other reformers with the "common" white American citizen was most likely a result of their written materials as well as their house-by-house marketing strategies and their work on the lecture circuits.

Much of the health advice used in the domestic care of the common American family was recorded in the receipt books of the female head of household. The contribution of receipt books to the understanding of the nineteenth-century patient, the nurse, and the use of botanical therapies will be discussed in more detail in chapter 4. The most broadly distributed and seemingly the most popular of all advice books were those written by the Regulars, the Botanics, and other healers.

Samuel Thomson's botanical therapies advice book, first published in 1820 as the *New Guide to Health, or, Botanic Family Physician,* was one of the most popular in America. It describes over thirty protocols for the prevention and cure of disease. The theory of increasing the natural heat in the body, especially in the bowels and the stomach, was at the center of Thomson's theory.[27] Between 1820 and 1834, Thomson sold thirteen editions of the advice book, and the Thomsonian system of botanical therapies was claimed to have been used by 2 million people.[28] The biggest rival to Thomson was Wooster Beach, the founder of the Eclectics discussed in chapter 2. His botanical advice book, *The Family Physician; or The Reformed System of Medicine: on Vegetable or Botanical Principles,* while perhaps not as widespread was also very popular, especially since he included a section in his book on midwifery.[29]

Women also were leaders in the advice book movement. Two mid-nineteenth-century women of note were Elizabeth Mott and Mary Gove Nichols. While little is published on the historical contribution of Mott (of England) to American health care, she is recorded as the model of a woman doctor that inspired Harriot Hunt, the first successful American woman physician. Mott and her husband, Dr. Richard Mott, arrived in Boston in 1833, and she returned to England in 1835 after the death of her husband. During her brief time in Boston, Mott not only influenced the life of an American health care pioneer, but she helped heal numerous women. The only extant accounting of her work is recorded in her descriptive advice book, *The Ladies Medical Oracle; or, Mrs. Mott's Advice to Young Females, Wives, and Mothers Being a Non-Medical Commentary on the Cause, Prevention, and Cure of Diseases of the Female Frame together with an Explanation of Her*

System of European Vegetable Medicine for the Cure of Diseases and the Patent Medicated Champoo Baths.[30]

Mott was the seventh daughter of a seventh daughter, often a birth position believed by early Americans to indicate an innate gift of healing in males or females. Her advice book does indeed indicate that she not only had a European background in health care but was a gifted healer. The book opens with a picture of her establishment and a description of her as a female "physician" who administers *her own* "Systematic Vegetable Medicines." While some historians have equated her system with the Thomsonian system,[31] Mott's *Oracle* and system of remedies, as well as the manner to which she speaks of her system of healing primarily with baths and botanical applications, do not reflect the popular Thomsonian botanical system of the period. In fact, it could be interpreted that she differentiates herself from the harsher, botanical treatments of the Thomsonians as well as the treatments of the Regulars when she writes: "Lest my fair readers should feel alarmed, I beg to inform them, Emetics, Cold Water, Hot Medicines, or violent applications form no part of this system."[32] Mott's system is much more reminiscent of European, in particular, French, tradition.

Mott mentions different modalities in general use in France in a number of places in her advice book. An excellent example of her unique practice in European herbalism which often includes hydrotherapeutic applications is in her description of the remedy for inflammation of the intestines.[33] Mott recommends a combination of remedies, including sitz baths, cataplasms for the feet, and a fomentation for the bowels made from chamomile, poppy heads, and cajeput oil, a wineglassful of "No. 1," charcoal water, and a "low" diet. The rational use of this botanical protocol for the purpose stated could even be explained by a naturopathic physician or herbalist today. For example, the chamomile is antispasmodic, especially to the intestines, poppy is used to relieve pain and is antispasmodic, and cajeput essential oil is also anti-inflammatory. She concludes the work with a humble farewell to her supporters and a word of assurance to those who had opposed her practice that she would continue her work because she is ultimately encouraged by her "inward monitor" that tells her that her work is empowered by "Divine Goodness."[34]

Mary Gove Nichols (1810–1884) was a mid-nineteenth-century pioneer in women's health, sexuality, and water cure. Her advice writings were published in journals, especially water cure journals. Her public lectures to women on anatomy and physiology, women's dress, and water cure also were published.[35] She collaborated closely with her second husband, Thomas Nichols, also a water cure physician, for the cause of universal happiness and good health. She wrote and spoke particularly to the needs of the nineteenth-century woman.

The role of the American woman was changing in the mid-nineteenth century. Advice books emerged in part to address the new needs of women in particular at a time when a new cultural ideology was emerging. Families were much more mobile, therefore, women often had increasingly less contact with and mentoring from their mothers and grandmothers. Domestic advice books were to quickly fill the cultural gap left in the separation of women from their family mentors.

One of the most popular mid-nineteenth-century advice books on the domestic arts was written by Lydia Maria Child. Although it was initially difficult to find a publisher due to the glut of domestic advice books on the market, Child was able to convince a publisher to take her project, *The American Frugal Housewife,* because it had been written for the middle-class woman, not the wealthy woman. A second edition of her book was published within three months of the first sales in 1829. Domestic advice books of the period typically covered health care and nursing duties as well as household responsibilities, cookery, and instructions on the care of children. Child's *The American Frugal Housewife* includes a number of "simple remedies" for conditions such as earache, dysentery, wounds, headache, lockjaw, and colds. She includes numerous botanical therapies, such as blackberry root and leaf tea or berry syrup for dysentery, which she said has "affected a cure when physicians despaired,"[36] as well as English mallows for colic and dysentery. She states, "Everybody knows of course, that English mallows and marshmallows are different herbs."[37]

While Child had no formal or informal health care, medical, or botanical expertise, her advice books were well received, save one, *The*

Family Nurse.[38] It was not the content that caused the poor acceptance of this advice book but the fact that Americans had learned of the author's allegiance to the antislavery movement that in the 1830s was a highly controversial subject. Regardless, *The Family Nurse* was first published in 1837. Because Child was not a nurse, she wrote that she relied on medical texts as references and a review of the book by a physician to ensure the "safety" of her advice. She also consulted "aged relatives and judicious nurses"[39] in preparing the advice book.

The Family Nurse includes an entire section on the use of botanicals entitled, "Common Medicines." The use of plants such as sage, dandelion, balm, hop vine, ginseng, burdock, and horseradish, for example, is described in minor detail. A section on how to make and apply certain botanical therapies such as poultices and ointments is also included. Women like Elizabeth Mott, Mary Gove Nichols, and Lydia Maria Child opened the door for the expansion of women's health networks through the medium of advice books and for the emergence of other media such as *Godey's Lady's Book,* a popular "lady's" journal of the mid-nineteenth century, which will be discussed further in chapter 4.

The Regulars' Contribution to the Advice Movement

While a number of Regular physicians added to the health advice book market of the nineteenth century, their history reaching out to the common person with health care advice had begun much earlier. Dr. William Buchan's advice book, *Domestic Medicine, or, The Family Physician,* originally written and published in 1769 in Britain and later published in America, was one of the first and was still popular in mid-nineteenth-century America. The subtitle of the book set the foundation for the purpose of all subsequent advice books: *Being an Attempt to Render the Medical Art More Generally Useful By Shewing the People What Is in Their Own Power Both with Respect to the Prevention and Cure of Diseases.*[40] Buchan's advice centered on lifestyle and diet, in other words, preventive health care. He wrote about the importance of proper child care as the foundation for health in adulthood, and he said that child care is the realm of women, not medical men. He identified the general causes of disease as "catching cold, unwholesome food, irregularities of diet, bad air, and infection." Particular causes of disease included "laborious employments, sedentary employments, and intense study."

Buchan also identified remedies to be used by the common citizen, including simple botanical remedies. Botanicals cited in *Domestic Medicine* include rhubarb, jalap, senna, Jesuit's bark, snake root, licorice root, wild valerian root, and syrup of poppies, oranges, and lemons, to name a few. Buchan said that these medicines should be kept in every "gentlemen's family." He also demonstrated his belief in the value of nursing practice in self-care and disease prevention when he wrote, "The first part of prophylaxis is calculated to shew the importance of proper nursing."[41]

Though he was a Regular, in his advice book Buchan also set the foundation for American health care reformers' opposition to the medical monopoly. He wrote the following about the practice of medicine:

> So far medicine is evidently found in nature, and is quite consistent with reason and common sense. . . . Every attempt therefore to monopolize or conceal anything that relates to the preservation of health or the cure of diseases must not only be injurious to the interests of society, but likewise detrimental to the medical art.[42]

Kentucky Regular physician John Gunn and other Americans followed suit. Not long after the first American printings of Buchan's advice books, Gunn too, wrote his own book, *Domestic Medicine or Poor Man's Friend in the Hours of Affliction.*[43] As the "poor man's friend," Gunn provides the reader with simple remedies and explanations for disease and health promotion. He wrote, "God, in the infinitude of His mercy, has stored our mountains, fields and meadows with simples for healing our diseases and for furnishing us with medicines of our own, without the use of foreign articles."[44]

The participation by Regular physicians, such as Gunn in the advice book movement, could be viewed as an act of cultural diplomacy. Many of the Regulars' advice books were written in an attempt to bring medical care back to the people and create an image of the learned physician as teacher and advice giver. The Regulars' advice books were indeed very popular. While the intent of some Regular physicians, such as Buchan and Gunn, may have been to change the course of medicine as it seemed to move toward professional monopoly, the ultimate result of their humanitarian efforts may have actually added to the ultimate success of endearing the American public to the cause of those Regulars who wanted full social and cultural authority in medicine.

Gunn's advice book extols the virtues of the uncultivated wild American countryside as a provider of thousands of plant medicines yet unexplored. He notes the importance of the scientific observations of Meriwether Lewis regarding the uses of medicinal plants by the American Indian during his expedition with William Clark from 1803 to 1806.

National Self-Care

Immigration to America can perhaps be viewed as European-Americans' first act of self-care. They believed the advice of friends and family, that there would be a better life in America. They also believed in democracy and followed leaders such as Thomas Jefferson in the quest to carve out a "new" nation. There was a parallel process between the self-sufficiency that Americans sought as a nation and the individual nineteenth-century American's search for spiritual, political, and health care reform that reflected the value of self-care. Jefferson, as a national leader, had stressed the importance of maintaining a self-sufficient, agrarian nation. One of the major acts of his presidency was commissioning the Lewis and Clark expedition.

The primary goals of the expedition centered on the need to explore the Missouri River and the West in an effort to ultimately expand trade to the Pacific Ocean and to engage Indians in trade with Americans. Another purpose of the mission is relevant to understanding the greater historical context of the success of the Botanical Medical Movement in the nineteenth century. The Lewis and Clark expedition also was a botanical expedition to explore American flora and the American Indian's botanical remedies.

Thomas Jefferson was a botanist and was fluent in a number of American Indian languages. He understood the value of beginning to study American botanicals for use in health care. He also knew the importance of diminishing American citizens' reliance on expensive botanical imports. In preparation for the expedition, Jefferson sent his good friend, Captain Meriwether Lewis, to Philadelphia for an education in botany with Benjamin Smith Barton, a leading botanist and physician of the time. Lewis also studied medicine with Dr. Casper Wistar, a German physician, and with Dr. Benjamin Rush, also a friend of Jefferson's.[45]

Lewis's healing skills would be tested a number of times during the expedition. His practice would "consist of the use of a few herbal and chemical medications, some of his mother's medical-herb knowledge, and some practical skills acquired during his army career."[46] Lewis's mother and botanical teacher, Lucy Meriwether Lewis Marks of Virginia, was well known throughout the county in which she lived for her healing and herbal skills.[47] She visited the sick in their homes well into her later years. Lewis demonstrated his botanical skills when he was sick with "violent pain in the intestens [*sic*]" and fever. He wrote the following in his journal on June 11, 1805:

> Having brought no medicine with me I resolve to try an experiment with some simples; and the Choke cherry which grew abundantly in the bottom first struck my attention; I directed a parsel of the small twigs to be gathered striped of their leaves, cut into pieces of about 2 inches in length and boiled in water until a strong black decoction of an astringent bitter taste was produced; at sunset I took a point [pint] of this decoction and about an hour after repeated the d[o]ze. By 10 in the evening I was entirely relieved from pain and in fact every symptom of the disorder forsook me; my fever abated, a gentle perspiration was produced, and I had a comfortable and refreshing night's rest.[48]

In June 1805, Lewis recorded the details of the health care he provided to American Indian Sacajawea, a woman who traveled with the expedition to facilitate the purchase of horses from the Indians. She took very ill after the birth of her baby and was initially bled by Clark. She was getting worse until Lewis used a number of remedies, including drinking sulfur mineral water from a nearby spring, oral opium for pain, cataplasms (compress) of barks, and laudanum.[49] Lewis and Clark's expedition was very successful. The two established many links with American Indians through their efforts. It is possible that the botanical aspects of the expedition, which concluded in 1806, may have contributed to the later success of the Botanical Medical Movement and the Thomsonians in the 1830s.

Botanical Advice—Herbals

Botanical advice books, historically referred to as "herbals," also are significant in understanding the nineteenth-century advice movement. Herbals, or books about the use of healing plants, often contain a description of each of the plants included in the text and suggestions for each plant's application in healing. Herbals can be identified historically throughout the literature by different names, such as "materia medica," "dispensatories," "formularies," or "botanicals," and they often are a major portion of other texts, such as housewife guides, receipt books, domestic medicine books, and health advice books. While many nineteenth-century domestic medicine books are titled "Botanic" or placed under the general heading "Botanic," signifying that they are written by a Botanic practitioner or include botanical therapies information, the differences between those written by the Botanics and the Regulars often are difficult to determine. For example, advice books, especially those written by physicians, both Botanic and Regular, include self-care tips characteristic of both groups. So it is not unusual to find advice books that reference the use of heroically strong remedies such as tartar emetic or the use of cayenne pepper to instigate a "puking" action that was considered a very important part of the healing process. Botanists such as C. S. Rafinesque (1784–1842), a Turk who had immigrated to America in

1815, complained that the authors of advice books who claimed botanical knowledge and called themselves "Botanics" often were herb doctors who had plant application knowledge but often did not have the knowledge of plants themselves, as did a botanist.[50]

One of the most popular herbals of all time, originating in England, is *Culpeper's Complete Herbal & English Physician.* It was written by Nicholas Culpeper (1616–1654), a seventeenth-century physician. In Culpeper's herbal, healing plants are classified by humoral qualities.[51] More than forty editions of the book have appeared since its inception. Americans, in particular those of British descent, continued the tradition of using Culpeper's herbal and remedies into the nineteenth century and beyond.

Perhaps more than any other modality, the use of botanical therapies often has been perceived by the public as being a gentler and simpler way of healing compared to the heroics of the Regular's orthodox medicine. Problems of toxicity with plant remedies have occurred throughout history, however, these were most often related to dosage. The historical records of a botanical's use in healing are part of a plant's safety record. Nineteenth-century Americans were not ignorant of the potential toxicity issues of their plant medicines, and self-care books often included education on the topic. One example of many is found in *The Family Nurse* in the entry on skunk cabbage *(Ictodes foetidus):* "The dangerous plant called poke root, or American Hellebore, grows in the same places (as skunk cabbage), and closely resembles it in early spring. But skunk cabbage has a larger root, and every part, when broken, emits the disagreeable smell, from which it takes its name."[52] Information differentiating one plant from another, in this case poke from skunk cabbage, is typical of the safety information found in herbals and herbal sections in advice books.

Some plants and plant parts are known to be toxic to humans, however, the mere presence of a toxic plant substance does not necessarily prohibit using that particular plant in healing. While herbal remedies, especially those used in household health care, can contain potentially toxic substances, typically they are prepared with small amounts of the plant material, thereby making ingestion or absorption of toxic amounts very remote.[53] This is why plant scientists, pharmacists, and clinical herbalists discuss the safety of healing plants and their centuries-old safety record as existing within their traditional or historical context. For example, if taken in small amounts, such as the inadvertent ingestion of an apple seed that contains cyanide, a person usually would not experience an adverse effect. The seeds also are embedded in an apple's core, the fibrous center of an apple, which makes it difficult but not impossible for the eater to find the seeds. Therefore, most parents teach their children that when eating an apple to avoid eating the core and the seeds. In addition, many herbs, if prepared properly are healing and not at all toxic. For example, peach pits, *tao ren* in traditional Chinese medicine, when used as a tea to "regulate blood" are cooked thoroughly (i.e., decocted in water for one to two hours) to deactivate the cyanide-producing component.

Health care professionals, in an attempt to assure the public of their expertise, often seek to distinguish their practices and remedies from the daily self-care practices and remedies of the domestic sphere. Most domestic, self-care herbal remedies are simples. Botanical practitioners often offer more complex remedies. Hatfield writes in her history of English domestic medicine that "It is possible that where someone became known as an expert in treating a certain condition, there would be a tendency for any treatment used to become complicated, in order to distinguish it from the kind of "simple" which was common knowledge."[54] When nineteenth-century Americans used the term *simple* to refer to their choice of medicine, it was not in any way derogatory. People valued their ability to heal themselves with botanical therapies that were simple enough to make and administer, and perhaps even to grow outside their own back door.

With the emergence of the professions of medicine and pharmacy, it was in the American spirit of competition that medicine makers and manufacturers sought to make each remedy special, unique, and new in some way. Americans were again culturally conflicted between their desire to self-care with remedies from their own home and their desire for commercialization of the newest and most exotic remedies, often imported and complex in formulation and ready and easy to administer. Botanical formulations, also called "composites," were the foundation for the products of American pharmaceutical companies. Nineteenth-century Americans supported the expansion of the drug industry. Access to drugs was a support for the self-help system. "When individual Americans obtained the drug, as in the form of Sappington's anti-fever pills, they quickly imagined themselves released from much of their need to rely upon doctors."[55]

Americans' views toward healers and therapies have been very diverse. While some nineteenth-century Americans most undoubtedly deferred to the "professional" expertise of the Regulars, many others regarded themselves as being as fully competent as the educated physician of the day. Few found the need to consult a physician for the numerous common illnesses that occur on a daily basis in some families. When people were able to make or obtain their own medicines, read self-care books, or have trusted relatives or neighbors suggest remedies, they often were eager to rely on such sources and on their own judgments rather than resort to putting their lives in the hands of a physician, especially for a common illness. Later it will be shown that exceptions included cases of injury and life-threatening illness.

The American Patent Medicine Industry

In reading any history that mentions botanical therapies, it is important to be able to differentiate between a botanical simple (and its numerous oral, topical, and environmental applications), a botanical formulation, and a botanical patent medicine that may be referenced. Simples and crude herbal formulations have been briefly discussed but patent medicines have not. Botanical simples such as sage (*Salvia officinalis*) tea, cannot be patented, because sage, like all medicinal plants, exists in the public domain. People can find it growing wild on their property and use it as they wish. However, while sage cannot be patented as being the property, intellectual or physical, of an individual, a product that is created and manufactured with sage as an ingredient can be patented. Botanical patent medicines are typically plant remedies that are formulations or recipes for oral use.

Samuel Thomson was not only an author of advice books and journals, but an entrepreneur as well. He was not only successful in patenting his botanical formulations but was the first to patent a *system* of botanical practice for promoting health and healing in 1813, listing it as *Fever Medicine*.[56] His was the twenty-sixth federal medical patent granted in the United States. From Thomson's perspective, patenting his system of botanical medicine was not antithetical to his beliefs in medical freedom and freedom from monopolies. A patent for Thomson was protection from those who would take his botanical system and adulterate it, making it eventually ineffective. He thought of the patent system as a quality control system. Thomson also believed that patenting his botanical medical system would keep others, mostly the Regulars and other Botanics, from depriving him of his livelihood and recognition for thirty years of work. He claimed that his purpose in obtaining a patent was to put himself above the reach of the state laws being created to restrict the movement of health care providers outside of the medical profession. He also patented his system to curtail the "machinations" of his enemies rather than to take advantage of an economic monopoly himself.[57] Thomson sold the right to use his botanical protocol to thousands of American families for twenty dollars a family.

All American patents are granted by the federal government to give an inventor "the right to exclude others from making, using, offering for sale, or selling the invention in the United States or importing the invention into the United States. What is granted is not the right to make, use, offer for sale, sell or import, but the right to exclude others from making, using, offering for sale, selling or importing the invention."[58] Because a medical patent actually revealed the inner "workings" of Thomson's botanical system, his move to patent his system may have been perceived in the early days of the nation as another way of empowering and educating the common American family that purchased the rights to use the system.

As discussed in chapter 2, nineteenth-century Jacksonian and Jeffersonian democratic ideology was part of the cultural core of nineteenth-century life. Thomas Jefferson, in his letters to James Madison, who at the time was a congressman crafting the Bill of Rights, advised that the document include the restriction of monopoly.[59] However, the Bill of Rights, in its final adoption in 1791, did not include any reference to the restriction of monopoly suggested by Jefferson.[60] Thomas Jefferson, when he wrote American patent law, however, attempted to ensure that no person would use patent law to create an economic monopoly that would subsequently infringe upon the freedom and creativity of other American inventors. Samuel Thomson put Jefferson's work to the test.

In botanical therapies practice, the term *patent medicine* is used to refer to the public registering or patenting of botanical products, such as those used in the Thomsonian system. While the nineteenth century may have marked the beginning of the formal patent medicine industry with the registering of Thomson's products, it did not mark the beginning of the American botanical medicine industry. Predating Jeffersonian patent law, Halle Orphanage medicines from Germany had been sold in America since the 1730s. Halle is the name of the town where the Francke Orphanage, a famous philanthropic and religious organization, was started in 1696. The organization was led by Pietist minister-physicians of the period who were recognized as experts in medicine production and patient education.

Physician-created, multiproduct "physic chests" were sold with accompanying advice books that extensively detailed the purposes and directions for use of each of the remedies in the chest. All advice books were written in lay language. The most popular Halle remedy, *essential dulcis,* was made from gold. Halle medicines, while including chemical as well as botanical remedies, were in general considered gentler than the medicine of the Regulars. Calomel was included in one remedy formulation but was on the "B" list of Halle Orphanage medications. In other words, it was not a primary remedy as it was for American Regulars, and, therefore, it was added to the primary physic[61] chest for an additional fee. It was used in combination with scammony and powdered oyster shells as a cathartic and an antihelminthic, and it was "not to be used more than twice in any given illness."[62]

Halle medicine was brought to American German and Swiss Lutheran and Reformed congregations by a number of generations of Pietist ministers and male and female physicians beginning in 1730.[63] The Halle Orphanage used its clergy throughout Europe and eventually in America to import not only its advice books and pharmaceutical products but also its distinctive health culture.

German and Halle medicines are rarely included in historical accounts of early American health care, however, Halle historian Renate Wilson presents clear and striking evidence not only of Halle practitioners' success as health providers, drug manufacturers, and educators but as leaders in the introduction of the botanical medicine industry to American consumers and health care providers in the eighteenth century. Prior to the 1820s, herbal simples, formulations, and chemical medicines were compounded by citizens themselves or purchased from physicians or apothecaries. Halle medicines demonstrated the desire of "industrial" participants to set standards for product quality, safety, and efficacy. These standards exist in the pharmaceutical and botanical industries today.

Halle medicines were marketed in America in the mid- to late-eighteenth century. The demand for these medicines declined significantly after 1805. Wilson describes a number of reasons for this, including the decline in German immigration to America in the late-eighteenth and mid-nineteenth centuries and the rejection of the connection between clergy and medicine decades earlier by Americans, a connection that was still prominent in Halle medical culture. In the eighteenth century, the Halle religious mission and the sale of patent medicines could not have succeeded without the advice books. Wilson wrote, "In the competitive American market, they could not have succeeded without the close link between the written word and the purchase of proprietary medicines."[64] As the American pharmaceutical industry began to emerge in its early stages and as Americans began to write their own advice books, German Halle trade was no longer necessary.

While it is certainly possible that the Halle medicine trade influenced the early emergence of the American botanical and chemical medicine markets and American botanical self-care practices, Wilson concluded: "Although the channels, markets, and mechanisms of commerce may have been similar, little evidence links the composition and indications of the Halle medicinals to the numerous products offered on the American market, the self-declared vitalism of representatives of physiomedicine notwithstanding."[65] The American market for industry-prepared, patented botanical medicines was growing throughout the mid-nineteenth century, while American health care reforms gathered momentum. It was in the latter part of the century after the Civil War and with the increase in industrialization that the patent medicine industry would rise to become a dominant part of American culture. The historical origins of the American pharmaceutical industry are found in the early years of the botanical patent medicine industry. A religious group known as the Shakers, discussed in chapter 5, has been credited with early leadership in the commercial exploitation of cultivated healing plants.[66]

Antimonopolistic concepts, medical freedom, health care reform, and advice books were most certainly not an invention of mid-nineteenth-century Americans. Americans did, however, take the ideas present in the earlier European culture of their ancestors and did begin to act on them as they applied to their lives in the United States. With the end of a series of wars, from the War of Independence to the War of 1812, Americans of the mid-nineteenth century became vitally interested in reforming an American health culture that would reflect their identity. It was in the cultural inclusion of American-grown botanicals in health practices, drug and remedy manufacture, literature, including advice books, and indeed in the American lifestyle that American patients and their healers, including nurses, began to define a new American health care.

Chapter 4

The Mid-Nineteenth-Century Nurse: Home, Herbs, and Women's Healing Networks

> One is much disposed to believe that the home system is healthiest and safer for the individual, in every way. Home, we may rest assured, will always be, as a rule, the best place for woman; her labors, pleasures, and interest, should all centre there, whatever be her sphere of life.
>
> — Susan Fenimore Cooper, *Rural Hours by a Lady*, in Kramer, *Women of Flowers*[1]

This chapter provides the historical context through which the mid-nineteenth-century nurse's identity and work come into focus. It contains two sections. The first describes the foundational domestic culture of the nineteenth-century woman that provided for the emergence of professional nursing in the public sphere. The second includes a historical profile of issues relevant to the nineteenth-century nurse and nurse-herbalist. One of the challenges in approaching the historical research of early nursing is the word "nurse" itself. The identity of a nurse has yet to be defined, even in the twenty-first century. Perhaps this is because the cultural identity of nurses is defined in relationship[2] to those for whom the nurse cares, and, therefore, the essence or identity of the nurse is not thoroughly captured when defining it in terms of specific tasks or the individual performing the task. Identifying the nurses of the mid-nineteenth century before the institutionalization of nursing education is even more of a challenge. While the 1873 institutionalization of nursing education may have been the first organized attempt in the history of American nursing to define and identify the professional nurse in the *public sphere*, and is, therefore, often considered the beginning of professional American nursing, it was not the beginning of organized, professed nursing in America.

Historians such as Susan Reverby recognize that "natural born" or "professed" nurses, who were paid for their caregiving expertise, had emerged by the time of the Civil War.[3] She defines the nurse as "A woman summoned to aid in the care of the sick and infirm. In the colonial period such women were well-known figures in their communities."[4] Rebecca Tannenbaum defines early colonial nurses as "ordinary women, performing ordinary female tasks for pay . . . who unlike midwives, physicians, and doctresses, nurses did not do anything beyond what an untrained housewife would do."[5] While Tannenbaum recognizes the varied levels of skill among nurses and acknowledges that some early nurses were expert caregivers, she still seems unable to concisely identify what that nursing expertise was compared to the physician, midwife, or doctress when using the healing task as the focus of a professional definition. This is not surprising given the cultural and sociopolitical challenges of the period. The boundaries between early American nurses and other health care providers were weak if not nonexistent and indeed were unnecessary. It was when the Regulars began to strengthen and enforce boundaries to justify their own claims for power, monopoly, and money that the "others," including nurses, perhaps saw the need to begin the quest for a more distinct definition of identity, especially as they brought their services into the public sphere alongside the Regulars.

While some nurses of the mid-nineteenth century may have been, in a sense, female domestics, the stories of the women nurses presented in chapters 5–7 demonstrate that the role of the professed or the professional nurse was different. Mid-nineteenth-century nurses responded to the needs of their communities, and their role was determined by their culture and environment. They could be long- or short-term home care or community nurses, infirmary nurses, or hospital nurses. They helped children, the elderly, men, and women. As midwives, they also birthed babies. Therefore, as mentioned in chapter 1, a broader working definition of "nurse" was used when conducting the research for this book. The definition of nurse used is a woman identified by her community as an expert in caring for the sick, pregnant, or infirm. A specific nursing task, the use of botanical therapies, is evaluated here and may indeed shed light on the identity of the nineteenth-century nurse; however, nursing, as nurse theorists and scholars have acknowledged, is not wholly defined by the tasks of the individuals involved in the acts of caregiving. Nursing, as expertise in caregiving, cannot and does not exist outside of the healing, caring relationship with a patient or a community.

MID-NINETEENTH-CENTURY AMERICAN DOMESTIC CULTURE

The domain of mid-nineteenth-century European-American women was the home. Domesticity, piety, purity, and submissiveness were the four cardinal virtues of the "true" nineteenth-century woman.[6] The goal of the woman in the mid-nineteenth century in Britain and America was to become the mistress of the domestic domain. It was her belief that by achieving her goal as "moral guardian and educator in the home,"[7] she would safeguard her family and her country. It was through the embodiment of these four virtues in acts of goodness and charity that women were believed to have the power to save their society and promote cultural progress.

The mid-nineteenth century was a time of important sociocultural changes and decisions for American women. On the one hand, women were to ensure the stability and improve the health of the family as well as the nation by tending hearth and home. And, on the other hand, within the message encouraging them to stay at home to "save the country" was embedded the subliminal message that *they*, American women, were in fact important to the success of the new nation and worthy of the political, economic, and social freedoms that American men were already receiving.

The social roles of men and women and the division between the public and domestic spheres are socially constructed.[8] In the mid-nineteenth century, the social or gender boundaries between the domestic and public spheres were not well defined. In general, a true woman was to be publicly subordinate to men and domestically oriented. Women of the period accepted this role not necessarily because they believed that they were inferior to men. Many believed that they were different but equal from men, and that by embracing a cultural structure that focused their work in the home they had the power to contribute to the preservation of American democracy. The nineteenth-century woman was to carve out a democratic life by staying within the domestic sphere. Many men and women found the ideal of the woman's domestic sphere and her preservation of moral purity through staying away from the corrupting standards of the public and political arena appealing.

Nineteenth-century women, such as the influential cultural directress, Catharine Beecher, author of the widely read *Treatise on Domestic Economy* (1841), provided leadership for many women trying to reconcile their role in a democracy where everyone was, according to the U.S. Constitution, equal; yet women were clearly politically and economically unequal to men. They were, in fact, the property of their fathers or, if married, their husbands. They also could not vote. Beecher's answer to resolving the dilemma was to encourage women to subordinate themselves *voluntarily* to men in the public arena as a way of demonstrating how to achieve social order in a democracy.

Voluntary subordination became associated with the nineteenth-century woman's peacefulness and power. Historian Kathryn Sklar wrote that Beecher suggested that the "mode of gaining influence and of exercising power should be altogether different and peculiar to women. Whereas a man may engage in public issues, the woman's influence should remain within 'domestic and social circle'; whereas a man may act aggressive to achieve his goals, a woman must conquer by 'kindly, generous, peaceful, and benevolent principles."[9] Beecher was most influential in creating and defining the way in which nineteenth-century women could act in the domestic sphere and what, therefore, constituted nineteenth-century American women's culture.

She spoke of the importance of beauty in reference to the decoration of the home and the influence of aesthetics on the young in particular. Beauty and aesthetics, she advised, contributed much to the "education of the entire household in refinement, intellectual development, and moral sensibility."[10] One of the most common home decorating strategies applied by mid-nineteenth-century women was the use of plants and flowers. Floriculture was indelibly linked to the image of the "true" nineteenth-century woman.

Many nineteenth-century women planted gardens for aesthetic and ornamental purposes. Renowned garden authorities of the period, such as Andrew Jackson Downing, encouraged women to work outdoors and to care for their own plants[11] as a way of promoting their own health. Gardening had been for the early colonial family a matter of survival. In colonial clergyman and physician Cotton Mather's *The Angel of Bethesda,* women were encouraged to grow helpful plants in their gardens and to keep their closets stocked with several remedies for the "help of their poor neighbors."[12] In the nineteenth century, plants, including herbs, were not only grown for their aesthetic value, they were an important part of women's healing culture too. For example, Lydia Maria Child's domestic guidebook *The American Frugal Housewife* includes health care recommendations related to over two dozen healing plants, including sage, hyssop, coltsfoot, motherwort, catnip, elder-blow, English mallow, and blackberry.[13] In the garden of the nineteenth-century woman, healing plants were most often segregated into special beds so that they would be found easily in case of an emergency.[14]

Women's Labor

While the nineteenth-century woman's ideal was domesticity, industrialization precluded many women, in particular the poorer classes of American women, from participating fully in domestic culture. During the colonial period in America and into the early nineteenth century, manufacturing, such as the making of cloth, had been primarily in the hands of women in their homes. Men's work centered on agriculture. But in the early nineteenth century, there was increasing growth in factory work, especially for women. In 1816, "well over half of the labor force in the cotton mills in the United States was female."[15] The conflict for women in mid-nineteenth-century American society was clear. Women wanted to continue to produce the goods they were known for producing, but they gradually had to leave the home and enter the factory to do so. The women's labor force was viewed by early manufacturers as a "national resource."[16] By the 1830s, many women were working at jobs outside of the home.

Women who did stay at home, especially middle-class women, often worked as hard as the factory women. They raised their children and maintained their households without hired help, and often with little to no assistance from their husbands. Those who held the belief in a female domestic mission maintained that women ruled child rearing and housekeeping, and that, therefore, a true woman had to bear these duties with quiet servitude. In 1838, Mrs. Caroline Gilman promoted the subordination of women and the suppression of ambition when she wrote in her advice to brides to "watch well the first moments when your will conflicts with his to whom God and society have given control. Reverence his *wishes* even when you do not his *opinions*."[17] And in the *Ladies Token* in 1848, advice on male-female relationships included "not giving one's advice to a male unless he asks for it" and not "retorting if he is abusive."[18] These criteria for women's domestic decorum seemed to have influenced many male-female relationships, ultimately including the male physician-to-female nurse relationships that were created as women nurses entered the hospitals of the male-dominated public sphere.

Woman As Nurse

Women throughout the nineteenth century typically comprised the majority of the congregations of Christian churches. Many ministers of the period believed and preached that women had a special affinity for religion as well as domesticity, in particular caring for the sick. One 1814 minister claimed that this was due to women's "sensibility, their vivacity, and sprightly imagination, their sympathy or tenderness toward distress and those in imminent danger of distress."[19] Nineteenth-century health care was centered in the home, therefore, health care, in particular nursing care, was the domain of the domestic woman. Visitation of the sick also was considered a part of Christian life[20] that should be encouraged in children and in true, pious, nineteenth-century women. Women participated in their church's benevolent societies' works to care for the indigent and suffering. Their philanthropic activities included feeding and clothing the poor.

Between 1800 and 1840, women's benevolent societies grew in membership into the thousands. The benevolent societies were predecessors of modern women's organizations. Some have attributed the success of these societies to the motivation women felt to serve others and to a "tremendous sense of optimism, a faith in their moral influence and their united power, to undertake campaigns that would alter American society in certain significant ways."[21]

Women took pride not only in their ability to comfort the sick but in the spiritual reflection it induced in them. "Popular culture encouraged nineteenth-century women to view themselves as a *sisterhood* 'of those who bear the mark of pain'. The extensive 'consolation literature' that arose in the middle of the century suggested that women could transcend suffering by reaching out to others."[22] During this time in American history when, for a number of reasons, women believed that they were inherently weak and fragile, nurses found their courage, strength, and identity in caring for patients. For example, "In 1857, Amelia Akehurst Lines wrote, 'Went with sister to Dr. Campbell's office. Sister took ether and had eight or ten teeth taken out. She did not take enough to make her insensible to pain, however, and suffered intensely. I stood by and held her hands through the whole. I did not know that I possess so much courage."[23]

In addition to her recipes for domestic success and descriptions of the proper home environment, Catharine Beecher, as creator of the image of woman's domestic domain, provided information on caring for the sick. Her books contain numerous recipes for the sick diet, such as milk porridge, beef tea, and tapioca jelly. She also includes herbal drinks. Balm tea, she wrote, "is often much relished by the sick," and "sage tea is also good."[24] She does not give very much information about the use of the remedies, however, but adds that pennyroyal makes a good drink to promote perspiration, demonstrating her knowledge of the common nineteenth-century health belief in the benefits of opening the pores and perspiring when ill. There also is a section in her book in which Beecher describes and illustrates the importance of creating a water bed, which she calls a "hydrostatic couch," for the bedridden, especially when patients had bedsores. The water bed was made with a wooden box and a rubber sheet.[25]

Beecher also discusses the importance of community nursing care that extended beyond the home. She wrote, "It would be a happy thing for the sick, and a most benevolent custom, if the young ladies of a place should practice cooking the various articles for the sick, and carrying them to invalids as an offering of kindness and sympathy. It would be a twice blessing, first to the invalid, and quite as much to the young benefactress."[26] Beecher did not believe that women were losing anything by not participating as men did in the politics and industry of the public sphere. She believed women were empowered by focusing on the development of their skills as housewives, mothers, and caregivers in the domestic arena. In her opinion, the power of the public political arena was ineffective anyway and was destined for self-destruction.[27]

Nursing the sick not only made a woman feel useful and accomplished but increased her influence. Some women, searching for purpose and fulfillment, and eager to exert their influence and power in the domestic sphere, may have gone too far at times. *Godey's Lady's Book* included a front-page correspondence, *A Tender Wife,* by a Sir T. Munroe in 1831, suggesting that women enjoyed having their husbands ill, because it "gratifies both their medical vanity and their love of power by making him more dependent upon them."[28] Consciously or unconsciously, women may have actually encouraged the sick role in their husbands and children.

Women As Invalids and Healers

The nineteenth-century woman, in addition to being adept at nursing the ill, also was quite often ill herself. She has even been described historically as a "perpetual patient."[29] Women were seen, especially by the Regulars, as being inherently weak and prone to illness. The most prevalent disease in women, excepting infectious disease, was that of invalidism, also known as "hysteria." Dr. Reese and the authors of the *Encyclopedia of Domestic Economy* (1845) described hysteria as being "very frequently symptomatic of some irregularity in the function peculiar to the womb; the periodical secretion from that organ being either deficient or in excess; irregular in its recurrence; attended with difficulty and pain." They described a hysterical fit as being preceded by faintness and choking and continuing with a "violent fit of screaming, and sobbing, mingled with wild bursts of laughter.[30]

Hysteria in American women, while present in the earlier part of the century, reached epidemic proportions in the mid- and late-nineteenth century. The recommended treatment for the hysterical woman included some of the common lifestyle remedies of the nineteenth century: fresh country air, exercise on foot and horseback, sea bathing, plain food, and warm clothing. In addition, the *Encyclopedia of Domestic Economy* encouraged families to curtail the mental "processes" of the woman, avoiding giving too much sympathy, guarding against religious fanaticism, and helping the woman avoid the "excitement of mixed society."[31] The family was considered vital to the success of the treatment. "If parents will not assist in the treatment of these complaints, the physician cannot restrain them [the fits], nor are they curable by any herbs."[32]

The definition of an able-bodied woman[33] was ambiguous, although numerous advice and domestic guidebooks and lady's journal writers tried to capture its essence. "For some health reformers, domesticity and able-bodied womanhood were one and the same."[34] The ultimate cure for the invalid woman was perceived to be that which might be the reason for her hysteria in the first place . . . domesticity. To heal, invalid women needed to stop their intellectual pursuits and seek the comfort, beauty, and serenity of the home.

One representation of the nineteenth-century woman "became the image of the disabled lady, the female invalid."[35] Were bourgeois nineteenth-century women really so ill? According to some tenets of nineteenth-century medical theory, women were *inherently* weak and defective and thereby a useful client base for the medical profession.[36] They were told by physicians that they were ill and weak because it was their nature to be so. Some women also might have been diagnosed as being ill due to having stepped outside of the boundaries of the roles for women defined by proper society.[37] "Invalid" is the word that one author has suggested "best describes the cultural definition of women in the nineteenth century."[38] However, this ignores the class-specific basis of this attribution, since working women could not afford to be invalids. Any nineteenth-century woman who was prone to invalidism had to reconcile her delicate nature with her domestic mandate to maintain a cheerful home and to be the strong, knowledgeable, supportive nurse when the family became ill.

Illness, related to both roles as patient and as nurse, was the domain of the nineteenth-century woman. Although doctoring was customarily seen as part of the man's domain, the words "nurse" and "nursing" were primarily used to refer to the caregiving practices of women. For women, nursing in the domestic sphere was not only a way of being useful in society, it also was a service where women who had been specializing in perfecting "women's work" could exemplify their skill and teach others.

Women's healing expertise in the domestic sphere grew as the national focus on personal accountability for hygiene and health intensified. With their knowledge of healing plants brought with them from Europe, their new knowledge of American healing plants, and their understanding of making botanical remedies, the health care practices and remedies of American colonial housewives was one of the highly successful home industries and traditions continued by nineteenth-century women. Industrialization, urban growth, opportunities for pioneer movement to the West, and participation in numerous social reforms, directly or indirectly, called women out of their homes to take part in the growth of the American culture. Women's domestic work, such as nursing the sick, followed, with its assortment of modalities, including botanicals. The history of nursing with botanical therapies often is recorded in the recipe books of nineteenth-century women.

Recipes for Healing

Just as women shared culinary secrets and tips, they also shared healing recipes. The sharing of recipes was vital to the success of women's ability to care for themselves, their families, and their neighbors. Women shared written as well as oral receipts. They had their own receipt books that they used like a journal for storing and recording their domestic exchanges from others, such as women friends, acquaintances, family members, Regulars, Botanics, and Indian doctors. The practice of keeping a receipt book and exchanging receipts was not new to the nineteenth century. Typically the receipts for foods and healing remedies appear together in receipt books. Sometimes they are intermingled throughout the book. Often, if reading left to right, the receipts for food appear right side up, and those for healing remedies are recorded upside down, starting from the back of the book.

As mentioned in chapter 1, receipt books have been usefully referred to as the "map of the social and cultural worlds"[39] that women inhabit. Recipe exchange or networking has been a vehicle for crossing cultural boundaries and entering into relationships, regardless of race, religion, class, or age. In receipt books, "Women have given history and memory a permanent lodging."[40] Early British-American women's receipt books often included British remedies, demonstrating that women's healing networks may have extended across the ocean to the homes of relatives for decades after the American War of Independence. One such example is that of a British doctor's seventeen-page remedy, "Dr. Stewart's Method of healing the pulmonary complaint." The source of a receipt is often recorded at the end of the recipe. For pulmonary remedy, Dr. Stewart is mentioned at the bottom of the receipt with an address reading "near Glasgow."[41]

Often receipt books provided health advice in the form of what today would be called a "case study." A case study of the care of a patient from Dusebury by a "Thompsonian [*sic*][42] woman" can be found in one collection of recipes.

> He had the blind piles. A Thompsonian woman carried him through a number of courses of Medicine and

> drove the canker from the internal to the external surface, and it appeared in large canker sores, then his friends were frightened and used their influence to frighten him, and they sent for Doctor Drew he came and said they were mortification sores and if they had given hot medicine a little longer he would have died in the operation of the medicine accordingly. Drew made his cold wet cloth applications externally and cooling medicines internally which drew all the determining powers inward, & he continued these applications, which worried and tormented the man about a week and he died. Then Dr Drew said it was the hot medium which he had previously taken that killed him.[43]

In creating a tapestry of women's healing history, quality receipt book information are those recipes that include the context for use of the remedy, in addition to the list of ingredients, such as found in case studies. Women's recipe books often contain the list of herbs used in making a remedy or the list of herbs with a note about how to make the remedy. What is often lacking, and critical to a thorough understanding of women nurses' botanical history, is the application of the remedy. After perusing the receipt books of women, and the receipts recorded in diaries, journals, newspapers, and texts of the period, I gathered those quality examples of remedies that included both substance and process. The remedies cited in the following chapters have been chosen to exemplify the broadest possible description of the caring context that surrounded the use of an herb or a therapy. Examples are fewer than I would have liked. Other women's historians have found the same challenge. For example, Ellen Gartrell wrote in 1987 that the recipe book of eighteenth-century American Elizabeth Coates Paschall fortunately stood out from the others she had read because of the detail of social context for the remedies included.[44]

Health care information, including botanical therapies information, was not only shared by mid-nineteenth-century women through written works, as in the receipts discussed earlier. Women also shared their knowledge through a communication network. They shared orally through lectures and community and domestic gatherings such as birthings, and through individual sharing, woman to woman. Women's gatherings and networking to share stories, receipts, and support often occurred at the time of illness.

Gathering and Networking

Women and men[45] throughout history have depended upon each other greatly for moral, spiritual, emotional, and physical support. This support often has been demonstrated in the sharing of health care knowledge. Women's sharing networks were prominent in American culture during the mid-nineteenth century. Charlotte Perkins Gilman, a late-nineteenth-century women's rights leader wrote: "The basic feminine impulse is to gather, to put together, to construct."[46] Networking experiences were an opportunity for women to identify their differences from men and construct their own cultural identity. In addition, historians have identified the importance of studying women's networks as "a crucial means of enabling us to appreciate and understand past and present lives and achievements."[47] The polarization of men to the industrial political public sphere and women to the domestic and private sphere led to a bonding of women in a new way where the social gatherings of mid-nineteenth-century women became very important to their education, health, and identity.

With the numerous societal and political reforms occurring, mid-nineteenth-century women focused on preserving their female peer relationships for support. "Women's work" became identified with the quality of relationships involved in that work and with the qualities of the heart. "Heartfelt caring was considered to be a woman's characteristic virtue"[48] in the nineteenth century. Who better to understand the feelings and heartfelt work of a woman than a woman? Margaret Fuller wrote in 1843: "I believe that, at present, women are the best helpers of one another."[49] Women found strength in gender solidarity. Examples of this solidarity include the early women's rights movement and women's community gatherings, such as the church benevolent societies mentioned previously and secular organizations such as the Ladies Physiological Institute (LPI) of Boston.

The LPI was founded in 1848 to promote among women a "knowledge of the human system, the laws of life and health, and the means of relieving sickness and suffering."[50] The 1850 annual report of the organization describes the values of the women of the organization as promoting a spirit of "true science," inquiry, and investigation in performing their roles as "wives, mothers, nurses, and guardians of youth."[51] The Institute's meeting minutes show that "nurses" were members of the organization; however, the minutes also include anotification that was circulated publicly, that "This Institute is not at all connected with the Female Medical Society, located in Boston, & designed to educate Females for Physicians, Midwives & Nurses; which also received a charter from the Legislature at the same session, & is successfully engaged in its appropriate sphere."[52]

The unbiased health activities, as demonstrated in the institute's behavior of hiring lecturers from both Regular and Empiric backgrounds (such as homeopaths and water cure physicians), were representative of the cultural diplomacy of the women of the period. "The Institute's unwavering, but almost unconscious, eclecticism is noteworthy in light of the sectarian clashes that divided American medicine. . . . Curiously, the Institute seemed unconcerned as the battle raged in the medical literature and professional societies of mid-century America."[53] Both Regulars and Empirics recognized the power of the organization as its membership grew exponentially each year. For example, the meeting records of September 1850 show that Alva Curtis, a Thomsonian physician from Ohio, corresponded with the institute and made a donation in support of its "diffusing of knowledge for the benefit of mankind."[54] The ladies also became powerful enough to recommend female as well as male speakers from among their ranks and a faculty of lecturers for other *public* functions.

In addition to attending public lectures and women's organizations such as the LPI, other, more indirect, nineteenth-century-women's gatherings and networking opportunities included subscribing to "lady's" journals, such as *Godey's Lady's Book*, one of the most influential domestic journals of the early nineteenth century. It contained recipes, editorials, fashion information, gardening tips, and domestic health care information. Other popular lady's journals were more specifically oriented to health and medicine. The *Boston Thomsonian Manual and Lady's Companion*, published under the direction of Samuel Thomson, began in 1835 as the *Thomsonian Manual, or, Advocate of the Principles Which Govern the Thomsonian System of Medical Practice.* The name was changed with volume five in 1838 to the *Boston Thomsonian Manual and Lady's Companion.* The addition of the words "Lady's Companion" occurs at the peak of the mid-nineteenth-century women's advice period. Women readers were known as "correspondents."[55] *The Lady's Companion* covered the usual Thomsonian topics of medical reform, Thomsonian philosophy, remedies and practice, and personal tributes to the cures achieved from application of the system. Ladies' journals were not only a resource of botanical and other health-related information for the nineteenth-century woman but also served as a connection between local women's health care networks.

Women depended upon each other to share time-honored as well as newer ways of caring for their families. Although medicine in the nineteenth-century public sphere stressed either reliance on a doctor or on "being your own doctor," women diplomatically did both. They were integrators of care. In addition, they incorporated their own gender's cultural healing values, providing friendship, care, and support for each other so they could indeed make the best choices for health care for themselves and their families. "Health and sickness were communal phenomena which engendered a sharing of medical services and remedies."[56] Communities depended upon their healing *networks* not only for help but also for survival. It is out of the nineteenth-century women's healing networks that the professed, community-recognized nurse emerged with her own special services of caring expertise, including the skill of supporting and complementing patient self-care.

THE MID-NINETEENTH-CENTURY NURSE

Nursing care during the mid-nineteenth century was an integral part of every woman's work in her domestic domain. As mentioned earlier, many women began to take an interest in their own health, understanding their anatomy and physiology and the ways in which they could heal themselves and their families. Because their sphere of influence was the home, they used whatever they had in their homes as instruments of healing. They utilized various foods and water therapy applications to comfort and heal. They learned how to create changes in their home environments to promote health. They used the flowers and herbs that grew in their gardens to nurse the sick in their care. In addition to being skillful in the kitchen, nineteenth-century American housewives were quite adept in the work of the stillroom. It was in the kitchen and the stillroom that a goodwife (or perhaps a servant in the case of the wealthy nineteenth-century woman) would practice her chemistry. She made cheeses, beers, wines, and herbal remedies, including salves, herbal oils, tinctures, and distilled fragrant flower and herbal waters. The stillroom also was a storehouse for botanical remedies.

While all nineteenth-century women were expected to have a basic knowledge of making botanical remedies and nursing the sick, there were many who became recognized as community *experts* in nursing and/or midwifery. They were not only helpful to their families and neighbors but were nursing experts to larger communities. Their spheres of influence sometimes included entire states. They performed their nursing work in the public domain, such as in infirmaries, hospitals, and the homes of strangers, as well as in their own homes and those of neighbors and friends.

European-American women of the period, like their British counterparts,[57] were interested in nursing the sick for a number of reasons. Perhaps the most important reason was their belief in nursing service as the expression of their duty to public charity, an essential aspect of Christian life.[58] Their strategy involved garnering power and support from the healing networks of the domestic sphere to promote health, thereby creating cultural changes. The nurses' intent was not to seek public power but to exercise their "familial influence more broadly."[59] This influence and contribution of women nurses will be described in the case studies of three religious communities in the three chapters that follow. The environments in which they performed their healing work, the healing networks they created to support their work, and the herbs and other modalities they used as their instruments of healing also will be discussed.

Many of the nurses profiled in the case studies, while socialized as nineteenth-century women, were neither wives nor mothers. By living in a religious community, they had already extended the typical definition of the woman's "domestic sphere" to what some historians refer to as the "borderland,"[60] a place between the domestic and public spheres. In all cases, it will be shown that the nurses were not only acceptable to their communities but also vital to the existence of those communities. The nurses were able to extend their influence "in a public activity sufficiently limited not to contaminate the moral purity that was perceived to be the essence of the 'womanly woman', and hence the fount of feminine influence."[61] Nursing work to alleviate human suffering was actually supported by society, especially male church leadership.

The nineteenth-century woman in general and the nurse in particular each had her own important role in society to fulfill in terms of health care. The nursing work of many women who had cared for the sick and promoted health in their communities for decades as a matter of course emerged in mid century with greater purpose. Women's *charitable* nursing work in particular opened the door for women to enter what had become defined as the "public sphere." American women and nurses networked with each other and found ways to sustain their role in expanding American domestic culture. While the Regulars and Botanics fought for dominance in the public sphere, nurses established an organized power base within their domestic community healing networks from which their public service and influence could emerge. Women nurses were not direct competitors with male physicians, because their caring work was performed either in the home or in the extended domestic sphere of the community. Their community work included numerous caring acts such as the touching of patients, that which had been defined as "ungentlemanly" by physician societies of an earlier period.

The Nurse-Herbalists

The healing or nursing work of American women, including their work with botanical therapies, did not begin in the nineteenth century. There is evidence, such as in the diary of midwife Martha Ballard,[62] that early European-American colonial women were most often the dominant caregivers in the community. Because American colonial women rarely kept their own records of their healing work within their families or with others, historians must often rely upon the records of male leaders for information about women's work. For example, one description of a colonial Puritan nurse is written by Cotton Mather, clergyman and physician. "It was an extreme satisfaction to him," wrote Mather of John Eliott, translator of the Bible for the American Indians, "that his wife had obtained unto a considerable skill in physicks and chyryugery, which enabled her to dispense many safe, good, and useful medicines and to the poor that had occasion for them, and some hundreds of sick and weak and maimed people owed praises to God for the benefit, which therein they freely received of her."[63] As had been customary in England, seventeenth- and eighteenth-century European-American clergy, with their wives as nurses, were often the ones who provided health care guidance and remedies for their communities when it came to matters of "physick." Popular English poet and clergyman, George Herbert, in his book *Country Parson,* wrote that the parson must be physician to his parish with his wife as his "helpmeet."

> If there be any of his flock sick, he is their Physician— or, at least his wife, of whom instead of the qualities of the world, he asks no other but to have the skill of healing a wound, or helping the sick. In the knowledge of simples, wherein the manifold wisdom of God is wonderfully to be seen, one thing would carefully be observed; which is to know what herbs may be used instead of drugs of the same nature, and to make the garden the shop. For home-bred medicines are both more easy for the Parson's purse and more familiar for

> all men's bodies. So where the apothecary useth either, for loosening, rhubarb, or for binding, bolearmena, the Parson useth damask or white roses for the one and plantain, shepherd's purse, knotgrass for the other, and that with better success. . . . she [the parson's wife] seeks not the city, but prefers her garden and fields . . . and surely hyssop, valerian, mercury, adders tongue, yarrow, melilot, and St. John's wort made into a salve; and elder, camomile, mallows, comphrey and smallage made into a poultice, have done great and rare cures.[64]

From early colonial times, European-American women developed extensive wisdom and skill in using plants for health and healing. Having herbs on hand and knowing how to make and apply the various remedies was very important to the nineteenth-century housewife and nurse. Women nurses, as will be shown in the case studies, learned the practice of nursing with botanical therapies from numerous sources. They read about botanical therapies in journals and books written by peers, health care reformers, Botanics, and Regulars. In the spirit of the bonds of sisterhood, they generously passed receipts to each other in their healing networks and shared stories of botanical healings at luncheons and lectures. And they were mentored by other nurse-herbalists. They also shared their knowledge with other professionals who used botanicals in caregiving.

For example, in a nineteenth-century account, recorded by botanical physician and leader of the Eclectics, Wooster Beach in one of his books on midwifery,[65] there is a description of a community "nurse's" communication of the traditional healing techniques of American Indians, specifically the Oneida, to him. It is a good example of the cultural diplomacy of mid-nineteenth-century nurses. Beach described an experience at a birth in which he spoke with a "nurse" who had lived "in the neighborhood" of the Oneida Indians for many years. He wrote that the nurse, Mrs. Davis, was intimately familiar with the practices of laboring American Indian women,[66] which included the use of slippery elm bark (*Ulmus fulva*). Dr. Beach was most likely interested in nurse Davis's information about the Oneida women because it was well documented in early-seventeenth-century European-American colonial records[67] that Indian women, unlike European-American women, suffered little pain in childbirth. Beach wrote that he ultimately preferred the "Indian method" (use of a supporting pole) for delivery that he witnessed with Nurse Davis. He also stated that the birth he attended with Nurse Davis had "terminated so favorably," more than any labor he had ever attended. He added, "And it has been a question in my mind whether I ought to impute it to the free use of the mucilage of slippery-elm bark for three months before confinement."[68] Nurse Davis, as cultural and herbal diplomat, shared her knowledge of the Oneida women and their use of slippery elm with a botanical physician and also gained entrée for the Botanic to observe a birth in an Indian community.

Nurse Davis's work was not that of a typical nineteenth-century housewife. Every mid-nineteenth-century American woman was expected to have a certain level of understanding of nursing others. Daughters were expected to care for their families and follow in the women's networking tradition of being on call for others in time of need. However, just as is noted of colonial women, that "several women in every community stood out from the others for the breadth and depth of their commitment,"[69] the same was true for nurses in the mid-nineteenth century. Davis was one such woman, and there were numerous others, as will be described in detail in the case studies.

The nineteenth-century nurse gained her knowledge and expertise in caregiving through mentorship with other women and through personal experience with her own family and neighbors. She prepared teas and topical botanical remedies; she changed patients' clothes, washed their bodies, sat up with them at night, prepared strengthening, healing foods, maintained a proper sickroom environment, comforted the dying, prayed, and prepared the bodies of the dead. She in turn taught others the nuances of what she had learned through her extensive experience in caregiving.

Nineteenth-century nurses also cared for patients who were contending with the results of the botanical and mineral remedies that were prescribed by physicians during the period. As mentioned previously, purgatives, emetics, and bleeding were very popular. But while medical histories describe the treatments, rarely is the patient's response detailed, nor is the art and science of nursing care that made the treatment bearable for the patient (and the attendants) described, let alone given credit for some aspect of the success of the treatments. Most assuredly without nurses managing the gross volumes of vomit, excrement, and blood itself (especially without the benefits of modern plumbing), there would be no reason for any rational patient to willingly pursue the purgative, emetic, and bleeding treatments of the physicians of the period.

"Professional" Nurses

According to sociologist Elliot Freidson, the "defining characteristic of a profession is autonomy, professionals' unusual independence in defining the scope and application of their expertise."[70] Nursing, by the dictionary[71] definition and the current vernacular, is often referred to as a "profession," but it has not been recognized as such in the same way that medicine, law, and theology have. Nursing is not referred to in the mid-nineteenth-century literature as a profession, however, the word "professional" is used here to differentiate between those nurses who were community-recognized healers and the general population of nineteenth-century women providing domestic nursing care.

There were two general "classes" of professional nurses in the mid-nineteenth century in addition to the domestic women nurses. Some nurses were hired from within the labor class. While certain documents reference them as "nurses," they, in comparison with other women community nurses, acted more as "attendants." Examples of attendants include the girl child nurse or the domestic nanny who cared for the children, the wet nurse, and some of the early hospital custodial workers. Attendants seemingly had little to no training, mentorship, or interest in anatomy or physiology, and at times they had no religious, moral, or social motive for alleviating suffering. An attendant might be a young girl fulfilling her family's social duty by sitting with a sick neighbor or family member. Although the attendant might be skilled in the one task of caring for children or breast-feeding a child, the historical records of these attendants do not leave one with a sense of the "nurse" as exhibiting a healing presence or as being a community-recognized nursing expert. The other class of nurses, which demonstrated professional expertise and experience, was mentored, educated, and often "called" or "set apart" as nurses. This group often held deep spiritual beliefs about the importance of its nursing work in the community. The case studies in the three chapters that follow about mid-nineteenth-century nurses are provided as examples.

Some have tried to define early nursing by its tasks.[72] Instead of a task-oriented definition, other scholars attempt to define nursing in regard to the process or approach and the knowledge the healer uses in applying herself or himself to certain caregiving tasks. One contemporary nursing theorist, Dorothea Orem, provides a definition of the process of nursing that is perhaps one of the most reflective of mid-nineteenth-century thought in its focus on the concept of *self-care*.

Orem defines nursing as a practical and didactic art "through which the nurse, the practitioner of nursing, gives specialized assistance to persons with disabilities of such a character that more than ordinary assistance is necessary to meet daily needs for self-care.[73] She adds that the "condition that validates the existence of a requirement for nursing in an adult is the absence of the ability to maintain for himself continuously the amount and quality of self-care which is therapeutic in sustaining life and health, in recovering from disease or injury, or in coping with their effects."[74] Orem's "self-care deficit theory" defines nursing in terms of supporting an underlying system of self-care where people willingly and knowingly pursue caring for themselves through internally and externally oriented health behaviors. When a person is no longer able to care for himself or herself and a nurse is needed, the nurse uses helping measures with the patient, such as doing for, supporting, guiding and directing, maintaining an environment, and teaching.[75]

The foundation of the American health care "system" in the mid-nineteenth century was self-care. For financial, philosophical, spiritual, and practical reasons, Americans started with self-care before seeking help from others. Housewives often took the lead in implementing the family self-care "system" by providing for their family's most immediate health care needs. If the self-care system was insufficient, it was often a nurse in the nineteenth century, who, like Orem notes in the twenty-first century, could provide the help that often satisfied the need. Many times, the patient's condition was such that the expert nurse's care was all that was needed to support the body's own natural healing forces. At other times, the family needed to seek help from other practitioners such as a Regular or Botanic physician.

Unlike Tannenbaum's description of early colonial nurse's skills that "did not differ much from those of housewives,"[76] some nurses of the 1830s to 1860s, based on historical records, had achieved a level of skill and a healing presence recognized by their communities that was significantly greater than that of the typical housewife. Tannenbaum also differentiates between the role of the doctress and the role of the nurse, based on autonomy and authority, and states that the doctress often took patients into her own home.[77] While it may have been easier to differentiate between one female health practitioner and another in the colonial days, it was not as easy among nineteenth-century women. For example, Hepsibeth Hemenway (1761–1847), a Hassanamisco Indian widow who was a laundress for the well-to-do in Worcester, Massachusetts, also was hired in her county during her later years to take care of the indigent sick *in her home* and was later well known in her community for her work as a baker of wedding cakes.[78] Was she a doctress or a nurse? Perhaps the answer depends on whether or not she administered remedies on her own volition in addition to caring for the patient in her home, as Homer Merriam's doctress had done. More than likely, the roles overlapped. It is highly probable that the "scope of practice" of the various practitioners varied from state to state and perhaps from town to town. The case studies in the chapters that follow further define the identities of nurses in the mid-nineteenth century, the role that botanical therapies played in the care that they provided, and the extent to which the nurses practiced autonomously and were health care authority figures in their communities as well as in sickrooms.

Sickroom Management Expertise

The sickroom was the key domain of the nineteenth-century nurse. Many domestic advice books and nurses' guides, long before Florence Nightingale's *Notes on Nursing*, which was first published in 1859, provided explicit details on the subject of "sickroom management." While no published books on sickroom management written by American nurses were found from the period,[79] quite a few physician-written books on the management of the sickroom were found. Physicians of the mid-nineteenth century not only used sickroom management advice books to disseminate their views as medical authorities on the subject, but they also included their commentary as moral authorities on what they perceived to be the poor state of nursing care in the United States. Their criticism centered on sick nursing in hospitals (the public sphere of male physicians) and nurses' lack of obedience to physicians. American nurses had been openly expressing their opinions on the care of patients to physicians in the spirit of democracy throughout the eighteenth and early nineteenth centuries, but physicians usually preferred, supported, and requested nurses who had served as assistant nurses in hospitals and who had been socialized not to express their own opinions, especially when they contradicted those of the physician. One physician wrote the following on sickroom management:

> When all the arrangements are completed in the sick-room, little benefit can be anticipated if a proper nurse be not obtained to render them available to the invalid. Before describing the qualifications requisite to constitute an efficient nurse, I cannot avoid embracing this opportunity of mentioning the great difficulty of procuring properly instructed nurses in this country. It is, indeed, to be greatly lamented, that, amidst the numerous improvements which characterize the present era, the females who assume to themselves the character of sick nurses, and are employed as such, are still left to acquire information, respecting the

> important duties which their office demands, from imperfect experience, or from accident. We expect that the skill of our medical attendants shall be certified by diplomas and licenses before they are permitted to practice; but we leave their orders to be executed by the ignorant and the prejudiced, who not only too often fail in performing what they are ordered, but who, with the usual temerity of ignorance, presume to oppose their own opinions to those of the physician. Every female, who wishes to act as a sick nurse, should be obliged to serve a certain time as an assistant nurse in one of the public hospitals, and to receive a certificate of her efficiency before she leaves the establishment. The advantages which the public would derive from a body of nurses educated in this manner must be obvious to every one who has had the opportunities of observing the miserable working of the present system. We should no longer have to lament the neglect of cleanliness; the inattention to ventilation and temperature; the obstinate and presumptuous opposition to the orders of the medical practitioner in reference to diet, which are now so prevalent.[80]

It seems odd that Regular physicians Griffith and Thomson, quoted here, specifically mention a concern about nurses exerting their opinions about diet for the sick when American domesticity guides of the period typically included instructions for the nourishing of the sick. Women housewives and nurses knew that the sick diet had been within their domain in the domestic sphere for years.

It is interesting to note that a statement identical to that written by Griffith and Thomson appears *verbatim* in another book on the management of the sickroom, written by another Regular. The book by Griffith and Thomson, written in 1845, was published in Philadelphia as a revised edition of a book written by a British physician and "Fellow of the Royal College of Physicians." The second book by Dr. Francis Smith, a physician at St. Joseph's Hospital, also was published in Philadelphia in 1851. The reference to "public hospitals" is most likely a direct quote from the original British document, since the few American hospitals in existence in 1845, including those that opened in the late eighteenth century, were most often semiprivate or privately owned[81] and/or directed by religious orders.

Mid-nineteenth-century *American* nursing quality, if taken in historical context, was perhaps not really as bad as some physicians would lead one to believe. Public almshouses, as differentiated from American hospitals, were indeed known as an "unfit place to recover from illness."[82] However, one American physician, William Symington Brown, when lecturing before the Ladies' Medical Academy in Boston in 1859, well before the institutionalization of nursing education in 1873, praised the children's nurses in one hospital. He said: "I am sure it is no slight pleasure for me to be able to bear witness to the admirable management of the children's wards in the Massachusetts General Hospital; the uniform kindness and patience of the surgeons; and the nurses' assiduous care."[83] It is uncertain whether the Regulars' statements about the poor quality of hospital nursing during the period, most likely copied from British sickroom guides, applied to the actual state of nursing care in the United States or whether the physicians who promoted the campaign against the nurses of the period were biased due to a feeling of interprofessional rivalry.

The public's and nurses' questioning of Regular physicians' opinions was the rule rather than the exception in mid-nineteenth-century America. One historian suggests that the tension that existed between nurses and physicians was not due to "simple boundary disputes" or "mere economic self-interest" but to an "ongoing, tortuous groping toward new ways to care for the sick."[84] This is quite possible, but evidence of professional rivalry does seem to exist in the writings of Regulars such as Dr. Smith. His complaints about nurses focused on the difficulty in working with an "opinionated" nurse. He wrote the following:

> There is not a greater difference between noon-day and midnight than between an educated and ignorant nurse. The former is often an aid to the physician, not

> only in carrying his orders into effect, but in observing and informing him of symptoms of great importance which have occurred during his absence: whereas the latter is a source of constant anxiety, and too often assumes the privilege of acting in direct contradiction to his orders, and according to her own opinion. The educated nurse, on the contrary, acquires from experience the capacity of observing changes in the progress of the disease which call her judgment into acquisition, and which justify her from pausing in the plan laid down for her guidance, until the physician is sent for, or repeats his visit. Her reasons for deviation from orders will be listened to by the doctor; and, without lowering his dignity, a useful hint from an intelligent nurse may be adopted and acted upon, much to the advantage of the patient.[85]

Smith equates the uneducated nurse with the opinionated nurse, who introduces "pauses in the plan" laid down by the physician without agreement from the physician. This statement was made in the 1850s. It was not long afterward, in the late nineteenth century, that domestic, sphere-based mentoring and the education of nurses by nurses was replaced with the education of nurses by Regulars in the hospitals of the public sphere.

It was during the sectarian "conflict" of the public sphere in the mid-nineteenth century, the same time as the 1847 emergence of the American Medical Association, that the domination of women nurses (and women physicians) was actively pursued by some Regular physicians in the sickroom management literature. This encroachment on the domestic sphere by physicians does not appear to have been addressed publicly by women. Interprofessional rivalry gradually abated as nurses became socialized to the rules of the public sphere. An examination of the details of this transition from mid-nineteenth-century accommodation to adoption of the public sphere as the focus of professional nursing practice and education in the later nineteenth century is beyond the scope of this book, however, it is noteworthy that the professional tension or rivalry prevalent in the mid-nineteenth century and referred to as the "legacy of early nineteenth-century reform"[86] has not gone away entirely. The emergence of nurse practitioner and physician assistant programs in the late twentieth century revived this conflict.

By the middle of the nineteenth century, Eclectic physicians had gained more professional power with the formalization of their botanical practice. They, too, participated with Regulars in the call for institutionalized nursing education. In an 1852 issue of the *Eclectic Medical Journal*, Dr. Cleaveland wrote, "*Some* should obtain a larger amount of knowledge than would be requisite for the mass of women. The more a person knows of the human system in health and disease, and the action of remedies, the less that person will be inclined to tamper with medicines, or to interfere with the physician. It is only the ignorant nurse or mother who presumes to give nostrums and quack medicines, of whose action they know little, to cure diseases, of the nature of which they know still less."[87] Concern over the "interference" of nurses with physician practice seemed to be at the heart of the support by Eclectics and Regulars for institutionalized nursing education programs.

It is not possible to assess how influential physician-written sickroom management books were, especially those that criticized the nursing care of the day. However, if one takes into account the direction that American nurses took in the later nineteenth century, that of focusing nursing education on following doctors' orders implicitly, it is probably safe to assume that the sickroom rhetoric of the Regulars from Britain to the United States had a significant effect on nursing in American hospitals. As the three case studies that follow illustrate, many professional nurses of the period were knowledgeable and experienced in patient care and by no means fit the stereotype of "nurse" put forth to the public by these physicians.

By the late nineteenth century, when American women had been entering medicine for decades, the medical profession's differentiation between nurses and doctors related to the attitude of the healer. A historian of women's entry into the American profession, Walsh, wrote: "The Woman's Journal accurately described the typical response of the male physicians: 'It's no argument at all to say that if we work with them as nurses we might just as well when they are doctors; that's a very different thing. Nurses are docile, submissive, and keep their proper place, while once let a woman study medicine and she thinks her opinion is as good as a man's.'[88] This sentiment was not only displayed toward female doctors but had been apparent toward educated, experienced nurses, before and after formal nursing training began in the late nineteenth century. One historian wrote that physicians have "consistently maintained and exercised the prerogative to define the scope for their own practice, and in so doing, they have claimed the right to set the limits of nurses' work."[89] Nurses, as they gain experience and confidence, have not simply subjugated themselves to the doctor. They have always been more than "the physician's hand."[90]

In their goal of providing patient care, nurses tried to honor the needs of the physician as well as the patient. At times the needs of the two could not be brought into balance. Experienced nurses had a greater opportunity for autonomy and creativity working in their communities than as hospital employees where the institutionally imposed goal for the nurse was not so much patient related as increasingly that of providing good service to physicians. The three chapters that follow contain case studies that discuss the autonomous status and skills of the professional, mid-nineteenth-century nurse who explored the use of botanical therapies during a foundational era in American health care history.

HARVESTING HISTORY—STAGE II

Sifting and Sorting

Before her remarkable service as a nurse and an herbalist during the Civil War, Mary Ann Bickerdyke of Ohio (1817–1901) was a popular and respected Botanic physician. She worked in private practice in Galesburg, Illinois, to support her children after the death of her husband. It is speculated that Mother Bickerdyke, as she was known, had trained in botanical therapies and the healing arts first with her Grandma Rogers as a child and then later with Dr. Zimri Hussey at the Physio-Botanic Medical College in Cincinnati, where, as was not common in the 1830s, women were accepted as students. While the history of her botanical education is not entirely clear, her war service is well documented.

It is recorded that Mother Bickerdyke followed a calling from God to work for the Union Army as a nurse. She rarely had an opportunity in the army to use her botanical skills, as her army medical superiors were, for the most part, Regulars. She did have occasion to put all of her nursing and botanical skills to use while stationed in 1863 at a pesthouse in Fort Pickering, Memphis, Tennessee, where she took a leadership role in healing the wounded. "She had the dead removed, the filthy bedding burned, and then she proceeded to clean up the place. . . . The patients were bathed, put to bed in clean clothes on clean bedding, dosed with black root and goldenseal, sassafras tea and beet juice, and fed all the milk and fresh vegetables they would take. A surprisingly large number of them recovered."[1]

Mother Bickerdyke fed, bathed, and bandaged "her boys" with skill and compassion. She was joined at one point by her friend, Eliza Porter, of Chicago. She kept Eliza busy cooking and preparing herbal teas. When the army ran out of medicine, Mother Bickerdyke used the herbs she knew about instead. She used blackberries for diarrhea and jimsonweed for pain, to name a few.[2] While some of her medical colleagues referred to her as the "old biddy," she was loved by many, from the lowest-ranking soldiers to Generals Sherman and Grant. General Sherman is quoted as saying that "Mother Bickerdyke outranked him" and reported only to President Lincoln. Mother Bickerdyke was known as the "cyclone in calico" and was memorialized with a monument in Galesburg, Illinois, for her tireless service.

It was the story of this particular nineteenth-century nurse-herbalist that first led me to believe that there were untold stories of other women who had participated in the Botanical Medical Movement of the mid-nineteenth century and whose stories were waiting to be harvested. The use of botanical therapies by mid-nineteenth-century nurses can be explored historically through the examination of individual accounts, such as has been done with Mother Bickerdyke and midwife Martha Ballard of the eighteenth century.[3] Based on the general women's history of the period, such as described in chapter 4, I thought that more information about nurses and their use of botanical therapies might be obtained by examining community rather than individual records, especially the records of the nineteenth-century spiritual communities and those in rural America, where Botanics and other healers were common.

Using the definition of nurse described in earlier chapters, I explored the archives of three religious communities. The histories of these three groups of mid-nineteenth-century women nurses and their use of herbal therapies—the Shaker Infirmary and Community Nurses, the Pioneer Nurses and Midwives of the Church of Jesus Christ of Latter-day Saints, and the Sisters of Charity hospital nurses—are included here. As mentioned in chapter 1, I vaguely knew of the connection that the Shakers and Latter-day Saints had to nineteenth-century herbalism. I chose to study the Sisters of Charity community, known after 1852 as the "Daughters of Charity," because of its history as early American nurses. I was not aware whether the community possessed any botanical knowledge.

Each of the three groups of identified nurses, the social foundation for each group's work, including community health beliefs, education in nursing, and the use of botanical therapies, each group's connection to the various leaders, philosophies, products, and services of the Botanical Medical Movement, in particular, Thomsonianism, and each group's relationship to American Indian healing practices, specifically in regard to botanical use, will be described in chapters 5–7. The botanical therapies, recipes, and remedies used in each group's nursing care also are included in the chapters for historical sifting and sorting. Chapter 5 opens this section with a history of the nursing and botanical therapies work of the Shaker infirmary and community nurses.

Comparative Time Line

	Up to 1815	1815–1829	1830–1839	1840–1849	1850–1860
General History	1801–09 Jefferson president 1803 Lewis and Clark Expedition 1813 Thomson receives patent for botanical system	1820 Thomson publishes 1st ed. *New Guide to Health* 1820 Florence Nightingale born in England 1826 Jefferson dies 1829 A. Jackson president 1829 L. Child publishes *Frugal Housewife* 1829 Beach starts Eclectic movement	1830 Indian Removal Act 1831 Midwives diminishing in big cities 1832 Cholera outbreak 1830s Regulars lose licensure	1843 S. Thomson dies 1840s D. Dix surveys institutionalized mentally ill 1847 American Medical Association established 1848 Seneca Falls Women's Rights Convention	1851 Nightingale trains at Kaiserwerth 1854 Nightingale provides nurses for the Crimean War 1859 Nightingale publishes *Notes on Nursing* in England 1860 Civil War
Shakers	1800 New Lebanon community mass-produces herbs for market 1813 T. Corbett is physician at Canterbury and establishes herb garden	1820 Marketing botanical remedies 1821 Millennial laws written and Order of Physicians and Nurses established 1824 Thomsonian Dr. Darling visits Harvard	1831 Thomsonianism introduced at Canterbury 1833 Many Shakers adopt Graham diet 1835 Canterbury's first herb catalog 1835 Harvard healers visit Dr. Gibson 1837 B. Hinckley physician at New Lebanon	1840–49 Nineteen Shaker communities in existence 1841-90 Canterbury Shakers produce sarsaparilla syrup 1849 P. Morrell writes *Choice Collection*	1851 E. Allard and others visit Indian doctor in Saratoga 1851 Rafinesque endorses Shaker products 1854 E. Myrick creates Herbarium 1854 P. Morrell writes *Receipts & Counsels* 1858 B. Hinckley receives med. degree 1860 Shaker women produce crude opium
Latter-day Saints			1830 LDS Church established 1831 Headquarters in Missouri 1833 M. C. West buys Thomson patent/ joins LDS 1834 W. Richards practices in S. Thomson's Boston clinic 1834 P. Sessions joins LDS 1836-49 P. Meek becomes root doctor 1836 W. and L. Richards baptized by B. Young 1836 M.A. Pratt travels to join LDS in Ohio from Maine with P. Sessions' husband	1840 Headquarters in Nauvoo, IL 1842 Women's Relief Society founded 1842 M.C. West to Nauvoo 1842 P. Sessions sealed to J. Smith 1842 L. Richards practices Thomsonian med. 1844 J. Smith murdered in IL 1844 Last meeting of Relief Society Ann Carling set apart as midwife/herbalist by J. Smith P. Sessions set apart by B. Young as doctor for women 1846 M.C. West teaches botanical nursing in Iowa 1847 Salt Lake established as headquarters and B. Young president of church 1848 Council of Health founded 1849 Negotiations between LDS and Ute Indians for land	1851 Female Council of Health formed 1851 M.C. West settles in Parowan, UT 1852 A. Carling settles in Fillmore, UT 1855 Sisters Meek and West set aside to teach nursing to Indian women 1860 Relief Society begins again Women sent East for medical education
Sisters of Charity	1809 Seton founds community in Emmitsburg, MD	1821 Death of E.A. Seton / R. White elected Mother 1823 Sisters help establish Baltimore Infirmary 1827-33 X. Clark Mistress of Novices 1829 M. Coskery joins Emmitsburg	1832 Establish Philadelphia almshouse and cholera hospitals 1833 Sisters administer Maryland Hospital (for insane) 1839-45 X. Clark is Mother	1840 Sisters resign at Maryland Hospital 1844 M. Coskery sister servant at Mt. Hope 1840-50 M. Coskery writes *Advices* 1844 Sisters purchase Mt. Hope 1845 -54 X. Clark Mistress of Novices 1846 X. Clark is recorded as writing *Instructions*	1860 Sisters nurse soldiers during Civil War

Chapter 5

Herbs and the Shaker Infirmary and Community Nurses

A blade of grass — a simple flower
Culled from the dewy lea;
These, these shall speak with touching power,
Of change and health to thee.

— From a Shaker catalog of herbs,
New Lebanon, New York, c. 1850

The United Society of True Believers in Christ's Second Appearing, more commonly known as the "Shakers," is a religious group led to America from England in 1774 by Ann Lee. "Mother Ann," as she was called by her followers, was believed to be the second incarnation of Christ. After being imprisoned in England for blasphemy, Mother Ann believed that she was directed by Christ to go to America. She and eight followers settled in New York, in a town called Niskeyuna, later known as "Watervliet."

In the early days of the movement in 1780, Mother Ann and other original Shakers were imprisoned in the United States for "disturbing the publick peace" and what the commissioners called "highly pernicious and of destructive tendency to the Freedom & Independence of the United States of America."[1] Over time, the Shaker movement grew in numbers and popularity. During the eighteenth and nineteenth centuries, a number of Shaker communities were formed throughout New England and the Midwestern United States. Each community had a hierarchical structure of two or more "families," each with leaders and responsibilities reflective of their age, spiritual accomplishment, and commitment (i.e., separation from "the outside world"). By 1840, fifty-six years after the death of Mother Ann, the Shaker movement had nineteen communities with approximately 100–800 members in each community and a total of 16,000 Believers in the entire Shaker movement. As of 2003, there were only four remaining Shakers living in the only remaining active community of Sabbathday Lake in New Gloucester, Maine.

Some Shaker historians report that the name "Shaker" was a derisive nickname given to the community by those who knew that their form of Quaker worship included ecstatic movement.[2] Elder Henry C. Blinn, recorder of the Canterbury and Enfield, New Hampshire communities, wrote of the early community in 1747: "This society accepted no creed, & subscribed to no form of religious worship. They were led by the spirit of God. . . . In their times of spiritual devotion they moved as directed by the Holy Spirit, which marked these seasons with a diversity of gifts, in speaking, singing, shouting & dancing. It was during some of these violent exercises that they received the name of Shakers."[3]

Shaker social beliefs included women's rights, nonviolence, equality among the sexes, celibacy, and the Second Coming of Christ as spirit in the Church, not as Jesus.[4] The essence of Shaker belief has been described as "love." "They wanted to escape from possessive and jealous love into a universal tenderness and compassion."[5] They not only believed in the equality of the sexes but races as well. Elder F. W. Evans wrote in 1859: "To the mind of the simple, unsophisticated Shaker it seems marvelously inconsistent for any human government to be administered for the sole benefit of its own officers and their particular friends and favorites; or that more than one half the citizens should be disenfranchised because they happen to be *females*, and compelled by the sword to obey the laws they have never sanctioned, and ofttimes in which they have no faith, and to submit to taxation where there has been no previous representation; while still millions of other fellow-citizens are treated as *property*, because they chance to possess a darker-colored skin than their cruel brethren."[6] The Shakers displayed their belief in the equality of the sexes and races by organizing communities that were led by men and women, often two Eldresses and two Elders. In addition, communities did not discriminate against blacks or Indians.[7]

A Shaker believed that "worship was a way of life, a continuous activity, so integral a part of his experience that it came almost as automatic as his breathing. To him every day was the Sabbath, and every deed an act of worship."[8] The Shakers were a very hard working people. Leader Ann Lee often was quoted as inspiring her community by saying, "Hands to work, hearts to God."[9] Following the biblical instruction from the Book of Revelation, 1:11, "What thou seest, write in a book," the Shakers documented their work and important interactions within their community, among themselves, and with the "outside world" when it did occur. The Shakers' Millennial Laws, or governing orders, stated that "two family journals should be kept by the order of the Deacons and Deaconesses, in which all important occurrences or business transactions should be registered."[10] Documentation was perceived by the Shakers as the fulfillment of sacred obligation. The community had experienced physical and legal attacks by non-Believers, therefore, documentation of their work was an act of protection, especially for their business transactions.

Initially reading and writing were only valued in terms of their purpose in spiritual development. Mother Ann was illiterate, and early on in the community, written texts such as the Bible, when used, were "in subordination to the primacy of orally conveyed teachings."[11] However, because of the reasons stated earlier, many Shakers did read and write, therefore, the work of the Shaker infirmary and community nurses is recorded to some extent. While much of the Shaker experience and history has been analyzed and recorded by scholars, such as Stein, Andrews, and Thurman, nursing and the Shaker community health "system" in general and the use of botanical therapies by nurses in particular have not been thoroughly explored. Thurman's research and writings are significant to the general understanding of the history of Shaker women, especially in the Harvard and Shirley, Massachusetts, communities. The history presented here attempts to expand the work of Shaker historians, such as Thurman, by providing a specific analysis of Shaker health care, nursing care, and botanical therapies used by infirmary and community nurses.

Shaker Health Beliefs

The Shakers respected human differences. They also believed that they were different from non-Believers and, therefore, should demonstrate that they had chosen a different life than that of people living in "the world." They wore different clothing than mainstream society and had their own speech patterns. "The Believers, in essence, developed a 'rhetoric of separatism' in which they characterized themselves as possessors of the 'truth' who could not be sullied by contact with the sinful world."[12] They believed in the spiritual gift of healing and that particular members, such as Mother Ann Lee and the Elders of the church, were blessed with the gift.[13] Early Believers were encouraged and inspired to seek their healing in God rather than in physicians and to use faith-healing and the laying on of hands. But as the years went on, Believers integrated their faith-healing practices with the practices of the "world" and "worldly physicians." This was often a point of controversy between the church leadership and Believers because Ann Lee and other early leaders had been biased against the use of worldly physicians.[14]

Some early church leaders, such as John Warner of the Harvard, Massachusetts, community, tried to limit the practice of consulting worldly doctors and complained about the Believers' overuse of physicians, both Shaker and non-Shaker. He believed that the Shakers should "bear" their illnesses as a "test of their faith rather than seek medical cures."[15] Believers' journals and daybooks show that Warner's opinions were not always heeded. But when the Shakers did seek help from a physician, it was not from a staunch Regular. Records demonstrate that they most often sought the help of a Thomsonian, an Eclectic or a water cure physician. For example, Dr. Kittredge of Lynn, Massachusetts, and Dr. Foster of Lowell, Massachusetts, were water cure physicians employed by the Harvard and Shirley Shakers. The bias against Regulars relaxed as the community grew. Thomas Corbett, a Canterbury Shaker who began his medical training at the behest of church leadership in the early decades of the nineteenth century, trained under physician William Tenney,[16] who was both a Thomsonian and a Regular.

Like many nineteenth-century Americans, the Shakers had very diverse approaches to health care. They used numerous healing modalities, such as hydrotherapy ("water cure") treatments, which included body steaming and body wraps with hot moist cloths, as well as special diets, botanical therapies, electrotherapy, and fasting. There are records of the Shakers consulting Regulars for broken bones, injuries, measles, and surgical procedures, such as the removal of teeth or cancerous growths. In the Harvard community, it is recorded that vaccinations were purchased and given to members.[17] The following entries from the infirmary journal from the Harvard community illustrate the variety of treatments used.

> June 1835. Mon 29th Pleasant. Benjamin Kendall took a steam.
>
> July 1835. Wed. 1st Mary Babbit rode into town with Mary Hatch & Lucinda Orsmint to have some teeth extracted.
>
> Fri. 3rd Pleasant. Br. Abel Jewett & Benjamin K. went into town to the doctor's. B.K. is very much out of health his back & shoulder is very lame.
>
> Mon 6th. Mary B. put to blister plasters on to Benjamin's back; by Dr. K's order.[18]

From early on, each community had its own nurses, who were women. Some communities also had physicians, many of whom were women. The Shakers believed that all Believers were equally entitled to health care. For example, the Harvard community's church covenant states: "All members that are or shall be received into the Church, shall profess one joint interest as a religious right, i.e, all shall have just and equal right and privilege according to their needs (in sickness and in health) in the use of things in the Church, without any difference being made, on account of what any one brought in (whether more or less) so long as they remain in obedience to the order and government of the Church, and are holden in relation."[19] The health beliefs of the Shakers are summed up here in their teachings to children about health:

> The preservation of health is a matter of great importance to all who desire to be useful and find enjoyment in the life. The privilege of the first consequence to a Believer is to obtain a standing in the work of God, and the next is to have health and strength to enable him to lay up a treasure in the gospel. If people by carelessness or imprudence do what will injure their health under their usefulness and render them a burden among Believers their reflection will be dreadful, and their loss beyond all calculation. . . . Overeating, as eating a great variety of everything, is one of the most common causes of debility and ill health among children. . . . These childish luxuries (nuts and fruits and confectionaries) often render them weak, feeble, serve to corrupt their blood and implant the seeds of disease and lead to a train of disorders. . . . If children are allowed to form a practice of taking a medicine for every little complaint they make to those who have the care of the sick they will be liable to establish habits that will corrupt their spiritual strength, destroy their health, and sap the foundation of a good and sound constitution.[20]

In general, the Shakers led by Elders, physicians, and nurses rejected the use of strong chemical drugs such as calomel and preferred herbal simples. Eldress Betsy Smith's travel journal describes a conversation on the subject between Brother Barnabas Hinckley, a physician at Mount Lebanon,[21] and the Eldress and other visitors from a South Union Kentucky community: "He conversed some on the subject of medicine. Said he considers water is good in some cases, but don't consider it a specific for all diseases. Uses medicine in some cases, and thinks to advantage, and says he would make use in certain cases, any human remedy to mitigate pain. But at the same time he would be cautious about using strong medicines of all kinds, and not use them where one more simple would answer."[22] Dr. Barnabas Hinckley, the head of the medical department at Mount Lebanon was an Eclectic physician.

The Shakers, like many nineteenth-century Americans, believed that one's lifestyle affected one's state of health, especially of women, whose work tended to be more sedentary. Because of the Shakers' values surrounding work and the fact that Shaker communities were in more rural areas, they were less likely to be sedentary than most nineteenth-century urban women. However, Shaker leaders still had some concern for the lifestyle and health of community women. Eldress Elmira Allard wrote in her autobiography, "Let the rising generation be trained to toil in the open air as we did, and there will be seen an improvement in their strength & health of body will return & prove a blessing. . . . Many females are too closely closited *[sic]* & bound to needle work, bowed down like a rain bow from early morn till evening gray with but very little relaxation."[23]

Like many nineteenth-century women, Shaker women were succumbing to the belief in the "weakness" of women. Eldress Sally Loomis of the Harvard community echoed the beliefs of John Warner in the concern with the overuse of the world's doctors, particularly by the sisters. Loomis "preferred that the sisters develop the gift of healing among themselves."[24] She tried to help the sisters by organizing a healing network, which included a series of health information meetings at which she read aloud to them Mary Gove Nichols's *Lectures to Ladies on Anatomy and Physiology.*

At times, community leaders attempted to mandate Believers' dietary practices. The Shakers considered good food, properly cooked and well digested, the foundation of excellent health.[25] In 1807, "A reformatory movement in dietetics was introduced as a universal gift among Believers. All were to renounce the use of imported tea. This gift continued during ten months."[26] A ban on English tea was being practiced by many Americans, because tea, as a stimulant, was considered encouraging to the "passions." Nineteenth-century

Americans and health care reformers often attributed the cause of disease to excessive indulgence of the passions.[27] Also, as discussed earlier, following the Jeffersonian presidency and the Lewis and Clark expedition, Americans with a sense of nationalism often felt obliged to become more reliant on botanicals and teas from American soil. The ban on tea was never fully embraced nationally or in the Shaker communities, however, and in 1808, after meeting with church leader Mother Lucy Wright, the ministry of Canterbury, for example, "gave permission to use imported tea"[28] again.

In 1833, many among the Shakers adopted the Graham (vegetarian) diet and healing system like other health care reform-minded Americans. It is recorded that the "Believers consumed a great deal of swine's flesh, and the younger ones could not digest it. This vegetable diet required the abstinence of condiments or stimulants. It was a great change. Meat, butter, tea, and coffee and tobacco were laid aside. Water was used for drink. Frequent baths were taken. Several undertook to carry out the system."[29]

The Shakers also demonstrated knowledge of community health promotion and prevention practices in their support of proper sanitation. Blinn wrote: "Although we are not made acquaintance with the prevailing causes of so much sickness, yet we are of the opinion that a proper regard to sanitary laws would have prevented large share of the ills."[30] The success of community health practices often is measured by longevity in a population. Many of the Shakers did in fact live long lives. There are a number of accounts of community members in the church family at Canterbury, for example, who lived to more than seventy years of age. Nurse Anna Carr lived to be eighty-six and James Hill seventy-nine.[31] Nurse Charlotte Thomas of Sabbathday Lake died of old age at eighty-nine and Nurse Lavine McIntire, who had been a chief Eldress, died at age eighty-four after breaking her hip.[32] In 1875, the average age of death in the Harvard community was sixty to sixty-eight,[33] and in Enfield, New Hampshire, and Watervliet, New York, members lived to be well over seventy-five years of age.[34] Believers gave most of the credit for their longevity to their sexual purity, for life, they claimed, was shortened by the "abnormal development of the passional nature."[35] As discussed earlier, the belief in curtailing passions as a means to health and long life was not unusual among nineteenth-century Americans, including those who were not living in religious communities.

Shaker Nurses' Education and Work

A number of sisters in the Shaker communities were identified as "nurses." For many years the nurses provided the health care in the communities that was needed beyond faith-healing practices. In 1837, Sister Elizabeth Lovegrove recorded in her diary her work of making candles, working in the kitchen, picking herbs, and making wintergreen lozenges. She also recorded some of the nursing care she provided during her time as a nurse in the New Lebanon community. Sister Lovegrove's nursing and botanical work included the use of teas and topical applications.

> Betsy B takes Phisic.
>
> Elder Sister is relieved some of her cough by the vaper [*sic*] bath and electricity.
>
> Lucy Bishop here to help sweat Elder Ebenezer with hemlock and hot stones.
>
> Commence polticeing [*sic*] Amy's face with chamomile and Marsh mallows.
>
> Elder Sister fell down and hurt her side — we resort to shocking. Rubbing. and bleeding her, likewise apply skunk cabbage leaves and make her tea of Johnswort and pepper grass seed, all have a good effect.
>
> Rachel Sampson severely afflicted with the sun headache, apply a blister to the neck and arm also oint the forehead with marrow of a hogs jaw and apply a bag of hops wet with vinegar, good effect.[36]

Nurses as well as physicians were identified separately by name in some Shaker demographic records, such as in the Watervliet, New York, community records.[37] Identified nurses were always "sisters." The brethren who helped with caregiving from time to time were not identified as "nurses." Male patients were cared for by male "attendants" when there was a question of propriety.[38] For example, the physicians' journal entry from March 25, 1835 read, "Joseph MM took a dose of No. 1 physic. Walter Adams waited on him."[39]

While some physicians in the various communities were male, many or all physicians in the Watervliet, New York, and Harvard and Shirley, Massachusetts, communities were females. It is often difficult to clearly identify from journal accounts and sickroom records what distinguished the role of the nurse from the physician. Some community members can be identified as patient, doctor, and nurse. For example, the Harvard community physician journal from July 20, 1834 recorded: "Mary B. [Babbit] has been his doctor & his nurse from that time to the present." On January 29, 1835, "Mary Babbit took an emetic also. . . ." In February 1835, "Selah W. is Mary B.'s nurse."[40] In the same community, on March 22, 1834, Susan Myrick was "appointed to live in the Physicians Order with Sister Eunice Wilds & Mary Babbit," and on February 2, 1835, "Sister Caroline, Mary Babbit & Susan K. M. [Susan Myrick] were the nurses."[41]

It also is not clear how a nurse or physician was chosen for his or her job. One record stated: "There were Sisters here set apart for nursing the sick, but Mercy was not one of them. She was there only to prepare their food."[42] Some Believers may have been "set aside" as nurses because they had received the gift of their own spiritual healing at one time. Lydia Lyon, a nurse appointed at the Enfield, New Hampshire, community in 1815, who died in 1863 at eighty-four, wrote of her own faith healing from diphtheria at age seven, when she and her family, all Shakers, were living outside of the Shirley community in Worcester, Massachusetts:

> My father was in great anxiety of mind whether we should yield to the solicitations of his friends or obey the convictions of his faith. We passed a sleepless night and

> on entering the room in the morning he asked me if he should send for a physician. I answered, 'Send for a man of God'. This pleased him, and he said that there was a healing gift for his daughter. . . . I was soon dressed and able to walk about the house. . . . My father was so anxious about me that he immediately went to Shirley to inform the Brethren and have one come and see me to make the gift permanent. . . . I have every reason to believe that my life was saved by the gift of healing.[43]

According to Shaker community records, achieving the status of physician was not the highest achievement in the community. Nurses and physicians often were "removed" to church leadership positions. As stated previously, Mary Babbit of the Harvard community performed nursing and physician work, and on September 16, 1835, she was "released from the physicians lot and put into the office for a Trustee Sister."[44]

Nursing in a Shaker community was defined, albeit loosely, by the Millennial Laws of 1821. The Shaker nurses, as described in the following excerpt from the Millennial Laws, "officiated" over health care in their communities.

> As the natural body is prone to sickness and disease, it is proper that there should be suitable persons appointed to attend to necessary duties in administering medical aid to those in need. . . . Brethren may not apply medical aid to sisters who are sick, without the knowledge and union of the sisters who officiate as nurses in the family. Neither should they administer any medicine to the sisters, without telling the sisters in care, what it is made of. And the sisters should do the same in respects to the brethren. . . . But all have liberty to request such medicines as they desire.[45]

Many sisters rotated through the infirmary at one time or another to provide care for other community members. Those Believers who were appointed by church leaders as physicians or nurses reported to the Elders of the community. They reported epidemiological data, such as how many community members had influenza or cholera. They recorded deaths in the community and trips to worldly physicians and treatments given, such as the number of "Emetics" given each week.[46] The activities of the health care facility of the community also were recorded. Different communities had different names for the building where health care was provided including, "infirmary," "sickroom," "nurses' shop," "physicians' shop," and "medical department."

The nurses provided what today might be referred to as "outpatient" and "inpatient" care in the building known as the "infirmary," "sickroom," "nurse house," or "nurses' shop." Some nurses' shops, such as in the Canterbury community, had the sickroom or infirmary in the same building as the nurses' dispensary or outpatient area. Some patients stopped by the infirmary for a remedy such as an emetic, and sometimes they stayed at the infirmary to be given round-the-clock care by the nurses. No records were found of patients staying for any length of time in the physicians' shop or medical department, however. In the manuscripts reviewed, patients and nurses went to the medical department to pick up a medicine, similar to going to a pharmacy today.

Nurses held leadership positions in the health care "system" of the Shaker communities. In 1792, the year the Canterbury community was formally established, Elizabeth Avery, a native of New Hampshire, was appointed head of the nursing department.[47] Due to Shaker beliefs against worldly doctoring and education (especially by Regulars), there were few physicians in the early years. For example, Eliab Harlow and Isaac Couch organized and worked in the physician order in the New Lebanon, New York community in the late eighteenth and mid-nineteenth centuries. They are recorded as having traveled to other communities to share their information. In the Canterbury community, it was not until Thomas Corbett was sent to study Thomsonian medicine at age thirty-three that the community had an on-site physician. "Previous to this date the Society had depended upon the Sisters, who had officiated as nurses. These had been furnished with a small printed volume containing medical prescriptions and directions for the care of the sick. They had also some recipes, sent from Br. Eliab Harlow of N.L. In cases of extreme sickness of dislocated or broken bones they employed a physician from Loudon, Dr. William Tenney."[48]

Shaker nurses performed many duties. They assisted in surgeries[49] and "fixed doses" of medicines[50] such as emetics. They had receipts for numerous remedies, primarily botanical in nature. The Shirley Shakers' *Nurse House Book* includes receipts for remedies, such as spirits of lavender, elixir of health (a formula of bloodroot, aloes, and bitters), tooth powder, tincture of rhubarb, simple syrup, pills for cough, divers powder (ipecacuanhna, opium, sulphate of potash), liquid laudanum, female pills (aloes, myrrh, caster, galbanum), and Dr. Parker's bilious pills (aloes, ginger, gamboges, bursteel soap, and a few drops of anis oil).[51]

How the nurses' medicines differed from the medicines received at the physician shop is not entirely clear; there may have been no difference. The following record demonstrates that Shaker nurses and physicians both used chemical and botanical remedies. "Feb. 1, 1823, Evening to physicians shop for Pills. December 22, 1825, Evening to nurse shop after powders of Golden Sulph & Panacea Ant. & Hulls physic for Augustus to take in lieu of an emetic."[52] The nurses also made medicines for the Shaker community and for sale to non-Shakers. Like other nineteenth-century women, the Shaker sisters had their stillroom for making medicines. But their still was often more than a room; it was a building. "Back of the infirmary was a distillery in a small building which was called 'The Still House'. In it they manufactured good spirit — and made many kinds of medicine."[53]

The sister-nurses also were clever businesswomen when it came to botanical remedies. They used their botanical remedy production skills to help support their communities economically. There is one example of Shaker nurses being required to find a way to pay for a patient's treatment by a worldly physician. Sister Aurelia Mace of the Sabbathday Lake community in New Gloucester, Maine, wrote the following:

> I have a record of Deborah Pote and Ruth Holmes. They were nurse Sisters. The record shows that they

> were business women. I think the Deacons were trying to make the Nurse's order pay all the costs — Doctor's bills and all — for the $8.39 for attendance on Josiah Holmes at Gray was set down against them, [Josiah broke his leg when thrown from his horse and was treated by a Dr. Whitney], and those two little Sisters did almost clear the costs. There was a great deal of rum and other liquors bought — But the work that was done by their hand was supprising [sic]. They worked the Distillery — Sold much what they called mint water which always brought a dollar a gallon, and Rose water which brought a higher price.[54]

The Shaker herb industry, which will be discussed later in more detail, was very lucrative for the community and highly respected by Shakers and non-Shakers alike for the quality of herbs and products. Unlike worldly nineteenth-century Americans who often had gardens for their beauty as well as their utility, the Shakers believed that gardens, including flower gardens, were purely utilitarian. They grew only those plants and flowers that could be eaten for food or used in making medicine. "Flower gardens were laid out in rows like vegetables and were considered to be crops. Flowers were used in the manufacture of dye for textiles as well as for medicinal products."[55]

Shaker nurses often lived in the infirmary. At Canterbury, the nurses' quarters and the pharmacy were on the first floor of the infirmary, and the patients' rooms were on the second floor. In the infirmary, the nurses administered emetics,[56] cathartics, steams, injections (enemas), and sweats for mild to moderate illnesses such as stomach pain and influenza. They cared for the patients sick enough to stay in the infirmary for nights and days, feeding and bathing them and turning them in their cradles.[57] They prayed and sang Shaker hymns for their patients, believing that their prayers and songs might be instrumental in bringing about a gift of healing or a miracle. As demonstrated in the story of Lydia Lyon, healings and miracles were not only observed by church Elders and Eldresses.

In addition to their infirmary work, Shaker community nurses made home visits to check on sick members[58] and escorted patients to worldly doctors and dentists.[59] They cared for patients with infectious diseases such as cholera during the national epidemics. Many, if not the majority, of the remedies the nurses used were botanical in origin. The nurses documented patients' responses, as shown in Harvard infirmary records from March 24, 1834: "Lucy Clark took an Emetic, it operated well, the sick are gaining."[60] The nurses were the ones to scientifically observe and record the results of the implementation of the community's new health care practices, such as the adoption of the Graham diet. At Harvard, they recorded: "The Graham system of diet has done some good, there has not been so little medicine taken in a week, for more than a year, as there has been the past week."[61] Nurses also dressed the wounds of human[62] and animal patients[63] and applied topical herbal remedies in the care of minor injuries.

Nurses did follow the directions of both the Shaker and worldly physicians if the physicians were involved in helping a community member. Mary Babbitt, a doctor and nurse, applied blister plasters under the "order of Dr. K."[64] One receipt used by the Canterbury nurses to make an "ointment or salve for cancers" instructs the nurse to "Take the juice of wood sorrel & dry it away in the sun — until a thick salve. To answer the directions of the Doctor this was to be applied to the affected part twice a day by rubbing it in carefully."[65] Physicians also took orders from other physicians, nurses took orders from physicians, and both, as well as patients, may have taken orders from respected community members, such as the Elders, for healing remedies, including herbal remedies. This is exemplified in the following infirmary entry, "William L. began to doctor for a humour in his head. Br.[66] Joseph Mayo ordered him to take Hellebore[67] Snuff, & some times to snuff up some Pepper, Cayenne annoint his nose & put a hot stone to his head nights."[68] The nurses were, for the most part, however, autonomous community healers. Suzanne Thurman, in her book on the lives of the Harvard and Shirley sisters, wrote: "Shed of familial responsibilities, these women fulfilled their female roles as nurturers and healers, but they did so not simply by following orders but by taking charge of an entire branch of medicine in their villages. These sisters were given the freedom to introduce and experiment with a new method of practicing medicine and to instruct others in it."[69]

Shaker nurses and physicians both utilized criteria for deciding when a Believer needed a nurse. "Fri. 27th Joseph Parker came here, he informed us that there was a number of the Brethren & Sisters sick at the N.F. [North Family] with the Cholera morbus & some of them were very sick. Sat. 28th Mary and Eliza Babbit went to the N.F. & found the number to be 10 that were *not able to wait on themselves.* Anna Mayo was there to assist them. Abigail Babbit is the only one in the Church [Note: a different family] that is sick enough to need a nurse."[70]

Shaker nurses used numerous herbs in their care of community members. Blinn recorded that "simple doses of root or herb tea entered into nearly every prescription."[71] Herbs used in receipts recorded in the Shirley Shakers' *Nurse House Book* include juniper, orange peel, snakeroot, Peruvian bark, saffron, myrrh, anis oil, bloodroot, lavender and rhubarb.[72] Another Shaker receipt book, possibly used by nurses, contains the receipt for "syrup for summer complaint," a blackberry and clove syrup used for dysentery recorded as being "an excellent medicine; and has cured many."[73] A receipt book, thought to be from the Mount Lebanon community, includes a very detailed account of *how* herbs were used in the care of patients. It is signed as being from the Groveland Shaker community, 1855, and it describes the use of the herb lobelia (for more information see Color Insert A), commonly used by Thomsonians:

> Lobelia is of great value in preventing sickness as well as curing illness. By taking a dose when first attacked by any complaint it will throw it off and frequently prevent long sickness. It not only acts as an emetic and throws off from the stomach every thing that nature does not require for the support of the system but extends its effects thro [*sic*] all parts of the body. It is searching, enlivening & quickening and has great power in removing all obstructions. But it soon exhausts itself and if not followed up by some other

medicine . . . to hold the vital heat till nature is able to support itself by digesting the food it will not be sufficient to remove a disease that has become sealed.

It clears all obstructions to the extremities without regard to the name of the disease until it produces an equilibrium in the system and will be felt in the fingers & toes producing a prickling sensation. This symptom is alarming to those unacquainted with its operation; but it is always favorable, being a certain indication of the turn of the disorder, and the patient generally gains in health from that time. In regard to the quantity to be given as a dose, it is a matter of less consequence than is imagined. The most important thing is to give enough to produce the desired effect; If too little is given, it will worry the patient, and do little good; if more is given than is necessary the surplus will be thrown off and it will be a waste of the trash!

Directions

To prepare for a course of medicine let the patient place his feet in hot water & drink freely of Composition and herb tea, until an easy & free perspiration is induced, & the veins in the hands are full. Then take an enema composed of a tea of Lobelia & raspberry leaves sweetened with molasses which should be retained as long as possible. Then take the Lobelia and some warm tea, either Scull-cap or Penny-royal. In about fifteen minutes take another dose, and so on, until enough has been taken to cleanse the stomach. If the stomach is sour take a little weak lye. If the patient should puke hard and the stomach be cold, drink freely of composition or herb tea, or take a little number six. Take a little crust water or milk porridge 2 or 3 times during the operation of the medicine.

> For a dose of Lobelia Tincture, from a teaspoon to a table-spoon in a little herb tea. Of the green herb pulverized, one or two table-spoons full steped in a gill or a half a pint of water is sufficient for our emetic. Divided into three or four portions, & if the patient prefers it sweetened, he may have it sweetened with molasses. If the the[*sic*] whole herb & seeds are mixed, it will not require as much, as the seed is more powerful in its operation. In some obstinate cases it may be proper to resort to the seed alone; if so a teaspoonful is sufficient for a dose, mixed with molasses.[74]

Another example of an herb receipt used by Shaker nurses can be found in the receipt book compiled by Sister Sarah Standish, *A Collection of Medicinal Receipts for the Use of Physicians.*

> Primhedge and Butternut Physic
>
> A great purifier of the blood; it destroys every species of worms in adults and children, it causes children to grow fleshy & sprightly. Most disorders in old people & children yield to this medicine. Preparation. Make a strong decoction of Blue Vervain tops and roots, mint, Catnep, Motherwort (Boneset- less than the others) Blacksnake Root, Elecampane, Butternut bark, proportionate, Primhedge berries 1/2oz. when strained to one gallon add 2 oz. mandrake root 1/2oz., Bloodroot 4 oz. Black Indian Hemp root in powder or 4 oz. Socotrine aloes — or quart Elder Berry juice or blossoms, — boil it add one quart of Molasses, boil it again to one gallon — strain it thro' a flannel bag, & add a pint of gin whilst hot. And it is fit for use, and safe in any case for old and young. Taken once in three months it preserves general health. Dose for an adult a wine-glassful, for a child a tablespoon full — for worms it should be given three mornings successively before the

> full of the moon, with a cup of cold snake root tea after it, and gruel thro' the day.[75]

Herbal remedies often were measured and taken by the wineglassful in the nineteenth century. The botanical "Primhedge" may be referring to the common name of the plant genus *Ligustrum*. *Ligustrum vulgare* was commonly referred to as "privet" or "prim" and was grown in hedges in England.[76] While the leaf was most commonly used, according to *King's American Dispensatory*, by Felter and Lloyd, the berry could be used as a cathartic too. When reading botanical receipts, it is often difficult to know exactly which plant is being referred to as the common names often are the ones used in the receipts. Primhedge is just one of numerous examples.

The receipt book by Sister Standish is somewhat unusual in that it not only includes instructions in the receipt for making a botanical remedy but also describes the *use* of the remedy, details often lacking in old receipt books and even more so lacking in contemporary herb texts and dispensatories. Older books may have excluded this kind of information about the process of using the herbal receipts, because many people still had a basic understanding of the preparation and application of herbs for healing. Standish's receipt book also is unusual in that it was compiled for the "use of physicians." This may indicate that the Shaker physicians learned healing methods and herbalism from Sister Sarah.

The Shaker sisters knew much about herbal therapies and the plants commonly used in healing in the nineteenth century. They were the ones who did much of the wild crafting of herbs, especially before the community medicinal gardens were started. "The sisters made numerous and continuous excursions into the woods, swamps, and fields to gather thousands of pounds of wild herbs. Later, 'botanic gardens' were begun in which transplanted wild herbs and acres of herbs from seed were grown within the village for easier harvest."[77] There are numerous accounts in various Shaker journals and church records of the types of herbs wild crafted and where they were obtained. For example, "June 8. A company of seven persons go nearly to the City of Concord to gather skunk cabbage. . . . June 22.

A company of seven persons went to Pembroke to gather some home tea, as the tea from China has been discarded to make place for this reform movement. The plant used was *Lysimachia quadrifolia*. It has several common names.[78] These journeys were made in one week to Pembroke to gather this plant and at other times they obtained it on the plains of Concord."[79]

The sisters participated in Shaker herbal operations from cultivation and harvest to processing and application with patients. One Shaker historian wrote: "The major part of the laborious and routine labor connected with the medicinal herb industry, such work as cleaning roots, picking and 'picking over' flowers and plants, cutting sage, cleaning bottles, cutting and printing labels, preparing powders and herbs, and 'dressing' or putting up extracts and ointments, was done by the sisters. They also made the ointments."[80] Joseph Hammond of the Harvard community kept a daybook that provided a description of his work as a broom maker and a healer as well as accounts of his medicinal herb work with the sisters. He did bloodletting and tooth extractions[81] and escorted the nurses of the community on home visits and on visits with patients to worldly physicians. His work as an attendant to the nurses and patients was carried out on an as-needed basis. He also did extensive work in the herb garden and did wild crafting with the Shaker sisters. The following is a selection from his daybook:

> Sept 14, 1820 Rest of day with Sisters cutting digitalis & fixing herb in loft. . . .
>
> Sept 15 Sisters distilled the fennel oil.
>
> Sept 16 Preparing herbs to go to Boston.
>
> Sept 21 Wrought with Sisters cutting last of things in garden such as S Balm, P mint, S mint, and various other small parcels of herbs.
>
> Sept 27th p.m. to S pasture after Sassafras roots.

> October 20 Wrought in the garden digging roots such as Aparabacca, Rhubarb, Comphrey & Garget root.[82]

In addition to the use of herbs as simples and combination herbal remedies, the Shakers also applied the philosophy and remedies of the Thomsonian botanical system. According to Henry Blinn, the Thomsonian system of healing the sick was introduced in Canterbury in 1831. "The first patient on the new plan was a Sister and she was to take a "pepper puke."[83] Thomsonianism may have appealed to the Shakers because of similar ideologies. For example, both Thomson and Ann Lee claimed to be illiterate and spoke about the potential for the corruption of society by an undue emphasis on formal education. Secondly, Ann Lee, many Shaker Elders, Eldresses, and Samuel Thomson opposed reliance upon Regulars. In addition, as farmers, the Shakers knew very well the importance of medicinal plants in promoting health, and Thomson's botanical system potentially served as a new level of organizing the way in which they used the remedies they knew.

Exactly how Thomsonianism was first introduced into the Shaker communities is unclear, but records of the early implementation of the system do exist. Harvard and Shirley community records indicate that Elizabeth Myrick was the first to administer Thomson remedies.[84] Shaker nurses probably learned Thomsonianism from the Shaker physicians and from itinerant Thomsonian practitioners. According to Joseph Hammond, on Sept 28, 1824, a Dr. Darling visited the community. "Dr. Darling & family & Sister of Boston been up to Ringe on a visit to his father's family. He is one of Dr. Thompsons [*sic*] proselytes or a Cayenne pepper Doctor."[85] Shaker receipt books also included Thomson remedies. For instance, a Hancock community receipt book contained recipes for "Dr. Thomson's Cough Powder and Sam Thomson's Strengthening Plaster."[86]

The Shaker nurses' practice also included domestic remedies they learned over the years from their healing networks of family, friends, and each other. A simple recipe that shows the connection between domestic healing and the infirmary/home health practice of the Shaker nurses is the Canterbury nurses' receipt for onion syrup.

"Slice your onions then put them in a vessel cover them with honey make your vessel air tight then let it stew gradually till the onion is done. Strain off the liquor & it is done."[87] Shaker nurses were as scientific about their botanical interventions as they were about their other nursing work. They recorded their observations and experiences with the use of botanical therapies in patient care. The following is an example of the nurses' choice of botanical poultice based on their scientific observation: "Sister Sarah K. wanted to have applied to Br. N. K.'s leg a poultice composed of the following articles, Beef brine, Feverfew, Mayweed Flowers, Wormwood, & Wheat middleings, it proved to be too harsh for it, caused some irritation & increased the swelling, it was taken off in the p.m. & the pumpkin poultice put on again."[88]

There is no specific record of the nurses receiving any education or training per se in medicine or the use of herbs, other remedies, or treatments. In fact, according to the Shaker Millennial Laws, Section XVI, number four, "No member but those appointed by the Ministry may study Physic, Pharmacy, Anatomy, Surgery, Law, Chemistry, etc. etc."[89] However, it is recorded that nurses received receipt books from Shaker physicians and receipts from worldly physicians, community members, and the Elders,[90] thus they learned through their healing networks. The nurses may have learned botanical practice from itinerant physicians such as Dr. Darling, and they may have visited worldly physicians at times for education. Although it is not specifically stated in the *Physician's Journal* from Harvard, it is possible that the group of Shakers that went to Dr. Gibson's in New Ipswich, New Hampshire on December 1, 1835 [91] was going for training. The group included nurse-doctors[92] Mary Babbit and Susan Myrick. Dr. Gibson's remedies are specifically mentioned for the first time on January 11, 1836 in the Harvard infirmary record, "Gibson's No. 1" for "Joseph M. M."[93] approximately one month after the nurses' trip to New Ipswich.

Botanical Therapies and Receipts

The Shaker nurses developed and exchanged receipts amongst themselves. In addition to learning orally from others, the Shaker nurses had access to and/or owned common nineteenth-century reference texts to guide their domestic/self-care and infirmary practice. Thomas Corbett's third volume of Wooster Beach's 1833 edition of *The Family Physician* is housed at Canterbury Village today. As mentioned previously, Shaker receipt books, such as those used in the Hancock, Massachusetts, community, demonstrate that the Shakers had access to remedies found in Samuel Thomson's *New Guide to Health.*[94] Sara Standish clearly had access to medical texts, as the descriptions of human physiology included in her receipt book are quite vivid, with full use of medical terminology.[95] The Shakers most likely used popular botany texts of the period by authors such as Amos Eaton,[96] Peter Smith,[97] and Constantine Rafinesque[98] to support the development of botanical therapies.

Like other women of the mid-nineteenth century, the Shaker infirmary nurses used receipt books containing descriptions of healing remedies, most often botanical in nature, in the care of patients. Their receipt books are collections of recipes and remedies from various sources identified either by the signature following the recipe or in the actual name of the recipe. Some examples of receipts include "Dr. Thomson's Rheumatic Drops"[99] (a mixture of blood-moving herbs — myrrh and cayenne), "Mother Lucy's liniment" made from gum camphor, pennyroyal oil, tansy, spearmint, and Bullock's gall,[100] and a cancer ointment recipe signed by "R. Johnson."[101] The giving and receiving of receipts was a significant part of Shaker women's culture. The Canterbury Shaker nurses' receipt book contains some recipes that demonstrate the nature of the Shaker's networking receipt tradition. The "Elixir Proprietatis" receipt is signed "With this little receipt receive a great portion of our best love. Janette and Caroline." The "Sarsaparilla Mead" recipe is signed "Dear Sister Leah, be kind as to accept with this my best love. From your Sister Deborah."[102] For the Shaker sisters, receipt exchange was clearly important to their caring tradition.

Two texts by Shaker nurse Prudence Morrell (born 1793) of the New Lebanon community are by far the clearest and most extensive example of the scope of the Shaker women's receipt network, as well as some of the best evidence of the expertise of Shaker nurse-herbalists. *A Choice Collection of Medical and Botanical Receipts . . . for the Consideration of Physicians and Nurses among Believers,*[103] collected and copied by Sister Prudence in 1849, totals 166 pages. Her second receipt book, *Receipts & Counsels Exclusively for Female Diseases,*[104] written in 1854, is twenty-two pages. In keeping with caring tradition, both books are written with "affectionate love" for her sisters as a "true friend and well wisher."[105] The contents, especially in the *Choice Collection,* included numerous botanical remedies, from "ginger bear" to "camphor plasters" and "lemon sirup." The receipts for female diseases included recipes for such things as "pills to promote the menses" and detailed instructions of when, how, and at what age a remedy should be given for specific conditions. The remedies contained herbs, such as blue cohosh, white hellebore, and lady's slipper. Sister Prudence demonstrated her knowledge of botanical theory and safety issues in herbalism and the nursing care of women in a section that followed her receipts for promoting menses, entitled, "A Short Word of Caution." She wrote that the receipts were for "removing obstructions of the menses" and that

> females are so constructed that they are not well, neither can they enjoy good health, unless they have their monthly courses, and every little thing will throw them further and further out of health and the above is particularly for the purpose of regulating the female system. But when a person is very feeble in body, and not sufficient strength of blood to have their monthly turns, it would not be wisdom to administer the above medicines: the syrup may be given if anything, or a syrup may be made of some strengthening roots and herbs, without any driving medicine in it; and after they have gaind [*sic*] their strength, then give the above mentioned pills to bring them over and you will go safe,

> and run no hazards. One more remark I would make. When a person is at the turn of life, never give medicine to promote the menses. But if they are in danger of flooding too much, you may check it slowly and carefully, and then you will go safe again on that wise: you will find medicine enough for that purpose in the following pages.[106]

In her preface, Sister Prudence confirmed that the remedies she included had been tested in the Shaker community and found to be "all good and beneficial."[107] Although she entitled the work as a collection of receipts from physicians, Sister Prudence demonstrated her knowledge of the importance of the expertise of the nurse in patient outcomes, specifically the nurse's ability to "persevere" with the patient. She wrote that she knows that the "great art or skill in curing up the sick and afflicted does not always depend on the knowledge of the Physician, it some times partly depends on perseverance; sometimes the sick is given over to die, when if the Physician had persevered the life might perhaps of been saved."[108] She described her experience of "persevering" with ailing patients and watching them heal and survive, because, unlike others, her conscience as a nurse would not let her give up on them.

Sister Prudence wrote about the importance of air, water, temperance, carefulness (with one's health), and exercise in promoting good health, which she stated is "our greatest concern one side of salvation."[109] Her purpose in writing the receipt book was clearly stated:

> And now what I wish is that every one that follows me in nursing the sick may be more successful than I have been, for I care for my fellow creatures, and desire their health, peace, and prosperity. For this reason I have taken some pains to preserve what little knowledge I have gained by my own experience these few years that I have been in this responcible[*sic*] place. . . . So I thought it not amiss to state some few things for the

> assistance [*sic*] of the new beginner [*sic*]. For I feel for them as I should like to be felt for in like circumstances. And I trust it will benefit some one for that has been my whole notion in doing it. It was not to please myself but rather through charity to my sisters, for they feel near and dear to me and if I can do anything to ade [*sic*] them in keeping their health I am much pleased to do it.[110]

She included another aid for new infirmary nurses at the end of her *Collection*, a table of medicine "necessary to be kept on hand for the use of the sick."[111] The table included doses and common words that described the general properties of each of the remedies listed as they were used in herbalism, words such as "mucilage," "cooling," "tonic," and "emetic." Sister Prudence's receipt books, with their directions, preface, cautions, and tables may be one of the few existing American nursing texts of the mid-nineteenth-century nurse.

Emetics were one of the most common remedies used by Shaker nurses in the care of patients. A common emetic recipe used by the Hancock nurses contained ipecac, bloodroot, and jalap. The ingredients were put into warm water, and two-thirds of the remedy was given to the patient first, then the remainder in fifteen minutes. The skill and control of the nurses in using the emetic botanical intervention were demonstrated in the remainder of the receipt, which includes three additional steps to the intervention. Boneset infusion was given when the patient began to feel nauseated. If the emetic did not "operate," then an elder flower tea injection (enema) with molasses and salt was given. A warm poultice was applied to the stomach when the patient wanted to stop vomiting.[112] It would be interesting to further explore whether this level of botanical precision was practiced by nineteenth-century housewives as well. Having evaluated numerous family receipt books, I think it quite plausible that the Shaker nurses, with their expertise and experience in providing nursing care, worked with plant remedies at a more sophisticated level than the housewife and were, therefore, able to use a strategy of botanical remedies, such as the aforementioned, to create a desired healing action.

Drugs such as laudanum, emetic tartar, saltpeter, and Epsom salt were used occasionally in the nurses' receipts, but the majority of the ingredients used in remedies were, as already mentioned, botanical. Vegetables also were used. As cited previously, stewed pumpkin poultices were used for Brother Nathan's swollen leg.[113] Water cure methods also were integrated into treatments. Most common were the steams for which the Shakers utilized steam boxes. The nurses also used water cures for local applications in combination with herbs. For example, in the treatment of bruises, the nurses applied hot water and then bruised wormwood and vinegar with a hot stone to keep the application warm.[114]

While the Shakers forbade the excessive use of alcohol, they had their own stills and made rose and dandelion wines[115] as well as herbal tinctures. They made and sold liniments and ointments and bulk herbs. They also made syrups, including poppy, Corbett's sarsaparilla, black cohosh, and Corbett's cherry pectoral.[116] Their receipt books contained instructions for making and applying herbal poultices, elixirs, tinctures, "sirrups," infusions, ointments, liniments, and dressings (what would now be called "compresses") to name a few.[117]

By 1850, the physic garden at New Lebanon used in Shaker herb production totaled fifty acres.[118] Acres of poppy (*Papaver somniferum*) were grown. Sister Marcia Bullard of the New Lebanon community wrote: "We always had extensive poppy beds, and early in the morning, before the sun had risen, the white-capped sisters could be seen stooping among the scarlet blossoms to slit those pods from which the petals had just fallen. Again after sundown they came out with little knives to scrape off the dried juice. This crude opium was sold at a large price, and its production was one of the most lucrative as well as the most picturesque of our industries."[119] Opium made from Shaker-grown poppy was used extensively during the Civil War and was sold at a large price.[120] (For more information see Color Insert F.)

The Shaker nurses and sisters made and sold gallons of mint and rose waters. The waters were sold as early as 1809 by the New Lebanon family.[121] According to Sister Marcia Bullard, " . . . a rose was useful, not ornamental. It was not intended to please us by its color or its odor, its mission was to be made into rosewater, and if we thought of it in any other way we were making an idol of it and thereby imperiling our souls. . . . It [rose water] was also kept in store at the infirmary, and although in those days no sick person was allowed to have a fresh flower to cheer him, he was welcome to a liberal supply of rosewater with which to bathe his aching head."[122] The Shakers used *Rosa gallica "Officinalis"* and *Rosa damascena* (damask rose) to make their rose water. The labels on the bottles of Shaker-prepared rose water claimed the water to be an "Unequaled fine cure for cosmetic and Dentrifice diseases of the skin, sore mouth, and a beautiful perfume." It also was applied to the lids of weak eyes before bed, used for bathing the temples for headaches, and used in baking.[123] (For more information see Color Insert G.)

The Shaker Herb Industry

The Shakers began by harvesting herbs from the wild, but as the market for their herbs and herbal products outside of the community grew, they used their gardening skills to increase their herb production. "The Industry was claimed by the Shakers to have been started at New Lebanon, New York, about 1800, and was the first mass production of herbs in this country."[124] The quality of the Shakers' gardens was renowned. "Their excellence drew a visible line of demarcation. The grass was greener on Shaker territory, the fruit larger, the grain more abundant. Consequently, acres that had for years been under Shaker plough and spade commanded a high price."[125] Both men and women worked in the gardens. The men did most of the planting and cultivating, and the women did the harvesting and processing.

Gardening was a part of the Shakers' spiritual life. "The Shakers compared cultivating a garden to cultivating the mind, and regarded weeding as a metaphor for spiritual cleansing."[126] Shaker gardens were constructed as neat squares, because Shaker Millennial Laws specified that "it is considered good order to lay out and fence all kinds of lots, fields and gardens, in square form, wherever it is practicable."[127] Careful attention to individual plants was "typical of the Shaker gardeners and a key to their success."[128] The word of God spoken to the elements in nature was believed by the Shakers to have played a role in their gardening success.

Elmira Allard recounts a story in her autobiography about Father Job controlling the elements.

> He said I fear the Brethren will have a heavy shower on their hay. Sisters I want you to pray it may not be wet. He steped [*sic*] out of doors, raised his hand towards the cloud, and said, go back go back, go back three times. The cloud seemed to hear his voice & wheeld [*sic*] a little southward. It had already begun to thunder & lightening [*sic*]; soon it began to sprinkle a little upon the field but did not disturb them in the least. But over the wall in the adjoining field, it poured down like a torrent mingled with hail & wind. . . . It seemed to me the very elements of nature obeyed his voice. . . . Father was a powerful medium.[129]

Their gardens flourished. By 1836, Shaker bulk herb production was 6,000 pounds, and by 1849, the Shakers had produced 16,500 pounds of herbs.[130] They produced more sage in bulk than any other herb.

The Shaker men, mostly male physicians such as Thomas Corbett, are credited historically with "starting" the herb industries in the communities most likely because of the prominence of their names associated with the expansion of the business of production and marketing in the public sphere. However, when reading the Shaker daily logs and journals, it is clear from the entries that the women were just as much a part, if not the backbone, of the success of the herb business. The sisters did much of the painstaking production work, and the nurses tested the remedies in their communities by using them in their caregiving. Without the knowledge of successful community use of the remedies in promoting health and healing (e.g., "clinical evidence"), the Shaker brethren, who marketed the Shaker herbs, would not have had the personal success stories to impress potential buyers.

The Shakers started their herb business with herbs gathered through wild crafting. There is no mention in the journals of how they learned to accurately identify the plants they sought. They may have learned from their interactions with neighbors, but most likely learned from community botanists such as Elisha Myrick of Harvard and physician and botanist Garrett K. Lawrence of the New Lebanon family. Lawrence and chemists, such as Alonzo Hollister, later expanded and capitalized on this knowledge and skill to include cultivated herbs and newly invented processing techniques such as the horse-powered herb press that could "process 250 pounds of herbs (leaves and tops) or 600 pounds of roots daily into solid cakes . . . weighing a pound each,"[131] Unlike the Amish, the Shakers welcomed progress and technology."[132] They were inventors.

The Shakers, both women and men, invented many things that are now part of everyday existence, such as washing machines, clothespins, the circular saw, and flat brooms, to name a few.[133] Their ingenuity grew out of their desire for self-sustenance. Elmira Allard wrote in her autobiography: "As years rolled by, changes occurred, machinery introduced, & work made easier. We got up some trades that brought us some money, so we were able to purchase cloth & yarn already for our needles. We gave up raising Flax substituted Cotton instead. So the spinning wheels were dismissed & long been idle. Our looms in like manner had their day & long since been idle."[134] In the nineteenth century, many Americans began turning to technology and other sources for their needs. By 1820, the Shakers' "newer" medicine-making skills, techniques, and resulting products were marketed to the "world" community, where domestic medicines were valued and yet people had less time to do the work of producing the remedies themselves. Shakers issued herb and seed catalogs to market their products nationally and internationally. They produced herbs and herbal products for physicians, pharmacists, Indian doctors, and other healers. Theirs was the largest botanical operation of the nineteenth century.

The Shakers were especially known for their production of fluid extracts, which was considered a great advance in therapeutics. "They were much more convenient and of more dependable strength than the infusions and teas made with herbs. They also gave impetus to the patent medicine industry in the United States."[135] "Previous to 1841 the 'Extracts both Inspissated and Boiled' were made by the Sisters, but the business became more than they could handle, and 'the Brethren took sole burden of the work'. However, the Sisters turned to other activities."[136] The Shaker sisters continued their wild crafting, produced rose water, collected the crude opium from their poppies, made ointments, sugared lovage root, and distilled witch hazel. They always had plenty of botanical work to do.

The Shakers were renowned for the compound herbal products that they developed and used in their infirmaries for years, such as Brown's Shaker Fluid Extract of English Valerian, Veratrum Viride, Mother Seigel's Syrup, Seven Barks, and Corbett's Shaker Compound and Concentrated Syrup of Sarsaparilla. The labels on the herbal products were colorful and the instructions for use were given in plain English . . for the "common person." The labels provide historians with botanical data that raises some questions regarding intellectual property related to the remedies, a common concern among nineteenth-century inventors. One example is Corbett's Sarsaparilla Syrup.

The Shakers at Canterbury, New Hampshire produced sarsaparilla syrup from the 1840s to the 1890s. Thomas Corbett, the Canterbury physician who invented the rocking truss for use in those with hernias and an electricity machine used in healing, is also said on the labels of the syrup and elsewhere to have "invented" the recipe for the syrup. There is no doubt that Corbett was knowledgeable about botanical remedies, but the claim to intellectual property for the syrup is not as easy to substantiate in Shaker archives. We know that Corbett grew up in the Shaker community, was the director of the Canterbury medicinal herb gardens for a time[137] and was a respected physician. A non-Shaker physician colleague described him in the following way: "His medical knowledge is very respectable. He has a very good library of medical books. Although not a member of our Society, he usually attends our meetings. He has performed some delicate operations on the eye and is considered safe in all his prescriptions."[138]

Corbett's sarsaparilla syrup, which contained a number of herbs, including sarsaparilla root (botanical name not given), yellow dock root (*Rumex obtusifolius*), black cohosh root (*Macrotys racemosa*), juniper berries (*Juniperis communis*), and Indian hemp (*Asclepias incarnata*),[139] was used to purify the blood and other body fluids, to heal indigestion and other diseases, and as a general tonic to restore health. This receipt was a top-selling Shaker remedy. What is perhaps of interest, botanically speaking, is that none of the details of any of the copies of Corbett's Sarsaparilla Syrup receipt found at Canterbury included the genus and species of the "sarsaparilla" plant used in the remedy. Other plants used in the syrup were recorded with both their common and full botanical names, as previously listed.

According to one source, "Most of the sarsaparilla syrups on the market, including the very first Shaker mixtures, were made from the root of the imported sarsaparilla, or *Smilax officinalis*.[140] Thomas Corbett, however, was said to have used the root of the indigenous wild American "sarsaparilla," *Aralia nudicaulis*. *Aralia* also is known as "false sarsaparilla" and was considered useless by Dr. Smilax, for whom the imported sarsaparilla was named. (For more information see Color Insert B.)

Despite the claims of Dr. Smilax about the uselessness of *Aralia*, Dr. Corbett and the Shakers enjoyed tremendous success with the health results and sales of their sarsaparilla (*Aralia*) syrup. It may be because of the sarsaparilla controversy that the recipes in the Canterbury archives do not list the botanical name of the sarsaparilla used. At the time, many Americans were using the common name "sarsaparilla" for the American *Aralia* plant anyway. Some labels on syrup bottles and printed, unattached labels in the Hancock and Old Chatham Shaker collections do list *Aralia nudicaulis*, however, as the main ingredient in Corbett's sarsaparilla.

The Shakers were leaders in the medicinal herb industry and had a reputation among botanists and physicians for the botanical accuracy of their products, so it is quite possible that at some point, the Shakers made the decision to stop purchasing sarsaparilla (*Smilax*) and to use the American *Aralia* instead. The Shakers did not, however, change the name of the product. How did the Shakers, in particular

Thomas Corbett, come to understand the effectiveness of *Aralia* when many experts, such as Dr. Smilax, considered it useless? Corbett may have come to his knowledge of the *Aralia* substitute for the imported and expensive *Smilax* through his knowledge of botanist Rafinesque's work.

The Shakers and Rafinesque did have a distant relationship, and Rafinesque may have suggested that the Shakers or Corbett use *Aralia* in the product. Rafinesque is quoted in 1851 as endorsing Shaker medicinal herb gardens as the "best in the United States"[141] and endorsing Shaker products in the Shaker 1851 catalog.[142] However, Rafinesque also was known for being "intensely individualistic"[143] and not inclined to align himself with any sect.

Corbett also may have consulted Elisha Myrick, a Shaker botanist and a contemporary of Corbett, and then made the decision. It also is possible that Corbett and the Shakers could have come to the knowledge of the use of *Aralia* through oral tradition, such as that associated with Mary Fowler Corbett, Thomas's grandmother. Mary Fowler Corbett, also a Canterbury Shaker, was kidnapped and forced to live among a tribe of American Indians in Canada for three years. It is possible that she learned about the Indians' use of herbs while living among them. There is a record of her being treated at least once by a "medicine man" while being detained.[144] She also wild crafted herbs while imprisoned and "gathered cranberries and other wild fruits for the market."[145] She may have taught any botanical knowledge of native plants she incurred to her grandson, Thomas, after rejoining the Shaker community.

The historical tracing of intellectual property for botanical remedies is very difficult, and data are often scarce. It is important to include the possibility of the contribution of oral traditions of intellectual transfer that existed within women's healing networks in the domestic sphere in historical analysis. Therefore, the speculation about the contribution of Mary Corbett is included here. While it is important to incorporate all potential links in the analysis of cultures for the benefit of further research, no definitive historical conclusions can be drawn, as in this case of Corbett's sarsaparilla.

Many of the Shakers' herbal products contained alcohol, often large percentages of it. Alcohol not only acts as a menstruum for the extraction of the healing constituents in plant material but also as a preservative for the finished product and as a quick carrier of the herb into the body. While many Shakers advocated temperance, and section three of the Millennial Laws forbade the use of cider or other spirits on Saturday and on the Sabbath, alcohol was permitted as part of healing practices. Spirituous liquors were kept under the care of the nurses and physicians to be recommended and/or dispensed judiciously.[146]

By the end of the nineteenth and early twentieth centuries, the law of prohibition had been passed, and the Pure Food and Drug Act of 1906 was in effect. It was much more difficult to sell medicines with a high alcohol content such as was in the Shaker tinctures and compound remedies. Sales dwindled. In addition, the Shakers were unable to keep up with production, because community members were aging. Shaker religious practice excluded procreation, therefore, the growth of the Shaker movement depended upon the recruitment of adult members. New members were not as plentiful as they had been in the earlier part of the century. Many of the herbal products were produced into the twentieth century with the aid of hired hands, but many of the bulk herbs were not. The Shaker Herbal Products Company was bought out, piece by piece, by pharmaceutical companies such as the Tilden Company, and it gradually went out of business altogether by the early twentieth century.

American Indian Herbalism and the Shakers

Shaker historian Edward Andrews wrote that there had always been a "curious affinity between the Shakers and the Indians."[147] The Shakers, like many American Indians existed outside of mainstream American social life. Did the Shakers have a relationship with the Indian, and if so, what influence did American Indian healing and herbalism have on the Shakers' healing practices and on the botanical work of the nurses? The Shakers accepted all people, regardless of race or color, who truly wished to embrace the life of a Believer. The early Shakers had themselves known discrimination in England and in America firsthand. Mother Ann and the community of Believers had even been suspected of witchcraft. Americans were fearful about the Shakers, much as they were of Indians, when they heard that their worship included the practice of entering trancelike states and speaking in tongues.

Shaker Elder F. W. Evans wrote in 1881 of his disagreement with the practices and beliefs of the Puritans and certain Christians in regard to the Indians: "The kingdom and dominion of the devil consisted of the infernal regions, in the spirit world, and of all Jewish, Mahomedan and heathen nations and their inhabitants on the earth. The American continent — New World — with its Indian population, was his special inheritance. He was, therefore, designated as a 'great land holder'. From these premises, anti-Christians conceived it to be their civil right and Christian duty to exterminate the Indians."[148] There is evidence that some Indians became members of the Shaker community. There also is a record of a man, Albert Randolph, leaving Canterbury Village on April 2, 1861, and taking his boys with him. He is described as "an Indian, a spiritualist, and a doctor,"[149] yet there were no other records found about him. Winifer Denbo, an Indian, was born on August 1, 1738, and died on July 16,1816. She was a member of the second family at Canterbury and described as a "good and helpful woman."[150]

The Shakers preached to the Indian tribes in the East and the Shawnee in the West. In 1807, "Dea. Richard Spires of New Lebanon brought letters from the Brethren, in July, which gave an account of a remarkable religious revival among the Indians,"[151] the Shawnee of Greenville, Ohio. For a period of time before 1845, Believers who were "receiving visitation through spirit" of various individuals also received Indians. "The mediums were more reluctant about accepting these wild, ignorant, & undisciplined savages than they had been of some of the spirits of a former date. . . . One could easily imagine that he was in an Indian camp & sometimes in the midst of a general powwow. The mediums would run from place to place, sit down on the floor. . . . During this time some of them made a very commendable progress, and their manifestations of spirit power, & testimonies of gospel light were keen & penetrating."[152] Another account of the event recorded the following: "Elders then urged upon the members the duty of 'taking them in,' whereupon eight or nine of the Sisters became possessed of the Spirits of Indian Squaws, and about six of the Brothers became Indians; . . . The Sisters and Brothers squatted down on the floor together, Indian fashion, and the Elders and Eldresses endeavored to keep them asunder. At the same time, telling the Indians that they must be separated from the Squaws, and otherwise instructing them in the rules of Shakerism."[153] The Shakers channeled Indian spirits seeking to convert them.

The Shakers traded with the Indians. Indian-made baskets sold to the communities can be found in Shaker museum collections today. The Shaker sisters may have learned some of their remarkable basket-weaving skills from the American Indians.[154] The Shakers and Indians may have shared healing and botanical medicine ideas too, especially during sales or trading. Elisha Myrick recorded in his daybook that "an Indian Doctress & her son came here to buy some herbs."[155] Occasionally an Indian name appears attached to a medicinal receipt in Shaker receipt books. The name is either in the title or in the signature area at the bottom of the receipt. For example, the receipt book from the nurses' shop at New Lebanon included: "For the sick headache Take flowers of Catnip, Steep them for a Drink, take when the pain begins. This from an Indian Dr."[156] The Indian doctor referred to here may very well not have been an actual Indian. The term *Indian doctor*, as discussed earlier, was used, especially later in the nineteenth century, by white physicians who had studied with an Indian and sometimes by someone using the name "Indian" to sell a service or product because of the popularity of the term among whites.

The Hancock receipt book contains a tonic and cleansing "Indian syrup" recipe made with boneset, wormwood, poplar bark, cayenne, and slippery elm bark.[157] While many nineteenth-century receipt books contain "Indian" recipes, most likely transmitted orally, one Shaker receipt book entry demonstrated, in the handwriting of the Hancock Shaker, direct contact with the Indian source. The receipt is for a two-part "Indian Remedy for the Piles": alder bark tea and hemlock/alder bark compress. The receipt is signed: "I received this from Meary Sorisa," and underneath the name "Sorisa" is the word "Wabanockah."[158] "Wabanockah" is most likely a white woman's phonetic variation of "Wabanaki" or "Wobanaki," an Indian tribe known to have lived in the area.[159] Linking herbal products with "real" Indian doctors or doctresses became more fashionable and marketable during the late nineteenth century. While the Shakers may have been inclined to use the word "Indian" in their public marketing campaigns for their products, the Shaker nurses' receipt books were not sold but they were part of the Shaker women's domestic sphere. They were only used by the community nurses and physicians and there would have been no reason for the author to use the word "Indian" in order to inflate the importance of the remedy. It seems more likely that the author(s) of the receipt books included the word "Indian" in the title of the remedies in the receipt books much the way the word "Eldress" or "Doctor" was included to identify a valued source of a botanical remedy.

There is some evidence that the Shakers did have knowledge of and did indeed value the healing practices of the American Indians. The Shakers frequently went to the ocean or hot springs for healing, as recorded in Elmira Allard's autobiography; however, the story of a certain trip to Saratoga Springs in upstate New York in 1851 sheds some light on how the Shakers (as well as other whites) felt about the Indians and their healing methods. Sister Allard told the following story of a trip to Saratoga, where a number of the sisters and brethren went to an Indian encampment.

> Elder Joseph and the rest of us continued on to the Indian forest. It was located in a beautiful grove of pines. The ground around the tents was trodden hard and as clean as a floor of a house. Each family had a tent of their own. Some of the swaws [*sic*] were cooking. Some making articles for sale. Some were making baskets, they manufactured moccasins & satches ornamented with beeds [*sic*] of various colors. Two male youth were making walking sticks. We went to the doctors tent half a mile from the rest. Elder Joseph asked him if he could cure his lip. He shook his head & replied, bad lip bad lip, he gave him ointment to try. There was a multitude of white people visiting him.

> We went there three times. Elder Joseph held a long conversation with the Doctor some of it was of a religious nature. The doctor said the white man was to blame for the Indians wickedness. They never would have known how to lie or steal or get drunk or sware[*sic*] he said the whites learned it to them; said they were cheated out of their lands & he talked very rough. Elder Joseph told him he would have to be careful or he would sware.[160]

A separate study of the Shakers and the Indians during the mid-nineteenth century is needed to more fully understand the nature of their relationship.

Herbal Expertise

The Shaker nurses were experts in the use of botanical therapies in caring for themselves and their communities. All of the Shaker women, including the nurses, were integral to the evolution and eventual success of the Shaker herb industry. The Shaker nurses used botanical therapies not just because the plants were readily available; they chose to use herbs in their healing practices often over the numerous other remedies and "cures" prevalent during the period. The Shaker women gathered herbs and tended their gardens out of necessity. Their work was tedious, processing barrels of horseradish into the night, avoiding thorns while picking rose petals by hand, and traveling by wagon in the hot, late summer sun to wild craft the herbs that would be needed for healing Believers who would take to their sickbed during the cold winter months.

The Shaker nurses, physicians, and community members worked hard to stay healthy using diet, sanitation, lifestyle, and botanical therapies as their main modalities of disease prevention and health promotion. When the brethren became interested in selling their botanical expertise to the "world," the disters and nurses supported them with their community- and infirmary-based botanical applications. They made sure that the Believers still had the herbs, remedies, and care they needed when the herb industry evolved. While the brethren and physicians took leadership in building the herb industry, the Shaker sisters and nurses continued what they always had been doing: caring for the community gardens and maintaining connection with nature in the forests and meadows that provided the original source of Shaker remedies.

The Shakers and the Tilden Company, which produced many Shaker remedies later in the nineteenth century, have been described as "Co-laboring pioneers in the field of American plant pharmacy . . . they were medicine-makers at an early date, perhaps the first pharmaceutical manufacturers on a commercial scale in this country."[161] The Shakers, women and men, pioneered an industry that ultimately would become the pharmaceutical industry we know today, the roots of which can be traced to the Shaker women and nurses who harvested, processed, and applied the plants in the care of their families. Without the knowledge of the Shaker nurses' successful use of the botanical therapies in their community infirmaries, the Shaker men most likely would not have had the ability or perhaps even the courage to enter the marketplace as they did.

The Shaker nurses used botanical therapies, packs, teas, salves, floral waters, and even pukes as instruments of caring. They had autonomy, freedom, and community support to explore their caring profession. The Shaker nurses actively participated in mid-nineteenth-century health care reform and the Botanical Medical Movement. They successfully created and demonstrated a level of caring in their communities that was palpable. One Shaker wrote of his care during typhoid fever: "I was treated with a kindness and watched with an assiduity unsurpassed by maternal solicitude or paternal vigils. Every night, after meeting, some of the leaders and brethren would bring to the infirmary where I was confined love from the 'spirit-land', spiritual medicines, balsams and balms, given expressly for me by all grades of spirits, save the wicked."[162] Nurse Lydia Lyon wrote that her grandmother once remarked: "Well, these Shakers do have a love and care for each other that could not be found elsewhere."[163]

Chapter 6

Herbs and the Pioneer Nurses and Midwives of the Church of Jesus Christ of Latter-day Saints

To soothe the heart. The swollen eye, /
When none but she and God were nigh.[1]

— Derr et al., *Women of Covenant*

The members of the Church of Jesus Christ of Latter-day Saints (LDS) were more often referred to by the American public in the nineteenth century as "Mormons." This religion with American roots began with a spiritual vision of the angel, Moroni, in 1823 to the prophet, Joseph Smith, and it was subsequently organized as a religion in New York on April 6, 1830. As a worldwide religion today, it has been said that "Mormonism is more than a religious movement; it is also a unique American subculture."[2] Latter-day Saints historians conclude that the LDS religion did not emerge as a restatement of other faiths or as a reorganization of an established religion or sect, as perhaps other new religions in nineteenth-century America had. "LDS authorities benefit from divine inspiration" as well as "have their eyes open to what is going on in the world generally."[3] While the LDS religion may have in some ways represented a social and spiritual statement similar to other nineteenth-century American religions, it also had many original beliefs and practices, many of which stemmed from the *Book of Mormon.*

The prophet Joseph Smith, (1805–1844) after his vision of the angel, Moroni, received a new revelation, *The Book of Mormon,*[4] a scripture that is considered by the LDS to complement the Bible. In 1831, Joseph Smith and other New York members moved to Kirtland, Ohio, which became the central focus for the LDS's activity. The church's second headquarters, designated "Zion," was established in Missouri until the sect was forced to leave that state in 1839 due to serious persecution. In 1840, Nauvoo, Illinois, became the headquarters for the church and gathering place for members from Missouri, Ohio, and the East Coast. The prophet also sent apostles from the church to England to begin preaching the LDS message there. Within one year, there were several thousand members in Great Britain, many of whom were hoping to emigrate to Nauvoo.[5] European immigrants, as will be shown in this chapter, brought with them their knowledge of healing, nursing, midwifery, and the use of botanical therapies with them to their new home.

Joseph Smith and his brother, Hyrum, were murdered by a mob in Nauvoo in 1844. Brigham Young, the president of the Quorum of Twelve Apostles, established by the prophet, became the leader of the church in accordance with church tenets. Honoring Smith's vision, the temple in Nauvoo was built. After its completion, Emma Smith, Joseph Smith's wife, and some others remained in Nauvoo; however, under the guidance of Young, and acting upon the visions of Joseph Smith, many LDS pioneers began trekking west and eventually found the land they believed to be the sacred place of Smith's vision in the Great Salt Lake Basin of Utah. They established the land, now known as "Salt Lake City, Utah," as the international headquarters for the LDS church.

Latter-day Saints' Health Belief

The Latter–day Saints' beliefs about health and healing are reflected in their scriptures and publications. Members of the church believe that the gift of healing can be bestowed by God or his prophets on certain individuals. "For behold to one is given by the spirit of God, that he may teach the word of wisdom; And to another, that he may teach the word of knowledge by the same spirit; And to another, exceedingly great faith; and to another, the gifts of healing by the same spirit; . . . And all these gifts come by the Spirit of Christ; and they come unto every man severally, according as he will."[6] The published *Doctrine and Covenants of the Church*[7] includes direction on a healthy lifestyle in a section known as the "Word of Wisdom." The prophet, Joseph Smith, revealed the interpretation of the Word of Wisdom when he wrote that it was "to be sent greeting; not by commandment or constraint . . . showing forth the order and will of God in the temporal salvation of all saints in the last days."[8]

Directions in the *Doctrine and Covenants* (D & C) include the importance of eating meat sparingly and including grain and fruit in the diet. The healthy lifestyle recommendations in the Word of Wisdom would not have been uncommon for any nineteenth-century American. However, whereas Americans outside of the LDS community might decide to follow such practices because of their belief in the health benefits, the broad adoption of dietary, lifestyle, and herbal practices in the LDS community was most likely due to the connection of the health practices to passages in the scriptures. Church leaders supported and promoted healthy lifestyle practices. Members of the Quorum of Twelve Apostles were often quoted responding to questions about the Word of Wisdom. Brigham Young was quoted in the *Deseret News*, a regional newspaper, as teaching the LDS that "tea and coffee are narcotic poisons." To this, the editors added: "and this is reason sufficient why it is not wisdom to use them. An additional reason is that those who use tea and coffee, generally drink them hot."[9] Drinking hot beverages was considered harmful to one's constitution by many nineteenth-century health care reformers and Americans, including the LDS.

Botanical therapies were very important to the LDS. Elaine Sorensen Marshall, a historical scholar of LDS nursing, wrote: "Early Mormons combined faith healing with the practice of Thomsonian medicine."[10] The LDS believed, like many other Americans, that herbs were a viable alternative to the horrors of the Regulars' medicine. The early LDS believed that, as written in scripture, herbs were sent by God and were proper medicine for the Saints[11] as followers of Jesus Christ. The LDS *Doctrine and Covenants* states:

> That inasmuch as any man drinketh wine or strong drink among you, behold it is not good, neither meet in the sight of your Father, only in assembling yourselves together to offer up your sacraments before him. And, behold this should be wine, yea, pure wine of the grape of the vine, of your own make. And, again, strong drinks are not for the belly, but for the washing of your bodies. And again, tobacco is not for the body, neither for the belly, and is not good for man, but is an herb for bruises and all sick cattle, to be used with judgment and skill. And again, hot drinks are not for the body or belly. And again, verily I say unto you, all wholesome herbs God hath ordained for the constitution, nature, and use of man — Every herb in the season thereof, and every fruit in the season thereof; all these to be used with prudence and thanksgiving.[12]

To the LDS who followed this health regimen, a promise was given: "And all saints who remember to keep and do these sayings, walking in obedience to the commandments, shall receive health in their navel and marrow to their bones; And shall find wisdom and great treasures of knowledge, even hidden treasures; And shall run and not be weary, and shall walk and not faint. And I, the Lord, give unto them a promise, that the destroying angel shall pass by them, as the children of Israel, and not slay them. Amen."[13]

Prophet Joseph Smith favored the use of Thomsonian medicine and often discouraged the use of "Regulars"; however, he did use both forms of medicine. In Levi Richards's[14] journal, a discourse given by Smith at a meeting in September 1843 describes his view on medicine that included a reference to lobelia, the common Thomsonian botanical remedy. "He spoke of the practice of medicine; He spoke decidedly against Dr. Brink's practice; and spoke in favor of Dr. Bernhisel's. He declared that he, Joseph Smith, never lost a patient where he had been the firsthand only one employed; and challenged the congregation to bring an instance. They broght [*sic*] none. He spoke of lobelia when the patient was too weak to bear it as being destructive. He said that calomel would corrode the stomach when it was empty. He said it was a poison; still it was a medicine and useful when it was used skillfully."[15]

The *Deseret News* was originally edited in the early 1850s by Willard Richards, a Botanic physician who held a Thomsonian patent.[16] He was a member of the Quorum of Twelve Apostles and founder of the Council of Health in 1848. The Council of Health, a group of LDS male and female healers, primarily Thomsonian Botanics and midwife-herbalists, was formed to educate and promote health in the church community. The *Deseret News* published a number of articles written by members of the council as well as others disparaging calomel and the practice of Regular physicians. For example, in 1852, Dr. Peter Humphrey of Michigan wrote: "Having attended 164 cases of the cholera on my own responsibility; I have not heard of one case of which has died. I attended 136 other cases, who had taken calomel, &c., before I saw them, most of whom, so far as I have heard, have recovered. Those who made common use of calomel, died, so far as I have heard."[17]

On May 15, 1852, a lengthy article by the council stated that the mission of the Council of Health was health promotion. This also was said to be the focus of healing in LDS communities after religious rituals such as prayer. In response to readers' questions about what to do if they were sick, the Council of Health responded in an article suggesting a hierarchy of interventions:

> Just as God has told you, call for the elders, unite their faith with yours; and if you are healed, thank God for the blessing; if not, act apon [*sic*] the word of wisdom, which is in perfect accordance with all the movements of the Council of Health, as established in our city some three years ago, for no other purpose than to devise ways and means to prevent disease, and for preparing and administering herbs and mild food to the sick, just as the Lord has said . . . and in the origin of the council to the present moment the Presidency of the Church have taken an active part therein . . . anyone who is opposed to the principles of the council

> are opposed to God and his government; and those who administer any of the poisons we have named, or poisons of any kind, as medicines, for the healing of the sick, are not approved of the heavens, or by the council of health, or by the servants of the Lord who hold the keys of the kingdom of God on the earth in these last days.[18]

The LDS journal *Times and Seasons* was published from 1839 to 1846 in Nauvoo, Illinois, and addressed issues pertinent to life as a member of the LDS community. In one 1843 article,"Physician Heal Thyself," the LDS's healing philosophy and current health belief systems were discussed. The article argued that the examples of community members' longevity provided in the article spoke "volumes against the common practice of medicine" and encouraged Saints that " . . . the just shall live by faith! No doubt but many cases occur, where medical operations may be requisite; but generally speaking, 'herbs and mild food' *with good nursing,* would be better for the patient's person and pocket than all the nostrums of materia medica."[19] The editor commented: "There is a good deal of sound common sense in the above remarks. We believe that if we only had faith, 'all things are possible to them that believe', and we would not plead our want of faith."[20] The editor went on to quote the *Doctrine and Covenants,* stating that while many of the sick can be healed by faith and the laying on of hands, some cannot (due to a lack of faith) be healed by faith alone, and that they should not be condemned. They should be "nourished with all tenderness, *with herbs and mild food, and that not by the hand of an enemy.*"[21] The editor then asked: "Who is to administer those herbs?" and "Who is the *enemy*?" The editor concluded:

> We should judge, then, from the above, that a person who is acquainted with the physiology of the human system, and the nature and medicinal properties of herbs, is more competent to judge of those things, and to administer with judgment and skill, than the one who is ignorant, both of the organization of the human

> system, of the medicinal properties of herbs, and of the nature and effects of disease. . . . We are aware that this community has been a good deal imposed upon by quacks; that nostrums of all kinds have been administered by injudicious hands, producing the most deleterious effects; and that many have slept in the dust, who, if they had been let alone, would still have in the land of the living; but that is no reason why those who have not faith should not be aided by herbs, administered with care and skill by judicious hands. If the heads of families are themselves acquainted with the nature of diseases, the medicinal properties of herbs, and the mode of compounding, preparing and applying them, so much the better. If they are not, the advice and counsel of those better informed, we think, could not be injurious. We have made these remarks, not so much with a view to instruct, or give counsel in those matters which we consider to be of a delicate nature, as to lay before our brethren and sisters the testimony of the word of the Lord on the subject, that they may read and judge for themselves.[22]

Neither the church *Doctrine and Covenants* nor the numerous LDS diaries, journals, newspapers, and histories of the church reviewed defines exactly what constituted a "mild food." As mentioned previously, meat was to be eaten by the LDS sparingly, and grain and fruit were to be eaten liberally. The prevailing health belief related to diet demonstrated in nineteenth-century domestic guides was that "stimulating" or unhealthy foods were meats, pastries, coffee and tea, alcoholic beverages, condiments such as mustard and pepper, and foods highly spiced with condiments. Beecher and Stowe wrote in *The American Woman's Home* that "life will be shortened just in proportion as the diet is changed to more stimulating articles."[23] "Mild foods" were most likely foods that were not "stimulating."

The Thomsonians considered herbs a milder form of medicine than the medicines of the Regulars. Herbs would most likely have been

perceived as a natural part of a primarily vegan, nonstimulating diet. The Council of Health leadership, being of Thomsonian ideology, would have taught the community that herbs (while they could be stimulating at times, such as in the use of lobelia as an emetic) were, if used correctly, a gentler or milder form of medicine. Whether the church used the Thomsonian system because it fit the health beliefs supported by scripture or was influenced in its scriptural health beliefs by Thomsonianism is unclear.

What is known is that the LDS believed first and foremost in the power of spiritual healing with mild herbal remedies as an adjunctive therapy. Brigham Young has been recorded many times asking the Saints to realize their own healing powers and to carry on the tradition of the laying on of hands. "I say, again, however that it is absolutely necessary that we all possess the gift God has seen fit to bestow upon His children to counteract the power of death."[24] Latter-day Saints believed in the possibility of healing miracles. Faith healing was considered, even for those who were very ill. "Scarcely a journal of the time fails to note at least one miraculous recovery from the most dire of circumstances."[25] Young also promoted domestic caregiving with gentle remedies. He said: " . . . It is our duty to have the medicine — the remedy to administer to that pain, to heal, to cure, to rebuke the disease and save the sick like a good physician, and not kill them by dosing down the medicine as do some of our doctors. Administer the medicine in all mildness, and with good judgment and discretion."[26]

In the early years, Young encouraged the Saints not to depend on professional physicians and to turn to the nurses of the community instead. He said, "I would rather have the sisters wait upon me in sickness than many of those who profess to be physicians."[27] He stated that he would rather have a wife knowledgeable in tending the sick than a professional doctor. He taught the LDS what he believed constituted a good doctor in physic. "It is that man or woman who, by revelation, or we may call it intuitive inspiration, is capable of administering medicine to assist the human system when it is besieged by the enemy called Disease."[28] Young spoke against the growing practice by physicians of applying the same remedy to all patients just because the

remedy had helped one individual. He cautioned against reliance on those who did not individualize care through inner spiritual guidance. "I say that unless a man or woman who administers medicine to assist the human system to overcome disease, understands, and has that intuitive knowledge, by the Spirit, that such an article is good for that individual at that very time, they had better let him alone."[29]

Young's belief about nineteenth-century doctors was clearly stated. "We had no sickness until we had doctors . . . and lived more richly."[30] He taught that physicians were "unnecessary," except in the case when someone had a broken bone or needed surgery. LDS Zina Hickman, a member of the LDS, is quoted in her oral history given to historian Kate Carter as stating that her father, Dr. George Hickman, had trained in medicine at Oberlin College and was one of the first doctors to settle in Utah. She reported that early on he counseled with Young, who told her father not to practice medicine because "he wanted to teach the people faith and dependence on God" for their healing. Hickman subsequently became a farmer and practiced medicine only when there were injuries and emergencies, such as the diphtheria epidemic.[31] In the later nineteenth century, Young's beliefs ultimately changed. He supported professional education in medicine and nursing and sponsored several women for attending medical school in the East.

Young, like many physicians and health care reformers of the period, affirmed the principles of people supporting and comforting the sick while relying on nature to cure. "Let the sick do without eating, take a little of something to cleanse the stomach, bowels, and blood, and wait patiently, and let Nature have time to gain the advantage over the disease."[32] He promoted self-care and family care, admonishing parents to know how to care for their children when sick. His instruction to parents included administering to children "by the laying on of hands and anointing them with oil, and giving them mild food, and herbs."[33] The oil used by the LDS was olive oil, called "sweet oil." Sweet oil was consecrated by the Elders of the church for use in healing[34] and was considered the most important botanical remedy by the LDS pioneers. It was taken internally for many ailments and rubbed externally into the skin.

Latter-day Saints Nurses' Education and Work

Latter-day Saints nurses and midwives learned their caring work in many ways. Some nurses brought their knowledge and skill from Britain. For example, Susannah Lippincott Richards, wife of Willard Richards, and Ann Lee[35] brought their nursing skills from England to their new home in Utah. Ann Lee took a course in home medicine and nursing in England before immigrating to the United States. She shared her knowledge by helping heal many people in her new home of Utah.[36] Latter-day Saints nurses and midwives also learned from each other, from wise community women healers, from books, and from physicians, both Regular and Botanic. The nurses and midwives were part of a healing network of women. In the LDS church, this healing network was not only organized in the work of the Council of Health. Women decided that they had their own special health issues. "In 1851 the Female Council of Health was formalized under the direction of Phoebe Angell, and by 1852 the organization had representatives in all but two of Salt Lake City's nineteen wards, again prefiguring the outreach that would come with the reorganization of Relief Society in 1867."[37] It was in these meetings that nurses such as Susannah Lippincott taught midwifery, herbalism, child care, and diseases of children.[38] The LDS nurses found organization in the Relief Society.

Relief Society

In 1842, in Nauvoo, Illinois, the prophet, Joseph Smith, appointed women to their first offices in the church, the leadership of the women's Relief Society. Women were elected to "serve as counterpart and companion to the men's priesthood quorum" and commissioned to "save souls and look to the poor and needy."[39] The nurses' calling to demonstrate caring for others was realized through the early efforts of the Relief Society started in Nauvoo and the subsequent works of the LDS sisters in Utah. Elaine Jack, in her forward of the book *Women of Covenant*, a history of the LDS Relief Society, wrote: "Through the works of women, done under the auspices of

Relief Society, we learn about the core gospel principles of charity, integrity, hard work, education, loyalty, and sisterhood. Our sisters made 'charity never faileth' more than an organizational motto; they made it a personal motto by which they lived."[40]

Many women, such as Zina Young and Emmeline Wells, who served as leaders in the Relief Society were among those originally trained in health and healing, nursing and midwifery by Thomsonian physician Willard Richards and his wife, nurse-midwife Susannah Lippincott. Patty Bartlett Sessions (1795–1892), nurse, midwife, and herbalist, also attended meetings with the Richards. She was a friend of Susannah Lippincott Richards. [41]

Friendships between the LDS women were "the heart of the expanding Relief Society network."[42] Sisterhood, the core of the network, was foundational for the women, as they not only sought education on nursing care and healthy lifestyle. The Relief Society also served as a forum for women's discussion about some difficult church doctrinal issues affecting women, such as patriarchal leadership and celestial or plural marriage. Society meetings stopped in 1844 as the LDS prepared for the trek westward.

The combination of loneliness and a rural pioneer life often strengthened the LDS women's needs for sisterhood and networking. In the early and mid-nineteenth century, the church recognized celestial or plural marriage. The emotional and physical difficulties of living in a plural marriage in a pioneer community are expressed in some of the LDS women's diaries, such as in Eliza Lyman's. She writes about the difficult birth of a baby to a woman, Carlie, who was very lonely for her husband, who was not with her during the birth because he lived in another town with another wife.[43] Midwife Patty Bartlett Sessions records frequently in her diary how lonely she was at night because her husband was with another wife. "Mr. Sessions has said many hard things to me . . . sorrow of heart has made me sick . . . I feel some better he has promised to treat me well [*several entries stricken out and ink changes color:* I lay alone."][44] The women found solace in the Relief Society and in their community work.

Formal Relief Society activities would not begin again until the 1860s but women still continued their networking, nursing, and charitable work. The LDS men were encouraged to support them. "Great exertions are made by the sisters to prepare themselves to nurse each other—the entire accomplishment of which is most desirable; and every good man will lend his influence and aid to accomplish this object, regardless alike of personal aggrandizement, and pockets full of gold."[45] The article continued by stating that women who desire a doctor instead of a female nurse and physicians who "delight in nursing women" rather than encouraging them to nurse themselves possess an "adulterous spirit."[46] The concern of Americans in the nineteenth century about male physicians treating women also was prevalent in the LDS community. The LDS women continued the tradition of female midwifery and woman-to-woman caregiving for this reason.

Nursing care, especially midwifery, was an important part of the LDS community from the early days of the church. Community women took care of each other's families when ill and knew how to lay out the dead. Eliza Lyman's journal refers to women "watchers" in the house when sickness was present and "girls to do the work."[47] But some of the LDS women's nursing, midwifery, and doctoring went well beyond the fulfillment of the common LDS community woman's duty. Expert LDS nurses were often acknowledged by church leaders, such as Joseph Smith, by being "set aside" as "nurses."

The nurses, who will be described in this chapter (some of whom were recorded as being formally set aside and some not), or their families often recorded their work in diaries even during their pioneer trek to Utah when they were living in wagon trains. For example, Mary Richards, the niece of Dr. Willard Richards, wrote during a storm that came upon them while trekking to Utah: "I got very wet. About the middle of the storm our tent blowed down & Walter also. Maria was obliged to make her way throw [*sic*] the storm to the wagon barefoot & in her night clothes. Soon after she was taken very sick & kept getting worse. I got Walter to make a fire & prepar'd for what might follow. I attended upon her all the night . . . 25 minutes before 7 Maria gave birth to a fine little Daughter."[48] In August, Aunt Rhoda Richards was not well and called for Mary to rub her with spirits. Mary "doctored" Aunt Rhoda all night getting up "9 times."[49]

After the pioneers settled in Utah and after some of the LDS women were trained in medicine in the East, the Deseret Hospital was formed, with women as house physicians in 1882. The hospital was directed by a very prosperous Relief Society. Nursing training in the late nineteenth and early twentieth centuries was provided by the Relief Society, the LDS women physicians, and the Groves LDS Hospital, which opened in 1905. Into the twentieth century, LDS Relief Society members were being "set apart" as nurses by the LDS priesthood. "When they returned to their home communities [after training], they were given thirty days' service in charity nursing as well as maintain a spiritual component in their practical work."[50] The spiritually based nursing work of the LDS women's Relief Society was continued by the church into the 1970s with a health missionary program in the disadvantaged areas of the church.

Botanical Therapies and Receipts

The LDS nurse-midwives were educated in the use of botanical therapies. In the mid-nineteenth century, nearly every LDS settlement had at least one botanically trained midwife.[51] Botanicals commonly used included arnica, horseradish, burdock, catnip, clover, dandelion, elderberry, fennel, feverfew, flaxseed, garlic, onions, ginger, hops, asafoetida, senna, peppermint, plantain, sage, sarsaparilla, lobelia, and saffron. Botanical applications included poultices, syrups, pills, oils, tinctures, teas, wines, bitters, salves, plasters, juices, and powders.[52] Some of the herbs, such as sage and onion, could be grown or harvested locally and some, such as asafoetida, most likely would have been imported[53] and purchased through local vendors.

Botanical wild crafting for medicine and food was important to the early LDS pioneers. "Many pioneer families, driven from Nauvoo in the winter of 1846–47, found relief from hunger in the artichokes and wild onions along the bottom lands of the Missouri River. It was probably a very unpalatable diet, but it proved to be a very good preventative against scurvy, cholera, and the disease known as black leg."[54] Cholera as a bacterial infection affects the gastrointestinal system causing marked diarrhea, vomiting, severe cramps and subsequent dehydration, as well as death in many instances. In the nineteenth century, cholera was feared for its ability to strike and kill sometimes within a day.

The LDS pioneers may have actually prevented cholera by eating the wild onions and artichokes. There were no records to confirm the genus and species of the plants eaten by the pioneers, but it is possible, if the plants they ate were of the genus *Allium* (onion) and *Cynara (artichoke)*, that twenty-first-century data may suggest an explanation for their success against cholera. One contemporary botanical text reports that "plant fructooligosaccharides have recently been claimed to have 'prebiotic' properties, i.e., to promote beneficial flora, and to be useful in dysbiotic conditions like candidiasis. They are a mixture of oligosaccharides consisting of glucose rather than fructose units. They are widely distributed in plants such as onions, asparagus, and wheat and in herbal remedies such as Cynara (artichoke leaf) and Urginea (squill)."[55] While artichokes and onions may have been quite popular among the people in the nineteenth century,[56] there is no mention of their use in the prevention of cholera or scurvy in the Eclectic's nineteenth-century *Materia Medica.*[57] However, the prebiotic properties of the plants may have helped in the prevention of the disease. The LDS pioneers perhaps would have learned of the botanical information through networking channels in the community.

The influence of Thomsonian botanical therapies is found in numerous, different LDS sources. For example, one of the primary Thomsonian herbs, cayenne pepper, was used to warm the interior of the body, primarily the stomach. In the LDS paper *Deseret News*, on April 3, 1852, J. D. Dunyon, a non-LDS physician, wrote to Thomsonian editor Doctor Richards about his recommendations for curing erysipelas, an acute infectious disease with symptoms of fever and skin inflamation. He recommended the use of the "salts and cream tarter" daily to purge the system.[58] The editor then wrote: "If any of our physicians will give us a better theory on erysipelas than the above, we would like to see it. To the prevention we demur in part; i.e., if you use *Salts*, follow the operation with *Cayenne Pepper*, sufficient to retain the natural warmth of your bodies, internally; if you do not, you run the risk of doing more hurt than good. The extracts of *Butternut bark,*

White Ash bark, or the *Red Osier*, or *Kinnakinic*, are either of them a safer and better article for cleansing the blood, particularly in hot weather, than *Salts*; make a tea and drink freely."[59]

Some LDS community members criticized Thomsonian practice by saying that cayenne and lobelia used extensively[60] were no better a solution and no safer than calomel. One gets a sense when reading some of the editorials that some of the LDS community must have opposed the conclusions and practice of the (primarily Thomsonian) Council of Health leadership. In the *Deseret News* in May 1852, the editors defended the use of cayenne (For more information see Color Insert H). They said:

> We have often heard it remarked in a wild, loose, or tantalizing manner, and by men in high authority too, "that pepper is a hot drink, and the word of wisdom proscribes hot drinks," . . . O ye elders in Israel, permit us to say to you, that when the revelation came to the saints of latter days to abstain from hot drinks, our Heavenly Father had no reference to pepper of any kind, cayenne, red, black, or yellow, or any other herb of a like nature, which is in perfect accordance with the principles of life and salvation. . . . Then what did he mean? Hot drinks, water boiled over the fire, . . . pepper and other articles of a like nature, pure and harmless in themselves as mother's milk, are good when colds or chills present themselves, to restore the natural life and energy of the human system, and are a prominent part and portion of the herbs referred to, and designed for the use of the saints, in the word of wisdom. We refer to these things with the best of feelings, hoping that no elder in Israel, from this day forth, will give way to his prejudices.[61]

As mentioned previously, because the emergence of the LDS church coincides with the emergence of the Botanical Medical Movement in the United States, it is difficult to determine whether LDS community members first believed in the safety and effectiveness of botanical therapies and in Thomsonianism or in the LDS doctrine regarding using herbs to promote health and healing, which then led them to the Thomsonian system. While the specific answers to these questions are not clear, what is apparent is that the mid-nineteenth-century LDS used botanical therapies extensively.

The church leadership of the LDS community today, as well as many members, no longer promotes or uses botanical therapies used in the nineteenth century. The controversy typical of the early nineteenth century between the "Regulars" and the "others" is evident in the LDS community after the Civil War and even up to the present day in writings, such as in the article by an LDS physician that was published in 1983. This late-twentieth-century article was written by Dr. Norman Smith for the journal of the Brigham Young University Medical Association, *The Journal of Collegium Aesculapium*, entitled, "Why Are Mormons So Susceptible to Medical and Nutritional Quackery?"[62] Smith wrote that many members of the LDS church used their scripture and journal accounts by early church leadership, in particular Joseph Smith's writings, to promote the use of herbs in healing and health promotion in modern times. He equated some LDS members' continuance of their tradition of using herbs in health and healing with a reliance upon quackery, which he defined as "enthusiastic, incautious promotion of an unproven or disproved method."[63] He explained many LDS's use of herbs in healing as being a result of feeling that "the right to choose even dangerous forms of quackery is part of the divine principle of free agency, and that any restriction on that free choice is satanic."[64] Smith expressed his concern that the LDS do not address the actual problems of using herbs, such as that of determining which herbs are "safe." He concluded: "Most promising medicinal plants studied are discarded because of excess toxicity. But they're *not* discarded by the herbalist."[65] Smith does not give any supporting scientific evidence for his statement that most plants studied are discarded due to toxicity, however.

Do the LDS really choose "dangerous forms of quackery" and is herbalism one of them? Dr. Norman Farnsworth, pharmacognosist and professor at the University of Illinois at Chicago, school of pharmacy, stated that based on published reports, "Side effects or toxic reactions associated with herbal medicines in any form are rare."[66] Perhaps the reason LDS are "susceptible" to the use of herbs and other "unproven" methods of healing, if in fact they are, can be found in their history of the use of herbs and the health beliefs surrounding this use.

Numerous accounts exist of the safe use of botanical therapies in the historical records of the LDS. People often do not require "proof" from clinical research that an herb is safe and effective to use in healing. According to folklorist Dr. Bonnie O'Connor's research: "*That* a therapeutic action works is more important than an explanation of *how* or *why* it works. . . . The long-standing prediction that as science and medicine progressed and education became more generally available, folk and popular beliefs about health, illness, and healing would steadily decline, must now be recognized to be wide of the mark."[67] People often rely on historical evidence of herb safety and efficacy and continue with the health practices that they know and trust.

It is often community women who, in the tradition of the healing network, keep "unproven" healing remedies such as herbs alive. In the LDS community, this seems also to be the case. Smith credits the *women nurses* who attended the Council of Health meetings, where the virtues of herbs were "extolled," with spreading herbalism in their small rural communities. He wrote: "The herbal philosophies of these councils of health, which the ladies took back to their communities, lay a basis for some of these strong family traditions of fondness for herbs and desires to keep away from the doctors, philosophies that carry down to our time, particularly in some small communities in southern Utah."[68] The next section of this chapter more closely examines the historical use of botanical therapies by some of those very nurses.

Latter-day Saints Thomsonians and Nurse-Herbalists

There are three men recorded in LDS medical history as being responsible for introducing, teaching, and/or promoting botanical therapies, specifically Thomsonianism, to the LDS community and nurses, Levi Richards, Willard Richards, and Priddy Meeks. Willard

Richards, a schoolteacher and lecturer on electricity and botanical medicine, practiced under the direction of Samuel Thomson in Thomson's infirmary in Boston in 1834. Willard and his brother, Levi Richards, were baptized into the LDS church in Kirtland by their cousin, Brigham Young, in December 1836.[69] One observer of the two doctors was Mary Ann Stearns Winters, who was three years old when she boarded in Young's home. Winters played with Young's daughters, Vilate and Elizabeth, and recorded her childhood experience of being treated by the Thomsonian doctors. It is interesting to note that it is a woman, Young's wife, who was the "convert" to Thomsonianism and who may have been initially responsible for introducing the Richards to the LDS community.

> During the winter the younger children of the family took the measles and my turn came with the others. I was very sick and always remember my suffering at that time. Drs. Willard and Levi Richards had just arrived from their homes in Massachusetts to investigate the gospel and were stopping at Brother Young's. They were Thomsonian doctors and Sister Young was a strong convert to that practice; so of course, we were liberally dosed with composition, Lobelia, etc. To me the red pepper was something dreadful, and taking the composition through straws did not help the matter much — and oh, how I did long for a drink of cold water. But we got well, the dear little twins and all, and I will not condemn the bridge that helped us safely over. About this time the doctors had asked to be baptized. I watched them as they departed, and upon their return, and when Sister Young shook hands with them and greeted them as "Brother Richards," I thought then they were all right, especially as I did not have to take more of their medicine.[70]

On a ship to England for a Saint's mission, Levi Richards served as nurse and physician. He wrote: "Engaged much of the time in nursing the sick."[71] He gave people enemas, emetics, and "composition" or composition and bitters mixed with a little "cayene [*sic*]." He also wrote: "I gave Elder John Kay a lobelia and took one myself; both operated.[72] Richards said: "Gave him a strong Thomsonian injection, which caused him to sweat all night," and he treated Mr. Brant's daughter's "female weakness and irritation" with "raspbury [*sic*] leaves" tea and a nighttime Thomsonian injection.[73] Levi Richards also treated the prophet, Joseph Smith, with Thomsonian therapies. He recorded providing an emetic for "Brother Smith" on April 26, 1844, and a tonic syrup for "President Smith" on May 11, 1844.[74]

Levi Richards primarily saw church elders, children, and men in his practice. He lectured on medicine and religious topics and had his own garden.[75] In 1849, he recorded his interactions with Dr. John Balbernie (whom he later baptized), who was most likely a water cure physician. Balbernie discussed his knowledge of "packs" and warm bath-cold dash techniques with Brother Levi. On July 31, 1849, Levi Richards, a true herbalist, wrote a critique of his colleague's water cure practices: "After dinner I had some conversation with the Doctor. I told him that I thought his practice required the use of herbs to perfect it."[76]

Priddy Meeks was a respected, self-taught "root doctor." Meeks wrote in his journal about how he arrived at his knowledge of herbalism.

> Bought a farm on the Illinois river with my wife who got hooping [*sic*] cough or in other words she was killed by the doctors who I was aposed [*sic*] to having any thing to do with her, only the folks over persuaded me and I am convinced that his medicine killed her. Here when the sickley season of the year came on I visited many of the sick and was very successful in releaving [*sic*] them with roots and herbs. So much so that the community insisted I should quit work & go to doctoring. Such an idea had never entered my mind. I

> said to them that I know nothing about doctoring, they sed, "you beat all the doctors." That expression brought me to my studies and I saw that it was a fact and I could not deny it.[77]

Later on, Meeks's wife became very ill. He could not help her, nor could anyone else. He met James Miller, who told him that he would be able to cure his wife if he had Samuel Thomson's *New Guide to Health*. He learned from Miller about Thomsonianism during a thirty-mile journey they made together.[78] Meeks wrote of his practice, "I had nothing but kayenne [*sic*] pepper and ginger for my composition powder and labelia [*sic*] and as I went along gathering green sumac leaves off the bush which answered well for kanker medicine and to make a tea to put the medicine in for her to drink. I mention this to show that we can get along without so many kinds of medicines as some would suppose."[79]

Meeks was partially responsible for the creation of the Council of Health. He wrote that he proposed to his two "pardners in medicine," Brothers Morse and Richards (Levi), that they form "some kind of association for giving information to the mass of the people in regard to doctoring themselves in sickness so as to help themselves and lighten our burdens."[80] They asked Apostle Richards (Willard), who agreed and named it the "Society of Health."[81] Meeks's journal entries also indicate that he was responsible for some of the botany work after the move to Utah. He wrote that he "scoured" the canyons for herbs and that each canyon had new plants that he presented to the Council of Health.[82]

In addition to the Richards brothers and Meeks, many other men and women promoted the use of botanical therapies and Thomsonianism. As discussed previously, Brigham Young's wife was a "convert" to Thomsonianism and supported it strongly, as did the prophet Joseph Smith.[83] Diaries and journals also demonstrate the active role that the LDS pioneer women, particularly the midwives and nurses, took in promoting general botanical use and Thomsonianism, in particular, to the LDS community. One of the most notable stories is that of Margaret Cooper West, who was born in Tennessee.

Margaret Cooper West (1804–1882)

Margaret Cooper West's story was told to Utah pioneer historian Kate Carter, a Utah pioneer historian, by May Riggs West.[84] Margaret West was known as a nurse in her community from early childhood. She cared for pets, for her father when he lay sick and dying, and for others in her town. When anything went wrong, the townspeople always sent for her and "for miles around when a child was born, people would send for Margaret."[85] In 1833, not long before Margaret was baptized into the LDS faith, a man came to the door of her home and sold her a copy of Samuel Thomson's *New Guide to Health* and the twenty-dollar patent to use the knowledge. While at first reluctant to spend the money, she realized after looking through the book that "The doctors I have known seem almost helpless to restrain its course or to give more relief than I have done. I have been reading right here that if a patient is given the proper care at the commencement of the fever it can easily and speedily be overcome. If this book can help me to learn more about the sickness and how to alleviate pain, how well paid we both will be."[86]

Margaret became a bona fide Thomsonian. She taught her husband, children, and patients the importance of the use of herbs, such as lobelia and cayenne. Margaret and her family left their home in Tennessee because they were being shunned for their religious beliefs. The men in the community were forbidding their wives to accept Margaret's help because of her religion. The West family moved to Kentucky after Margaret helped many of her patients document the herbal remedies she had used to help them.

In Kentucky, Margaret became a bonesetter as well as a Botanic nurse. While Regulars did bonesetting work, it was not unusual in nineteenth-century America and earlier, especially in the rural areas of the country, to find a healer who only set bones. For example, Tannenbaum recorded the activities of Mrs. Parker, a bonesetter, who had her own equipment for pulling bones into place, splinting and bandaging.[87] Margaret may have been somewhat unusual in the level of "cross-training" she had. She was a nurse, a Botanic, and a bonesetter. Margaret also used water cure techniques, including sweats and steams.

When the West family was again forced to leave their home in Kentucky because of their religious beliefs, in 1842 they went to Nauvoo, where they stayed until 1846. Margaret continued her nursing work with herbs and water cure. "How many days and nights Margaret found herself making the familiar sweat tent with sheets and blankets, a raw-hide bottom chair, if possible, covered with a blanket for the patient so that the steam could better reach him. . . . The nurse and her helpers would be perspiring quite as freely as the patient, and when sweat began to pour from every part of the body, he was carefully rubbed until cool with clean clothes dampened with either vinegar or alcohol. The patient was then put to bed and closely watched, for the perspiring might continue."[88]

After the murder of the prophet, the West family, like many other LDS families, moved to Kanesville, Iowa, the fourth state where Margaret practiced nursing. Carter recorded that it was in Kanesville that Margaret taught other women to care for the sick. "The knowledge she had gained from the little book [*Thomson's New Guide to Health*], and from her own rich fund of experience, she gave to all who wished to learn."[89] She was an experienced herbalist at the time and in preparing for the trek to Utah engaged the help of her family in preparing a large stock of herbal remedies to bring to their new home, where she would not be familiar with the local plants. Carter wrote: "They gathered herbs and barks which they pounded into powder. They filled bottles and cans with these powders and dried hops and parsley. She gathered vast stores of cherry stone meats and peach stone meats and pounded them fine. She made the following syrup in large quantities to take with them: 1 lb. each of poplar bark and the bark of bayberry root, boiled in 2 gallons of water and strained, add 7 lbs. of sugar. Scald and skim, then add 1 lb. peach stone meats or the same quantity cherry stone meats, pounded fine."[90] The syrup was used to strengthen the stomach and bowels and was also used in dysentery, a condition that Margaret expected might occur on the trail.

Margaret Cooper West settled in Parowan, Utah in 1851. She continued her work as a nurse, midwife, and water cure and botanical healer, and her successes are recorded in such accounts as the healing of her son-in-law, George Smith, from tuberculosis. She used steams, emetics, hot herb teas and herbal syrups, and a chest protector to heal him. Her nursing work was known in many towns. It is recorded that "Sometimes the people at Red Creek, Beaver, and Greenville, and even as far south as Washington, would send for her with good results."[91]

Mary Ann Stearns Winters (1833-1912)

Mary Ann Stearns Winters was the child of Mary Ann Frost Stearns Pratt, wife of Nathan Stearns and Parley P. Pratt, member of the Quorum of Twelve Apostles. Mary Ann's autobiography (cited earlier) is unique in that it provides a child's experience of the socio-medical culture of the period, including the Thomsonianism experience, pioneer nursing care, herbal and home remedies, and woman's herbal networking. Mary Ann Winters' account of the trek to Utah demonstrates the healing talent of her mother (also named Mary Ann), the trust that community members had in her mother's knowledge of healing and herbs, and the importance of herbs to pioneer women.

Mary Ann described the level of healing expertise her mother had indirectly in her story of how a box of medicine came to be possessed by the pioneer group. She related the following:

> Brother Robison and Brother Winters had worked all day and drank freely of the warm river water, and at night Brother Robison became very sick with cholera, and Brother Winters was the first to call for a dose of the medicine. Before leaving Kanesville, Brother Winters has gone to the drug store and handed the druggist five dollars and told him that he wanted some of his best cholera remedies to take with him on the plaines [*sic*]—all had been advised to provide themselves with cholera medicine, and mother had a good portion along with her, among other things a quantity of pulverized charcoal. The day before we arrived at Loup Fork, Brother Winters brought his box

> of medicine to mother and said she would know how to use it better than he did.[92]

Brother Winters got remedies from Mary Ann's mother that evening for Brother Robison. Her mother's preparation consisted of charcoal and molasses, laudanum or paregoric, camphor and a little cayenne pepper, and flour, and "it proved to be a good remedy, for all that took it recovered except Brother Robison, and he passed away after two days suffering."[93]

Sister Pratt treated many others on the wagon train on the way to Utah. Mary Ann recorded the success of one of her mother's simple remedies, hot porridge.

> Mother called around to speak to the sick ones, and see how many there were, and found many of them very weak and dejected and discouraged. When we opened up the porridge it had stopped bubling [*sic*], but proved to be well done, was piping hot, and after adding sufficient milk we started on our rounds of distribution. There were seven that accepted it joyfully, and I believe the surprise, under the discouraging circumstances, did them as much good as the refreshment. . . . Then she roused me up to take them (the porridge) to the people, these were mostly sisters — only two of the men folks of this camp had been taken sick . . . some of them afterwards told mother that they believed that those warm drinks were the means of helping to save their lives.[94]

All recovered from "the cholera," and there was no further sickness for the rest of the journey.

The LDS women's community healing networks were expanded to others on the pioneer trail. Mary Ann recorded an incident regarding the herb asafoetida (For more information see Color Insert C) between her pioneer nurse-mother and an Oregonian woman they met on the trail. The following story about Sister Pratt demonstrates the simplicity and importance of the pioneer nurse-herbalists' healing network:

> We had overtaken and passed several other companies, and one day we came up with a company of Oregon emigrants and camped with them. They seemed quite well-to-do people and our company bought some provisions of them—some got flour and some dried fruit or whatever they had a surplus of. In the evening one came over to talk with mother and she inquired if there was any one that has some asafoetida that she could get. She had been in the habit of using it before she left home and had brought a quantity with her, but it was all gone and she was quite miserable without it. Mother told her we had a piece somewhere, but she didn't know whether she could find it. She replied, "O you must find it. I cannot be this near to it and not get some. She was over early the next morning, and mother hunted till she found it. (It was some we had at Kanesville in the small-pox epidemic and the children had little bags with some of it hung round their necks), and it was strange the effect it had on her, for she said, "Now I will be all right," and she took it so caressingly in her hands saying, "Oh, I am so glad to get it and will pay you anything you ask." Mother told her she was perfectly welcome to it and was glad if it would do her so much good, and she went back to her wagon a very happy looking woman.[95]

This account not only demonstrates the importance of herbs to some women but the importance of the healing network that often was the source not only of healing information but of the products of healing. This account also shows the depth of the relationship, especially in terms of health beliefs, that women had with their remedies, and how nurses supported, without question or judgment, a person's choice of remedy. Sister Pratt simply told the woman she was "glad if it would do her so much good."

The LDS women's healing network most likely began forming before the pioneer trek to Utah and even before the founding of the first church headquarters in Nauvoo, Illinois. Mary Ann Winters and her nurse-herbalist mother were originally from Bethel, Maine. In 1836, after Mary Ann's father, Nathan Stearns, died, she and her mother set out on their journey to Kirtland, Ohio, to join the LDS community aggregating there. They left Maine in the company of Father David Sessions,[96] who had been married since 1812 to midwife-herbalist Patty Sessions, also of Newry and Bethel, Maine. Mary Ann wrote that when they arrived in Nauvoo after their difficult boat trip, her mother and stepfather went to the mansion of Brother Joseph Smith. She continued: "Some of our friends insisted on having part of our family, so Aunt Olive and we children were taken up to Mother Sessions [Patty Bartlett Sessions], where she nursed us up to good health again—the little ones that were not quite over the effects of the measles—and I had the chills and fever while on the boat."[97] Patty Sessions also would record in her diary having Mary Ann Pratt visit her at her home in July 1862.[98] Mary Ann Pratt and Patty Sessions knew each other in Maine, and it is quite possible, though not recorded in the diaries studied, that Patty Sessions, who had been practicing nursing and midwifery in Maine since 1812, delivered Mary Ann Winters and may have taught her mother the work of caring for the sick that she eventually used on the Utah trail. The women were contemporaries in the LDS women's healing network.

Patty Bartlett Sessions (1795-1892)

One major contributor to nursing, midwifery, and herbalism in the LDS community was Patty Bartlett Sessions (1795–1892). Her complete diaries (1846–1888) are preserved in the LDS church archives and have been published. Patty Sessions reportedly delivered 3,977 babies in her lifetime.[99] While living in Nauvoo, she was set apart by church leaders Brigham Young and Heber Kimball as a "doctor for women."[100] As mentioned earlier, Sessions had been a midwife and nurse since the early part of the century in Maine. She may have gained some of her understanding of midwifery and botanical therapies from Indian women.

Historical accounts of the early medicine of Bethel, Maine, include stories of an Indian, Molly Ockett, who was a midwife to many of the women in the region. She "knew roots, barks, and herbs from which she concocted salves, drinks, and poultices for the sick. . . . Patty may have gained some of her extensive knowledge of herbs from the area's last resident Indian practitioner."[101] Ockett may have taught Sessions, Pratt, and many other women about midwifery and the use of local plants in healing and in easing childbirth.

Sessions most likely learned herbalism and midwifery from a number of sources. For example, she owned a copy of Wooster Beach's *The Family Physician*. She must have used it often, as the book cover was quite worn from use and contained Sessions's cross-stitch of the saying "Remember Me."[102] Beach wrote medical books in the nineteenth century on midwifery, health, medicine, and botanicals. The 1843 edition of *The Family Physician* contains 107 pages on preventing disease and promoting health and longevity, approximately 100 pages on "general principles of the reformed practice of medicine," nearly 300 pages on "internal diseases," a section on "surgical diseases," twenty-nine pages on midwifery, sixty pages on "vegetable materia medica" (herbs), and thirty pages on pharmacy and applications, such as poultices, bitters, and oils. There also is a small section on diet for the healthy and sick, on anatomy, and on the teeth.[103] Owning a book by Beach in a predominantly Thomsonian community might have been viewed as irreverent, given the fact that Beach and Thomson were rivals with the Beachites accepting some of the practices of the Regulars. Nevertheless, Sessions's book remained in her possession throughout her life.

In addition to learning from Beach's book, Patty Sessions may have learned about botanical therapies by sharing information with LDS Thomsonian doctors Willard Richards, Levi Richards, and Priddy Meeks. Records show that Sessions knew Priddy Meeks, and her diary includes an entry of visiting the home of Sarah Meeks, his wife.[104] She also knew Willard Richards because he performed her sealing (celestial marriage) to Joseph Smith in 1842.[105] In addition, Sessions was also a participating member and leader of the Council of Health, established in Utah by Willard Richards.[106] She regularly attended

Richards's wife's nursing instruction,[107] which most likely included information on botanical therapies, given the health beliefs of the community at that time.

While the Thomsonians supported midwifery practice and women's roles in healing, Thomsonian books have little information on midwifery compared to Beach's books. Sessions may have chosen to own the writings of Wooster Beach for that reason. She may have been a Beachite who later turned Thomsonian in Utah. Common Thomsonian techniques such as steaming and lobelia do not appear in Sessions's diary until she reaches Utah, where she writes about her interaction with Willard Richards on the council. In July and August 1850, she recorded counseling with Willard Richards and then going back to a patient to give her an "emetic."[108] She made entries in her diary such as, "took Julia Baldwin through a course in medicine," and " . . . give him an ametic [*sic*]."[109] On December 8, 1852, Sessions said for the first time that she herself took "cayenne & lobelia" when ill, and then later that month, she recorded giving patients a "composition & lobelia" injection or a "tincture of lobelia" on a number of occasions.[110]

Sessions's nursing work included laying out the dead, home or wagon visits, putting women to bed (delivering babies), the laying on of hands on the sick,[111] speaking in tongues,[112] dressing wounds,[113] working with doctors who saw LDS members in cases of injury or more serious illness,[114] and making wine[115] and remedies, such as "canker" medicine.[116] As in many receipt books of the period, Sessions recorded some of her healing receipts upside down on the page. For instance, she recorded a receipt "for salve for old sores the bark of indigo weed root boiled down beas wax a very little rosin" and "For bowel complaint take one tea spoonful of rubarb [*sic*] one forth carbnet soda one table spoonful brandy one tea spoonful peperment [*sic*] essence half tea cup ful warm water take a table spoonful once an hour untill [*sic*] it opporates."[117] Also upside down and folded is her receipt, "cure for gravel wild rose berrys boiled long drink the tea."[118]

In addition to teas and salves, Sessions also recorded using an herbal poultice for a patient with a hand infection. "Br Filawry came here a week ago with a very bad hand it was poisoned by skinning a cow that died did not know what ailed her he had a small place on his finger where the skin was scrat[c]hed off and it swelled verry [*sic*] bad & made him sick all over, to day he is better I have took care of his hand polticed [*sic*] it with catnip & Lobelia mostly put in salt & soap and molasses his finger turned black & the flesh dead ~~when the~~ [*sic*] but it begins to come to its feeling a little now."[119]

Like colonial nurse-midwives[120] and Shaker nurses, LDS nurses and midwives grew their own botanical remedies. While rarely mentioned in her diaries, perhaps because it was a "common woman's" activity, Sessions did report maintaining a garden. On August 22, 1855, she wrote: "Worked in the garden gather herbs & seeds."[121] "Dug about my pye plant."[122] "Puled [*sic*] the peas took care of the flax."[123] Sessions did not, however, specifically mention using flaxseed poultices in her care of others. It may have been grown for other purposes, such as the production of cloth, or it may not have been mentioned, because flaxseed poultices may have been too common to be noteworthy.

Sessions interacted with a number of community physicians and healers. She was very active in LDS community health care. In January 1855, she presided over the Council of Health when Brother Richards could not be at the meeting.[124] Throughout February 1855, Sessions went to meetings of the midwives, and on March 8, 1855, she went to the "council of midwives."[125] In addition to working with Willard Richards and the Council of Health, Sessions recorded buying "medicine and other things"[126] from a Dr. Pearson. She also attended a lecture in April 1852 by Albert Carrington on the topic "Doctors and Their Practices."[127] There is a distinct change in Sessions' diaries around December 1852, following that meeting.

Sessions began to record the detail of her interactions with physicians on patient care issues. For example, on December 2, 1852, she wrote: . . . I would go and see Dr Richards or Sprague. Friday 3d as I was preparing to go Dr P Richards came after me to go with him and see a woman he had been attening we caled [*sic*] as we went along and sister Forsith and girl found them better he thought they would get well if they took no cold: said I had give them all he could think of then."[128] Is it possible that at the April meeting Sessions and the other nurses were told to have more interaction with doctors? Sessions seemed to believe that she needed to seek out and consult a doctor on her cases, as she had not done before, or at least had not recorded as having done before.

Some entries in Sessions's diaries may indicate that she had some concerns about another issue related to physicians, that of the quality of some of the physicians moving into Utah. From her diaries, we know that Sessions attended lectures on "Midwifery and the Management of Women and Children" by a Dr. William France, a LDS from England who had settled in Salt Lake City, where he had set up his medical practice in 1850.[129] Later on in her diary, we see two entries regarding the practice of Dr. France. She wrote on September 11, 1855: "Went to see calebs babe it is dead dr France tended on it sister Steed washed for me and Br Smith. . . . Thursd 20 cut peaches to dry called to sister Whitehead found her very sick Dr France has Drd her.[130]

Dr. France published a "report of the health of the city" in the *Deseret News* in 1855. In it he included statistics on his monthly caseload, including the number of patients he saw with specific disease such as canker, lung disease, piles, and fits, and the numbers cured (thirty-five), the number remaining under treatment (sixteen), and the number died (one).[131] Though he may have appeared to Sessions and others to be more of a Regular physician than a Botanic, Dr. France clearly showed his deviation from the Regulars when he wrote the following:

> Hence they [people] fly for aid of the use of nausecous [*sic*] drugs; which, although for a time they may relieve, can never cure disease. This is a fact now admitted by the most intelligent modern physicians, that medicine never did, can never cure disease. . . . In a word remove impurities of all kinds, cleanse the body outside and inside, cease to clog up the delicate machinery of the system by improper food or otherwise; then, and not till then, will the Spirit of the Lord be poured out in the ordinance of anointing and the laying on of hands, and the sick shall be healed as in days of old—then, and not

> till then, physicians in our midst may close their offices—drugs, along with other Gentile abominations, be banished from the community—and I for one will have cause to rejoice in being relieved from the care and anxiety inseparable from a faithful discharge of the duties now devolving upon me.[132]

Sessions's diary may have reflected the tension in the mid-nineteenth century between physicians and midwives regarding obstetrical care, which also was occurring across the nation. In the East, male physicians had begun to dominate obstetrical care in the early part of the century, especially in larger cities such as Philadelphia. In 1831 Philadelphia, only twenty-one female midwives were left in the city out of 155 accoucheurs . . . at least among those documented as sending in reports.[133] Female midwives continued providing their services for the poor and working classes, but they lost most of the status they had achieved during the colonial period.[134] Even though nineteenth-century women began to insist that male care in obstetrics was improper, and women midwives were encouraged by health care reformers such as Thomson and Beach to take back their practices, American midwives' status never returned to what it had been.

From the middle to the later part of the century, women entered medical schools and then ultimately offered what might have been considered by some women citizens the best of both worlds—the caring expertise of the nurse-midwife with the expertise and training of the physician.[135] The replacement of nurse-herbalist-midwives first by male physician encroachment and then the replacement of male physicians with medical school-trained women physicians occurred in Utah a few decades after the transition in the East after the community was settled in the Great Salt Lake Basin. Sessions's legacy remains strong. Her birthing record, her work with the Council of Health and the Midwives Council, and her work with botanical therapies and Beach's and Thomson's systems are preserved in the diary of her life of healing service. The LDS historians have concluded: "She earned a place as a leader among women in spiritual and practical ways."[136]

Ann Green Dutson Carling (1799–1893)

Ann Carling, known by many as "Grandmother Carling," was born in England and died in 1893 at age ninety-four. Carling had been in Nauvoo, Illinois, when angry mobs were demonstrating against LDS members. Ann Melville Bishop, granddaughter of Carling, wrote that when her family lived in Nauvoo, her mother, Jane, suffered the effects of the poisoning of the family well by the mobs "for the rest of her life."[137] Bishop wrote of her grandmother: "Grandmother was set apart by the Prophet Joseph Smith to be a midwife and was told to use nothing but herbs and she would be successful which she was. She was Dr. and Nurse for a number of years for the people of Fillmore, Holden, Meadow and Kanosh [Utah]."[138]

In 1852, Carling moved to Utah, where she settled, raised a family, delivered many babies, and trained other women to nurse the sick. Her fee as a midwife was either three dollars or payment in produce.[139] She was renowned for her skill. Carling often was called upon into her old age to travel great distances from her home in Fillmore to deliver babies when the local midwife had done all that she could. The following is just one account of the community's respect for Carling's skill:

> Carlie's sufferings during this day are past description. No mortal but a woman can suffer so and live. May I never witness such suffering again. Platte stood by her like a brother and his wife Adelia did all she could as also Sister Caroline and others, but no one could do any good till Sister Carling came and she soon brought relief and the best sound I ever heard was when I heard the Baby ~~cried~~ [*sic*] cry.[140]

Carling grew her own medicinal herbs. She was a very trusted community "herb doctor" in addition to being a midwife and nurse. Her granddaughter, Ann, recorded that she gave saffron tea to newborn babies to help clear their skin. She bruised the feathery leaves of yarrow and used them in making ointments for wounds and gave her patients with mountain fever or neuritis wild sage tea.[141] These were just a few of Carling's remedies. Another of Carling's granddaughters, Florence Dutson Nielson (born 1857), also became a successful nurse and herbalist. She in turn handed her herbal remedies down to her two daughters, Florence and Margaret, who recorded their family remedies. A sample of the receipts follows:

> Plantain leaf steeped in new milk was given for dysentery. One baby who was suffering from this was given up by the doctors. The Childs mother appealed to Florence for help. After giving him this remedy for a few days he was completely healed. A blood tonic of bitters used for vomiting and stomach trouble was made from Mountain grape roots, kin-a-nic bark, raspberry leaves, peach leaves marshmallow roots and a small amount of dried hops. This was steeped and made up with beer root and yeast like root beer. It was then used in small amounts several times daily. [142]

The writers of the Dutson family history recorded that, "Even the Indians came to Ann for medical assistance. This she discouraged because of their superstitions and customs. The Indians trusted the white 'herb doctor' in every way. Ann was kind to them."[143] To this day, a picture of Ann Carling hangs in a museum in Fillmore, Utah; however, no primary source materials were located in Fillmore, Salt Lake City, or with her family that could shed more light on the work of this extraordinary nurse-herbalist and her relations with Indians in Utah. The women in Ann Carling's family had kept to an herbalist tradition by passing on receipts orally. They did record their herbal remedies in the mid-twentieth century. The following is an example of a receipt from Anne Carling's botanical heritage:

> Onion syrup was made by slicing the onions and pouring boiling water over them, then letting them steep on the back of the stove. This when sweetened with a little honey was used for cough syrup and to

treat a sore throat. The water off from the onions was also used for packs to be placed on the throat; the onion syrup was also used internally.[144]

American Indian Herbalism and the Latter-day Saints

Pioneer nurse-herbalists of the LDS community had ample opportunity, as in the case of Grandmother Carling, to interact with the Indians. The nineteenth-century LDS nurses presented here lived in Indian territory. The LDS church leadership had to negotiate with Indian leaders to obtain the land in Utah for the community. The nature of the relationship with the Indians from the perspective of the Latter-day Saints had much to do with their religious beliefs stemming from the teachings of the prophet Joseph Smith. One belief of the Saints in the nineteenth century was that the North American Indians were "Lamanites," part of God's "Chosen People."[145] American Indians were believed to be descended from the Hebrews. According to the *Book of Mormon*, the Indians had once practiced an advanced form of Christianity, having been taught its principles by Jesus Christ after his Crucifixion, but they had become mischievous. Church members believed that Christ, after his Crucifixion, appeared in the Americas, where he brought his teachings of peace to warring indigenous peoples. Around 421 a.d. Indians began warring and killing each other again.[146]

The LDS believed that they were to introduce the Indians to the *Book of Mormon* and teach them the ways of their ancestors, who once followed Jesus. "The Latter-day Saint view combined under a religious canopy the duty to convert and civilize with a respect for the past accomplishments and the religious record of the Indians and with an attitude of awe towards a chosen people of destiny whose prophesied role in the divine economy was equal if not superior in some ways to that of the white Mormons."[147]

The LDS spent many years actively working on their relationship with the Indians when they began settling in Utah. A number of indigenous communities were already well established in Utah and surrounding areas, including the Ute, Shoshoni, Hopi,

Navajo, Apache, Gosiutes, and Paiutes. According to the LDS's records, the LDS leaders secured the consent of Ute tribal elders to settle in Utah by promising to share livestock and produce. Mary Richards, Levi Richards's and Willard Richards's niece, recorded a meeting between her uncle and the Indians on December 12, 1846, in her uncle Willard's home. She wrote: ". . . next called at Uncle Willard's house, where we had the pleasure of being present at a Council held between the Twelves & the Natives. There was present 10 Indians two chiefs & two Interpiters [*sic*]. One a French man or a half breed we was quite interested to hear them talk & see them act."[148] In June 1849, Brigham Young and H. C. Kimball met with Chief Wakara (Walker) and twelve Ute to come to an agreement for the LDS to settle the Sanpete Valley of central Utah.

The developing relationship between the two cultures was an ongoing issue in Utah as well as in the nation's capital. At one point, the U. S. government believed that the LDS community was aiding and abetting the Indians, during a time when the national policy toward the Indians was one of containment, not negotiation. Other reports claimed that the LDS were killing the Indians. In her diary, Mary Richards recorded that on May 9, 1847, church leader Parley Pratt gave a speech that included the following words:

> They say that we say kill the Indians, Bro Brigham said we should not kill the Indians, no one has ever heard me say kill the Indians or Bro T either we never said it, but we shall say you shall not kill them, neither shall you let them come in to the City and kill off all your Cattle or the Cattle of ~~them~~ [*sic*] belonging to the Wives of those who have gone in the Army.[149]

Mary Ann Stearns Winters' diary account of the trek to Utah contained a number of references to fears regarding an Indian attack.[150] It also included an account from 1852, in which she helped her mother make orange-and-blue ruffled calico shirts for the Indians, who were going with Brother Joseph Johnson to Washington to speak with the "Great White Father."[151] The women in the LDS community formed an Indian Relief Society of which Matilda Dudley was the first president. Midwife Patty Sessions also was president at one time.[152] The purpose of the society was to make clothing for the Indian children and women. Months after the initial work began under Dudley's leadership, Brigham Young "reinforced" the sisters in their work and said that the relief societies should clothe the "poor brethren" in addition to clothing the Lamanite women and children.[153]

Some records exist of the increasing interaction between the two communities, especially in terms of the sharing of cultural information and resources related to health, healing, and botanical therapies. An entry from 1854 in Thomas Bullock's journal included a story of a Dr. Sprague, who was recorded as "calming" Chief Walker and helping the Chief's child to recover from illness. Dr. Sprague, often cited as being the first "physician" in Salt Lake City, who was not a Thomsonian, also was the vice president of the Organic Horticultural Society and is credited with planting the first flower garden.[154]

In the LDS community, the women, nurses, and midwives often demonstrated courage, compassion, and diplomacy in building relationships with the Indians. Nurse-midwives such as Ann Carling shared their botanical medicines and wisdom with the Indians. The LDS women's abilities to reach out to others in the Utah community regardless of race were recognized by the LDS leadership. In his speech to the LDS in central Utah to encourage members to reach out to and teach Indians, Brigham Young said: "I am sure there are women present who have spoken in tongues that they would have to go among the Lamanites & instruct them to sew to knit to wash & perform all domestic works. . . . Now I tell you the time has come that you will have to carry out that which you have seen years & years ago."[155] In 1855, some of the women of Parowan, Utah, including sisters Meeks (most likely the wife or relative of Priddy) and West (likely Margaret Cooper), were set apart as nurses and teachers to the females of the [Pai-edes] Indian tribe, to "teach them their organization, the taking care of children, &c., and to nurse according to revelation, that is by laying on hands, anointing, and with mild herbs."[156]

As compassionate as early LDS may have been toward the American Indians, there is evidence of a subtle discrediting of their healing traditions. The renaming of certain plants used traditionally by

Indians is one example. Indians have often traditionally named plants with words that describe some aspect of the plant's healing qualities so that others are able to find it in the wild and know the use of the plant. The LDS named two plants they came upon in Utah "Mormon tea" and "Brigham tea." Mormon tea was most likely the common name for a species of *Ephedra* (*nevadensis, trifurca*, or *californica)* that grows in the arid, rocky areas of the American West and that has been used "possibly since prehistoric times as medicine."[157] Mormon tea often has been confused with *Equisetum* (horsetail) and *Ephedra sinica* (Chinese ephedra, also known as "ma huang").[158]

One source recorded "Brigham tea" as being recommended by Brigham Young to the LDS community as a common replacement for Japanese tea.[159] However, the same source described the plant steeped as a tea as coming from a rush "growing on the side of a stream." If the plant used for common tea and named after Young was found by water, it was most likely *Equisetum hyamale* (horsetail,) not *Ephedra nevadensis* or Mormon tea. *Ephedra nevadensis* grows in arid regions, and horsetail grows in wet areas, such as on the sides of streams. How Young came upon the idea of substituting one of these plants for Japanese tea is unknown. The taste of neither of these plants is really a substitute for Japanese tea, especially if Young was referring to substituting something for *Camellia sinensis,* the aromatic plant drunk by many whites as "tea." *Ephedra* and *Equisetum* were known to have been used medicinally by Indians.[160] The church members' decision to name plants after their own culture might have been a common practice of any immigrant or settler, however, the practice does not demonstrate cultural sensitivity to Indian tradition.

There were some occasions, according to LDS sources, when the Indians shared their knowledge and wisdom of botanical healing with the whites. One example of Indian women sharing botanical knowledge is found in the diary of William Atkin, the son of Thomas Atkin, a prominent LDS bishop, who tells the following story of his father's cure of a serious injury to his calf due to a dog bite:

> It was impossible to find any medicine that would effect a cure. However, one afternoon two Indian squaws

> were at our home on west Vine Street and as they noticed my father doctoring his leg, and on being told of his having been bitten by a dog and how impossible it seemed to find a cure, they talked together in their own language, and the younger of the two Indian squaws who had a papoose in one of the little carrying cradles gave the older squaw charge of the little papoose and started out up towards one o'clock mountain. In about one hour she returned bringing some wild Indian carrot, a wild plant, which at that time I believe now, is growing in the small canyons and forks of the hills south of Tooele. The leaves of this plant resemble very much the leaves and the entire plant is very much in appearance like the tame carrot. The taste of the root is very bitter and I have known of some people using the root of this plant as a blood medicine. These two Indian squaws took the roots of these plants and after thoroughly cleaning and washing the roots they found some smooth rocks and after they had thoroughly washed and cleaned the rocks they used them as grinders and ground the roots until it was more like a salve, and my father after using this ointment or salve was able to completely cure the dog bite in a very short time. Through his kindness and considerate nature my father had the love and respect of many of the Indians, and although in the earlier days he had been called to ride in a company of armed militia to help protect the early settlers, in later years all was peace between them.[161]

Fresh herb poultices have been used throughout history by traditional healers and nurses[162] for healing wounds. The Atkin story about wild carrot (For more information see Color Insert D) is a good example of the power of the herb not only as an agent of healing for Atkin's wound but also as an instrument of herbal diplomacy that allowed for the exchange of compassion, caring, and healing knowledge and wisdom from the Indian women to a bishop of the church. It is unknown whether the women were taking a risk in sharing their botanical skill, knowledge, and human compassion with a white LDS leader or were acting on behalf of their tribe to increase relations with the whites.

Continuing the Tradition

The Latter-day saints housewives, community nurses, and midwives used botanical therapies extensively in their care of the ill in the mid-nineteenth century. Their healing networks were at certain points in the early history of the community centered on botanical use. Use of botanical therapies in the LDS community did not rely upon the support of the practitioners of the Botanical Medical Movement however. The pioneer LDS nurses and midwives, who had used herbs before they found Samuel Thomson, Wooster Beach, and the Richards brothers, continued their use of herbs well after the success of the Botanical Medical Movement waned. One source stated that the herbal therapies and sweating associated with Thomsonianism were gone from the LDS community in Utah by the 1870s, but there were residues of the practice recorded some thirty years later. Mary Fowler recorded giving a good sweat to a patient with possible pneumonia on November 23, 1899, preparing "herbs to make bitter pills" on December 18, 1899, and gathering medicinal herbs with "Eben and Harry" on July 21, 1900.[163] The LDS nurses had integrated Thomsonianism, Indian herbalism, and other aspects of botanical healing into an expert knowledge base that would survive the emergence of medical technology and the beginnings of institutionalized, hospital-based nursing—at least for a little while.

While botanical therapies may not be included in the present-day LDS nursing curriculum,[164] as they were in the mid-nineteenth century, the botanical healing legacy of the LDS women nurses is part of a history of LDS women's relief work and the "completeness of the beautiful order" envisioned by the prophet.[165] Joseph Smith's sermon to the Relief Society included the statement: "Women were to continue in their exercise of spiritual gifts. . . . Who are better qualified to administer [to the sick] than our faithful and zealous sisters, whose hearts are full of faith, tenderness, sympathy, and compassion. No one."[166] There may be no one better to continue the spiritual tradition of the LDS botanical use than the knowledgeable nurses and midwives of the LDS community, their children, and their students.

Chapter 7

Herbs and the Sisters of Charity and Early American Hospitals

> The greater our charity the greater our participation in this divine light which will inflame us with the fire of Holy Love for all eternity.[1]
>
> —Louise de Marillac, in Sullivan, *Spiritual Writings of Louise de Marillac*

The third group history presented in this chapter discusses the use of botanical therapies by American Sisters of Charity (SOC) nurses. While I knew that the SOC had provided some of the earliest formalized nursing care in America, I was initially unsure about whether or not that nursing care had included the use of botanical therapies. As I began to search, I found that the SOC had used herbs, but there were few records of the specifics of their nursing work in general, let alone their work with herbs. I discovered, however, that the French counterpart to the American SOC, the Daughters of Charity (DOC), and some affiliated organizations had an extensive centuries' long history in the use of herbs in their care of the sick poor. Therefore, while the stories of the nurses of the Church of Jesus Christ of Latter-day Saints and of the Shaker movement originated in America, as did their religious organizations, the history of the use of botanical therapies by the American Sisters of Charity[2] originated in France. This chapter begins then with a brief sketch of the French DOC and their botanical healing traditions as part of the foundational health history context for understanding the use of botanical therapies by SOC nurses during the American Botanical Medical Movement.

Botanical Therapies and the Daughters of Charity

The history of the use of herbs by the French DOC in their nursing service to the sick poor began with the founding of the communities created by Vincent de Paul (1581–1660) in 1625, called the "Ladies of Charity" and in 1633 the "Daughters of Charity." The very first confraternity of women, commonly known as the "*Dames de Charite,*" (1617), was comprised of wealthy society women. Their mission was to "imitate the Divine Savior" by bringing corporal and spiritual nourishment to the sick poor in their homes.[3] Vincent de Paul then founded the apostolic community of *Filles de la Charite,* or the Daughters of Charity (DOC), with an aristocratic French widow, Louise de Marillac (1591–1660), in 1633 as a community of "lay women vowed to apostolic service of the poor."[4] The Daughters of Charity were unusual in that while they did take vows, they were not cloistered. In 1660, Vincent de Paul said that the DOC were not religious "but women who come and go like seculars."[5] He voiced his support for the spiritual role of women in providing healing services in his address to the Ladies of Charity in 1657.

> It has been eight hundred years or so since women have had public roles in the Church. Previously there had been some, called deaconesses, who were charged with grouping women together in the churches and instructing them in the ceremonies which were then in use. However, about the time of Charlemagne, by the secret plan of Divine Providence, this practice ceased and your sex was deprived of any role and has had none since. Now this same Providence has called upon some of you, in our day, to supply for the needs of the sick poor of the Hotel Dieu.[6]

Vincent de Paul's statement, made at a time when the effects of the Inquisition upon women were still apparent, was perhaps, in retrospect, one of the first steps in the formalization of nursing as a profession for women in the Western world. For 300 or more years, during the Inquisition, women healers, in particular midwives and herbalists, risked their lives to help others. They risked being accused of heresy and witchcraft. Wise women healers were suspect, even when trying to relieve the suffering of someone who wished to be healed of being bewitched. The guiding text for Inquisitors, the *Malleus Maleficarum* stated: "Again it is pointed out that the common method in practice of taking off a bewitchment, although it is quite unlawful, is for the bewitched persons to resort to wise women, by whom they are very frequently cured, and not by priests or exorcists. So experience shows that such cures are effected by the help of devils, which it is unlawful to seek; therefore, it cannot be lawful thus to cure a bewitchment, but it must patiently be borne."[7]

The use of healing herbs was scrutinized during the Inquisition for herbs were thought to be the favored source of the "witches' poison."[8] Physicians judged whether or not an illness was caused by witchcraft.[9] Because physicians during the Inquisition period used herbs themselves when caring for patients, the church doctors had to determine whether the way in which an accused person used the herbs was an instrument of witchcraft or genuine medical treatment.

Nursing, in particular, midwifery, during the period of the Inquisition, was often accompanied by fear, confusion, and superstition. Women were perceived as manifesting original sin and inherently prone to working with the devil in any activity, including healing and birthing. Their redemption for the original sin of Eve in the Garden of Eden was, among other penances, suffering pain in childbirth. Midwives often alleviated the pain of childbirth with herbal therapies, yet their care and comfort of laboring women were viewed by Inquisitors as malevolent. The *Malleus* stated: "No one does more harm to the Catholic faith than midwives."[10]

Nurse historian Sioban Nelson wrote: "Care of the sick as a serious and skilled activity is argued to have emerged in seventeenth-century France with Vincent de Paul's Daughters of Charity."[11] The successes of the DOC in caring for the sick poor subsequently inspired the works of other renowned health care reformers such as Theodore Fliedner, the Protestant pastor who in 1836 initiated the German lay order of deaconesses of Kaiserwerth, where Florence Nightingale received training.[12]

The services of the DOC were guided by the *Common Rules of the Daughters of Charity*, which allowed for the nursing of the sick poor in their homes in addition to French hospitals, something not commonly done in seventeenth-century France. The unique charitable work of the Ladies and Daughters of Charity with the sick poor gained the healing women notoriety. The *Common Rules* were first published in 1672 and guided the lives of the DOC until 1954.[13] The DOC nurses were given education and guidance by Vincent de Paul and Louise de Marillac in their spiritual as well as corporal duties to the sick poor. The DOC nurses also learned from physicians. They were encouraged by Vincent de Paul to observe the work of the "city doctors" and then to "do the same"[14] for the sick poor, especially for those in the rural provinces, where the DOC most often worked. The DOC often were the only source of medical services in a community. They were, in essence, the physicians and nurses for the poor. They gave medicines and did the bleeding and cupping treatments popular in that day as part of providing nursing care and comfort.

The French DOC had written guidelines for the care of the sick poor documented and followed since the time of Louise de Marillac. In the early years, de Marillac conducted her trainings through lecture, demonstration, and practice.[15] Her letters, now published in the *Spiritual Writings of Louise de Marillac*,[16] demonstrate that the training of DOC nurses occurred as a result of an oral tradition of mentoring and instruction. For example, de Marillac demonstrated in one of her letters knowledge of infectious disease when she admonished a sister-nurse, "I beg you not to go to visit the sick without rubbing your nose with vinegar and putting some on your temples."[17]

Her writings also demonstrate an extensive use of herbal knowledge employed in her nursing care. For example, one recipe for a purgative "potion" is included in her letter to Monsieur L'Abbé de Vaux in 1641.

> Forgive me, Monsieur, if I take this liberty as well as that of telling you that, if you have not already been purged, I would be pleased to render you this little service by preparing you a potion which I believe should be made up of the weight of three copper coins of senna steeped overnight in a good mixture of refreshing, pleasant-tasting herbs. To this add one-half ounce of cleaned black currants mixed with an ounce of peach syrup (the pharmacist here has given me some that is excellent) or, if this is not available, the same amount of pink rose syrup. However, I believe that you should wait until the pain which is causing the inflammation has subsided completely, or at least for a week, so as not to bring on another attack.[18]

It is not clear from the letter exactly what the man's condition was, but in general it was an inflammatory condition. Black currant berry juice is diuretic and diaphoretic and has been used in people with febrile disease, sore throat, and inflammatory conditions.[19] The French still prepare a liquor called "cassis" from the berry. The herb senna (*Cassia spp.*), which de Marillac recommended as a purgative, is still used today with caution as a laxative and purgative for the large bowel. De Marillac completed her advice with recommending the best time for the patient to take the remedy. Her recommendation to wait to take the senna purgative until an "attack" had passed demonstrated her belief, similar to that of other practitioners' beliefs of the period, in the importance of purgatives.

She was knowledgeable about and instructed other sister-nurses in the administration of purgatives and in bloodletting. "The sisters shall be careful to purge patients and to let their blood only when necessary because of the dangers associated with these procedures. . . . When the patients have an intermittent fever with recurring shivering they shall be purged by a laxative tea. The sisters shall be very careful not to administer any remedies while a patient is shivering or sweating."[20] In another letter, de Marillac recommended a purgative for Vincent de Paul, a mixture of chicory and peach blossom syrups.[21] She also prescribed for him increasing doses of remedies in an attempt to "draw off the heavy fluids" in his body. She wrote: "You could take either 24 grains of cornachin powder or the weight of two écus of senna or a few crystals and some rhubarb in an infusion of our good peach blossom syrup."[22] De Marillac also recommended boiling chicory root and a little bayberry as a quick-acting remedy for Sister Claude's intestinal inflammation. Knowing that herbs, such as a chicory/bayberry decoction, can be very bitter tasting, de Marillac suggested the holistic, spiritual advice of accompanying the remedy with "a remembrance of the bitter drink offered to Our Lord on the Cross."[23]

Louise de Marillac may have learned herbalism through her personal connection with renowned French herbal healer Madame Marie de Maupeou Fouquet (1590–1681). Madame Fouquet wrote a number of books on herbal remedies. De Marillac mentioned the presence of Madame Fouquet in some of her letters.[24] One source reported that every establishment of the French DOC possessed a copy of Madame Fouquet's collection of remedies, first published in 1670.[25]

In addition to Madame Fouquet's remedies, books on botanical therapies were also written specifically for the French Ladies and Daughters of Charity to use in their care of the sick poor. Louis Daniel Arnault de Nobleville (1701–1778), a royal physician, wrote the first edition of *Le Manuel des Dames de Charite, ou Formules de Medicamens Faciles a Preparer* in 1760, as well as subsequent editions. The fifth edition of his work, published in 1765, includes a written dedication to his biological sister, Angelique, a Lady of Charity. He not only dedicates the book to her but also states in his dedication that she is the source for many of the remedies quoted in the book. He wrote in French that the little book was "as much a fruit of her work" as his.[26] These texts and the writings of de Marillac seem to indicate that some, if not all, of the French Ladies of Charity and the DOC had extensive knowledge of the botanical therapies used in nursing care and contributed to the information documented in the herbals used by the nurses.

The French DOC wild crafted their herbs and purchased herbs from local women vendors.[27] In a letter to a sister serving in Nantes, France, Louise de Marillac requested that the sister speak to a Monsieur

Lambert to "put a stop to our sisters going out to gather herbs in the countryside; such high-quality herbs are not needed in the pharmacy. It is enough to have the common and most needed ones."[28] De Marillac demonstrated her knowledge of herb gardening as well in her letter to Vincent de Paul in which she discusses licorice. She wrote: "Licorice is used in making infusions, and I sent you some small bits of it so that you can use it more easily. However, it must be used fresh; only cut what you are going to use, because it blackens quickly. I would not dare boast that it grows in our garden, because so far we have only seen leaves and flowers."[29] And to a DOC she wrote: "I hope that our sister gardeners are hard at work while God is giving us beautiful weather. I would ask them to take special care of the chicory. I am sending you a few nice beans so that, as they are gathered in, you might remember the war. I beg you to tell Sister Francoise that I believe the essence of cinnamon must be placed in the sun like the other distilled waters."[30] The DOC also networked and exchanged herbs. Louise de Marillac wrote to Sister Genevieve in Chantilly: "I would be delighted if you sent me some juniper berries when they are ripe."[31]

The DOC were especially adept at making rose, cherry, and peach syrups and were instructed to "take care to make preserves and syrups at the proper seasons."[32] Some sisters were more than syrup makers, however; they were pharmacists. They prepared the herbal remedies for the nurses to use in their care of the sick. In a letter, Louise de Marillac asked Sister Jeanne Lepintre, who was working at a hospital in Nantes, France, to train a sister who already knew how to "prepare medicines and other remedies to mix compounds."[33] The sister pharmacist was second in authority after the sister servant, who was the head of the hospital, infirmary or asylum; however, the sister servant was to seek advice from other knowledgeable sisters regarding the care of the sick. In particular, the sister servant was to seek advice from the sister pharmacist because she had "better knowledge of the state of the sick."[34]

The sister pharmacist took care of the drugs and utensils used in preparing remedies and made sure that remedies were given at the appropriate times. She also made sure that all of her pots and bottles were kept well covered at all times to preserve the quality of the remedies. She oversaw the work of the sister infirmarian ensuring that the sick were given the appropriate remedies and that the infirmarian did not say anything to sadden the sick. The sister infirmarian had to "be most exact to notice any change or accident which occurs in patients so that she can notify the doctor or the sister pharmacist."[35] The sister pharmacist also was responsible for selling remedies at a cheaper price than the apothecary shops. She kept an account book and was responsible, as were the superioress and the treasurer, for the strongbox and for counting the money taken in.[36]

The making and administering of herbal teas, also known as infusions and tisanes, was a common activity for the Ladies of Charity. Herbal infusions were considered necessary for patients. In the documented Orders of the Day, the French Ladies who served the sick were instructed to "keep a constant watch on their needs such as wood, linen, preserves, infusions, and other necessities."[37] The assistant to the infirmarian administered teas. "The duty of the assistant infirmarian will be to sweep the Infirmary, make the beds, attend the sick in common cases, give them teas and victuals according to the directions of the Infirmarian, in a word, render to the sick any service which their state may require."[38]

However, there was a limit to the authority and freedom the sisters had in providing such a broad range of modalities to the sick poor. The DOC were not allowed to interfere with the livelihood of the French physicians and surgeons. The infirmarian was responsible for ensuring that anyone in a town who had the means to be bled by a surgeon had it done by a surgeon, not the DOC. "Others in need of being bled and Ladies who do not appear to be very sick shall not be bled unless they are well-known by the sister pharmacist, or, at least, not without the advice of a doctor."[39]

The French DOC were so knowledgeable in treating the sick given their understanding of herbs and other treatments, that Louise de Marillac had to counsel them on how to act diplomatically in regard to their knowledge. She wrote to Sister Barbe Angiboust: "Be vigilant so that your experience in treating the sick and your knowledge gained from the doctors do not make you too bold and cause you to jump to conclusions, which prevent you from listening to their prescriptions and obeying any order they might give you. When someone does you the honor of asking your advice, answer with great humility, saying quite simply that you have been taught thus."[40] The foundation for this instruction is found in the sisters' *Common Rules* on obedience, which will be discussed later.

The American Sisters of Charity

While there is ample evidence of the French sister-nurses' knowledge and expertise in the use of botanical therapies, the same cannot be said for the American Sisters of Charity. In general, the SOC nurses did not document their work as did the American Shaker and Latter-day Saints nurses. While the SOC kept exacting accounts of expenditures,[41] there was no instruction from church leadership to the sister-nurses to record nursing or botanical activities as occurred in the Shaker communities. However, information from public records, community records such as patient records from the cholera outbreak in 1832, letters and biographies of the SOC leaders, and two manuscripts of instruction written during the mid-nineteenth century by SOC leaders have been used in this case study to formulate a description of the nursing work, including the botanical therapies used by the SOC during the Botanical Medical Movement. These documents were reviewed in an attempt to discover whether or not the American SOC nurses carried on the tradition of herb use in nursing the sick poor that had been so prevalent in the nursing care of their French counterparts.

The history of the American SOC begins with Elizabeth Ann Bayley Seton. Mother Seton (1774–1821), widow, mother of five, and Catholic convert in 1805, moved to Baltimore in 1808 to establish a Catholic day school under the guidance of a Catholic bishop and priests. In 1809, she founded the Sisters of Charity of St. Joseph's in Emmitsburg, Maryland. Between 1809 and 1841, the SOC opened eleven missions. The work of Mother Seton and the SOC was not without opposition. Mother Seton had converted and begun her Emmitsburg mission during a period when anti-Catholic sentiment was very high. Catholic worshippers such as Mother Seton often were heckled. She was estranged from her Protestant family and friends as a result of her conversion, denied inheritances from her godmother and uncle,[42] and lost her social standing. She was not to be deterred however.

Mother Seton was determined to bring the spiritual teachings and mission of Vincent de Paul, Louise de Marillac, and the French DOC to the United States. Catholic priests such as Rev. Simon Bruté (1779-1839), a friend and spiritual guide to Mother Seton, helped bridge the works of the French DOC and the American SOC. However, during Mother Seton's lifetime, there was some controversy over how much influence the French community would have in the establishment of the community at Emmitsburg. During the period 1810–1812, some of the clergy proposed that the French DOC be brought to Emmitsburg to provide training in the *Common Rules* of Vincent de Paul. The French DOC never came to the United States. Some historians have concluded that this was due to the French government denying them visas. However, there may be other reasons why they did not assist the Emmitsburg community during Mother Seton's lifetime. For example, from Mother Seton's letters, it is clear that she was uncomfortable with the possibility of the French sisters' influence.

Some, including Mother Seton, had concerns that the *Common Rules* that the French sisters would be teaching would preclude Mother Seton from continuing in her leadership role because of her duty as mother to her children. Yet as historian Annabelle Melville concluded: "The issue of the French sisters went beyond the question of Elizabeth Seton's personal position, however. It involved a disagreement over general policy."[43] Mother Seton and her superiors were divided over the American implementation of the *Common Rules*, an issue that would have affected the nursing mission (and, therefore, potentially, the transfer of the French DOC's botanical expertise).

If strictly adhered to, the American SOC would need to fulfill two services as part of their mission: services of charity to the sick poor and education. Mother Seton, while she welcomed the service to the sick poor, argued that the primary focus of the earliest American SOC should be education. Some of Mother Seton's superiors disagreed with her and advocated importing French Sisters to help establish "charitable works" (e.g., nursing). Bishop Flaget, who brought the

Common Rules from France and originally favored the importation of the French Sisters soon wrote to Simon Bruté, "I dread the arrival of the religious women who are to come from Bordeaux. . . . Their hopes will be frustrated. . . . I would wish at least that they be informed in detail of the spirit which reigns in the house at Emmitsburg, of the slight hope of serving in hospitals."[44]

Bishop Carroll and Father Dubois, on the other hand, believed, as did Mother Seton, that the time was not right for a union with the French DOC, and that the rules for the American SOC would need modification. Bishop Carroll wrote that the proposal for the American SOC to merge with the French DOC and their rules, while conforming as much as possible to the Institute of St. Vincent, was "soon and wisely abandoned for causes, which arose out of distance, *different manners, and habits of the two countries*, France & the U.S."[45] Carroll most likely made this statement after assessing the American hospital culture of the early nineteenth century, which was predominantly, if not completely, Protestant. In 1818, Archbishop Maréchal wrote in a report to Cardinal Litta of the Emmitsburg Sisters: "Sisters who live according to the rules of their holy founder, the exception of the modifications demanded by American customs and dispositions. They do not take care of hospitals, nor could they since the administration of these hospitals is Protestant. Their principal work is the pious education of Catholic girls, those of the poor as well as those of the rich."[46]

Therefore, the primary focus of the mission of the SOC during Mother Seton's lifetime was the establishment of schools and care of orphans. According to a letter written by Father Cheverus to Mother Seton, he and Father John Dubois, the first and Mother Seton had known when first moving to the Emmitsburg area with her children and followers, apparently agreed with Mother Seton and Bishop Carroll about "the propriety of your establishment remaining independent from the Sisters of Charity [France] & continuing to be merely a house of education for young females."[47] Melville concluded:

> Although both the Rule of St. Vincent de Paul and the openly-avowed purposes of the St. Joseph's community included educational and charitable work, the

> communities in France at this time were predominantly engaged in charitable activities while the Emmitsburg group was chiefly concerned with the school for girls which was their solitary means of support. There was no question of incompatibility. . . . He [Bishop Carroll] was still convinced in 1814 that while in France "the soul and life of St. Vincent's institution" was attendance on hospitals and the sick, "yet here in America no more can be required of [the sisters] than a disposition of readiness to embrace the charitable duty, if imposed on them."[48]

Ultimately, Bishop Carroll's lead would be followed by the other American-based bishops, and the SOC would be encouraged to establish their own way of life, separate from their European counterparts.[49]

Mother Seton and her supportive superiors seriously questioned the prudence of bringing in expert Catholic French sister-nurses during a period when the "habits and manners" of the United States, as Carroll called it, would not have tolerated the women. Could the "habits and manners" that would not have been receptive to the French DOC have had anything to do with the fact that in addition to being run by Protestants the American hospitals of the early and mid-nineteenth century were run by Regulars, who might have vehemently opposed the French sister-nurses who, over centuries, had developed an expertise in the use of herbs in the care of their patients?

Mother Seton's primary concern was the establishment of the Emmitsburg community. She knew firsthand the dominant position and hostilities of Protestant Americans toward Catholics. She had come from that very culture herself. She most likely also knew, being the daughter of one of the most respected Protestant Regular physicians in New York, the controversy that might occur if her new community of apostolic women, trained by French sister-nurses who had been operating autonomously in society for years—with herbs—entered the Protestant hospital culture of Regulars at the wrong time. It may be possible that Mother Seton had some concern, given the growing medical sectarianism and rivalry between the Regulars and the Botanics that would fully emerge in the 1820s with Samuel Thomson, that the success of her community and its practice of providing hospital nursing might be put into jeopardy if she trained her sister-nurses in the French culture of nursing care that included herbalism. This discussion will be revisited later in this chapter.

Mother Seton did succeed in establishing the community at Emmitsburg, a school, and an orphanage before succumbing to disease, possibly tuberculosis, at age forty-six. After her death, Sister Rose Landry White was elected Mother and Sister Mary Xavier Clark her assistant. Rose White (1784–1841), who had served as assistant to Mother Seton, also nursed Mother Seton's children on occasion and had charge of an orphanage in Philadelphia.[50] Mary Xavier Clark (1776–1855) was mistress of novices from 1827 to 1833 and 1845 to 1854 and was Mother herself from 1839 to 1845. Mother Xavier's "solicitude for the sick knew no bounds; she was always planning for their comfort, any little delicacy sent to her was immediately given to the infirmary."[51]

It was under the guidance of Rose White and Mary Xavier Clark in 1822 that the American SOC were first called to hospital work. At the same time the Botanical Medical Movement and health care reforms were gaining momentum, the SOC were asked to help establish the Baltimore Infirmary (1823), the Philadelphia Almshouse and Hospital (1832), and the cholera hospitals in Philadelphia and Baltimore (1832).[52] The three purposes for founding the hospitals were "pestilence, lack of local hospitals, and requirements of medical education."[53] The presence of the SOC in hospitals made it possible for medical students to receive their clinical experiences. The SOC of Saint Joseph's entered into hospital work in three infirmaries attached to medical colleges. "Their nursing service in the infirmaries filled a twofold need: it supplied devoted care to the patients and contributed indirectly to medical education."[54]

Connecting with the Regulars

The nursing practice of the American SOC was greatly influenced by their relationship with Regular physicians. Foundress

Mother Seton relied primarily on the services of Regular physicians for her own care and for the care of her children. Her father, Richard Bayley (1744-1801), as mentioned previously, was a renowned physician educated in England. He and his brother-in-law, Dr. John Charlton (1731-1801), also a prominent physician in New York, had a successful practice together. After Mother Seton's mother died, Dr. Bayley married the daughter of Andrew Barclay and Helena Roosevelt, whose father was the founder of the Roosevelt dynasty. Mother Seton was raised in a privileged home as the daughter of a wealthy physician who was at the heart of the emerging medical "establishment" in New York. In addition, her sister, Mary, married a Regular, Dr. Wright Post (1766-1828).

Mother Seton's physician father served the military where he had begun controversial scientific work in human dissection. He set up an anatomical laboratory in New York after the Revolutionary War and began his work. The New York Doctor's Riot of 1788 was instigated after one of Dr. Bayley's students poked fun at a group of boys playing in the street by shaking the arm of a cadaver out the window and saying it belonged to the mother of one of the boys. A mob descended upon the lab and would have gone through the Bayley home as well had it not been for the intercession of city leaders.

In the late 1790s, Dr. Bayley, after returning from England, was appointed to the first health office of New York. "Bayley's career and his humanitarianism advanced swiftly, hand-in-hand; in fact, one fed the other. Shortly after his return from Europe in 1790 he had helped organize the New York Dispensary for the benefit of the city's poor. . . . In 1794 Bayley helped reorganize the Medical Society, with his brother-in-law, Dr. Charlton, as head."[55] Bayley also was renowned for his research on epidemics such as croup and yellow fever. He often spent time seeking funding for his research in the Albany and Watervliet, New York, areas, where the Shakers had begun establishing their community twenty years earlier.[56]

Having grown up in a family environment with two influential and talented Regulars, who did have aspirations of helping the poor, it is not surprising that biographical accounts of Mother Seton demonstrate that she relied upon her father and other Regulars, such as Dr. Pierre Chatard, for the medical care of her own family as well as for her followers. There is no mention, however, of Mother Seton or the SOC being attended by water cure, homeopathic, or Botanic physicians. Mother Seton was very good friends with the aforementioned Dr. Chatard, a French physician residing in Baltimore, and his wife. Chatard (1767–1848), an eminent physician, midwife, and ophthalmologist, was a member of the Medical Society of Baltimore, beginning in 1804, and also was a consulting physician to the Board of Health and the Public Hospital in 1812.[57] According to one source, Dr. Chatard immigrated to Baltimore in 1797 from Saint-Domingue, a French colony in the West Indies, with others, including Bishop John Carroll, superior and good friend to Mother Seton.[58]

Mother Seton also was very close to Rev. Simon Bruté, her spiritual guide. Rev. Bruté's maternal aunt, Sister Francoise Le Sanier De Vauhello (1740–1802), was a DOC. Among her missions was the Hospital Saint-Andre at Bordeaux. Rev. Bruté too, had been in health care as an official medical doctor in France before entering the seminary in 1804, after which he moved to Emmitsburg. Rev. Bruté did not practice medicine after attending seminary, which was partly due to a church prohibition against priests shedding blood.[59] As bloodletting played a large role in the practice of the Regulars at that time, Rev. Bruté would have had to make a choice between medicine and joining the ministry. There was continual correspondence between Rev. Bruté and Mother Seton, and he gave the American SOC "the full benefit of his spiritual and intellectual accomplishments."[60] It is quite possible that while he did not practice medicine, he may have taught the American SOC what he knew.

In 1814, Rev. Bruté returned from France to Emmitsburg with his personal library, which included his medical books. His library is housed today at the Old Cathedral Library at St. Francis Xavier Catholic Church in Vincennes, Indiana. The collection contains more than 10,000 volumes of Bruté's original library, mostly books on theology and philosophy, however, there are a number of medical books in the collection. The majority of the books are in French and some in Italian, including works on botany, anatomy, physiology, chemistry, and hygiene. The presence of a single American medical book in the collection, *The American Domestick Medicine, or Medical Admonisher*, written by Horatio Gates Jameson, M.D., an honorary member of the Baltimore Medical Society, may indicate that Rev. Bruté knew about the work and skill of prominent medical doctors in the Baltimore area. He also may have known Dr. Chatard through his association with Mother Seton. While primarily including anatomy and disease information, Jameson's book also includes botanical therapies information about hops, valerian, sage, hyssop, slippery elm, burdock root, sarsaparilla root, sassafras bark, lemonade, and apple water.[61] Jameson wrote: "The hop, which is used in making beer, is supposed to have anodyne properties. It may be used by laying a small bag, containing good fresh hops, under the head of patients; but it is a remedy which I cannot recommend from actual experience."[62]

Hops (*Humulus lupulus*) was not only a very commonly used healing herb but in the early nineteenth century it was fast becoming an important commercial product and source of income for Americans in the eastern United States. (For more information see Color Insert E.) Hops is used in the production of beer. While it is well known for its commercial benefits in urban as well as rural areas, it is possible that physicians, in particular, a Regular such as Jameson, may have been completely unaware of the health benefits of the herb. Rev. Bruté, because of his French and botany background, most likely had some knowledge of botanical therapies, perhaps even of the healing plants found in the United States.

The presence of one book in Rev. Bruté's collection demonstrates that he was, at the very least, aware of the botanical tradition of the French DOC. The Bruté collection includes a very small, pocket-size reference book written in 1767, *Description Abrege des Plantes Usuelle. A vecleurs vertus, leursufages & leurs proprietes. Par l'Auteur du manuel de Dames de Charite & pour server de suite au même Ouvrage. A Paris Chez Debure pere, Quai des Augustrus, a l'Image Saint Paul.* The French translation of this title indicates that this pocket-size herb book was written by the same author who wrote the nurses' botanical manual for the French DOC, the same Louis Daniel Arnault de Nobleville mentioned previously. It is possible, with Bruté's understanding of the French DOC tradition in herbalism and the use of botanicals in the practice of medicine in France and with his strong ties to Mother Seton and the American SOC, that he may have had discussions with and/or provided instruction to the SOC about using botanical therapies in their care of American patients. Is there any evidence in the archives of the American SOC that herbalism was learned from those such as Rev. Bruté, the French sisters, or other healers and physicians in the Baltimore area?

Botanical Therapies and Instruction Books

With the help of French priests such as Father Dubois and Rev. Bruté, the American SOC patterned their nursing services somewhat after the works of their French counterparts. They contracted with hospitals to perform the duties of "corporal care of the sick, spiritual instruction of persons in health and sickness, bleeding, giving remedies, furnishing a proper diet to the patients, maintaining cleanliness, preparing the sick for death, laying out the dead, and providing the means for a decent burial."[63]

The American SOC kept few records describing their nursing work in general, let alone the details of the remedies they used during their nursing missions. They did, however, have a strong oral tradition in which novice sister-nurses were trained by a mentor, often for a year or more. The SOC learned their nursing work from each other, especially from those who had achieved a level of mastery in ministering to the sick poor. There are two instruction books in the SOC archives written by an SOC on the care of the sick that capture the essence of the education the nurses received from their expert mentors. One was written by Sister Matilda Coskery and the other a copy apparently written by a student of Mother Mary Xavier Clark. Both contain some mention of botanical therapies.

Sister Matilda Coskery (1799-1870)

Matilda Coskery (1799–1870) was born in Maryland and joined the SOC in 1829. Her major appointments included the Maryland Hospital in 1833 and Mount St. Vincent's (later known as

Mount Hope) in 1844. Sister Matilda was "Sister Servant" (i.e., Superioress) at the hospitals and asylums in which she worked. According to the records, her teachers were "the Saintly Bruté, Hickey, Mothers Rose and M. Xavier"[64] Sister Matilda was assigned to Mt. St. Mary's Infirmary near Emmitsburg from 1831 to 1833, and Rev. Bruté was at Mt. St. Mary's from 1818 to 1834. Rev. Bruté may have instructed Sister Matilda in medicine, botany, and botanical therapies in addition to issues of the spirit.

Mother M. Xavier referred to Sister Matilda in the following way when speaking with a new sister-nurse in training: "My child, you are going to a saint, study her well, she is a good book for you to read daily."[65] The nurse in training wrote this of her experience: "Before giving me a charge she taught me how to act, what to say and what to expect from those to whom I ministered. . . . She [Sister Matilda] would frequently come when I was preparing drinks for the sick to see how I did it. On one occasion I was preparing toast water for them when she entered, looking at it, she said, smiling: 'take pains with that, and remember for whom you do it. Every thing we do is calculated to raise our heart to God."[66]

Sister Matilda served as a nurse during the Civil War. She wrote about the work of the SOC (by then the DOC) during that war and then returned to the Central House in Emmitsburg, where her service included the instruction of new nurses until she died in 1870.[67] At some point during her service, Sister Matilda also wrote a thirty-eight-page book, *Advices Concerning the Sick,* for the SOC nurses. The original document is not dated. There is internal evidence that Sister Matilda wrote the work during her time at Mount Hope in the 1840s or early 1850s. First, Mount Hope was a hospital for the mentally ill, and much of *Advices* is aimed at instructing the nurse about the patient with mental illness. Second, Sister Matilda devoted two full pages in her book on dressing blisters.[68] The use of blisters was considered a "heroic" therapy used by Regulars, along with calomel, bloodletting, and purgatives. Statistics, such as those gathered at Massachusetts General Hospital, demonstrate that prior to 1850, blisters were often used in hospital treatment, but after that date, heroic modalities such as blistering were much less common.[69] Sister Matilda, as an expert in nursing care, especially of the mentally ill, most likely would have prepared her students for the care of patients undergoing the most current treatments of the time. Therefore, her instruction book probably was written in the 1840s or early 1850s while she was Sister Servant at Mount Hope and while blistering was still a common practice with the Regulars.

Sister Matilda included detailed instructions on botanical applications in her book, such as mustard footbaths and plasters, apple tea, camphor temple rubs, lemonade, flaxseed tea, cabbage leaf dressings, hops tea, and spirits of cayenne pepper rubs.[70] In the "Teas, Tonics, etc." section of her instruction book, as in the two excerpts that follow, Sister Matilda clearly defined the level of authority and autonomy that the SOC nurses had in health care decision making in general and in particular in the use of botanical therapies, such as hops tea:

> Make them strong, & in a clean vessel, have the water boiling—keep them covered while boiling or steaming. When done, strain & cover it. In warm weather do not make too much at a time, & keep it in a cool place. Nurses are often careless in these things, thinking they are only simple matters, thus, they prepare them negligently, & are irregular in giving them—or give them after they are sour & mouldy, & this makes the stomach sick, or getting them irregular does no good. The Dr thinks it is the fault of the tonic & changes it for something stronger, perhaps brandy or some other thing that does real harm—He loses confidence in that tonic, names it to his students and Medical friends, who likewise discontinue it, in all these cases that fall into their hands, some stronger thing is given, when the thing itself was right, <u>in right hands.</u> How often, these, <u>seemingly</u> small things, are the beginnings of the death-bed & in many, many cases, Life and Death is (in) the hands of the nurses, more than in the Physicians.[71]

And in the section on the treatment of "*mania a potu*" (insanity arising from the use of liquor, also known as "delirium tremens"):

> After the Dr has named the kind, quantity and frequency of the opiates & stimulants, there is still much depending on the attendants, as in many cases these remedies increase excitement & shd therefore be discontinued until the Dr. comes again, & telling why these were not given—Hop tea is a good substitute as opiate & tonic; & often serves better than opiates or spirits. Chicken soup is a good remedy, also, because it strengthens them.[72] The office of "Nurse" is one of awful responsibility if its duties be properly considered; for on the faithful discharge of them, will the life of a fellow being, in very many instances, almost exclusively depend. Where there is a Medical Attendant, the duties of a Nurse are reduced to two simple, but highly important rules; the observance of which should be rigidly insisted upon. First, to do every thing that the Physician orders to be done, and this is the strict letter of the commands. Second, for it is fairly to be presumed, that the Physician will direct to the best of his knowledge, whatever he may think is essential to the welfare of his patient.
>
> There are however, exceptions to these remarks, that the Medical faculty admit of, that is; when the nurse is experienced and faithful, and has also shewn herself equal to her duty, she may, and should, withhold medicines, drinks, etc. which she observes acts contrary to the designs or wishes of the Phyn[sic], but this liberty is only to be exercised between his visits, and she should relate to him as soon as he comes of what she has done, & why.[73]

These excerpts from Sister Matilda's book demonstrate that her instructions included exercising autonomy in patient decisions for the good of the patient, especially when the physician was not present. She also demonstrated the importance of nurses' knowledge of botanical preparation and application not only in the care of the patient but also in medical decision making, policy, and procedure, that is, whether certain remedies would continue to be used or not. She emphasized that the nurses' right to the use of botanical remedies affected the accessibility of those gentler remedies to future patients.

Sister Matilda's expert care of the mentally ill included an approach that was extraordinary for her time. She was instrumental in reforming mental health care. She and the sister-nurses were convinced early on of the need of the mentally ill for kindness, relaxation, nutritious food, and a healing environment when the routine care of the insane at the time resembled the care of the incarcerated. The SOC looked upon their patients as "given them by their Divine Master Who has taught all His disciples to look upon even the most neglected and repugnant of men as His brothers and members of His mystical body."[74] The SOC were not alone in their belief about reforming mental health care. Many were beginning to put forth a new philosophy that insanity was no different than physical disease. The physicians attending the 1844 first meeting of the Association of Medical Superintendents of the American Institutions for the Insane in Philadelphia also reached the same conclusion.[75] The sisters had doctors on their resident and visiting staff at Mount Hope Retreat, such as Dr. William Stokes, who were "sympathetic" to the needs of the mentally ill and to the philosophy of the SOC.

Sister Matilda, like the leaders of the French DOC before her, set forth instruction for nurses that ultimately resulted in the establishment of the SOC's reputation as knowledgeable expert nurses in the care of the sick, in particular, in the care of the insane. While the SOC may have learned about patient care from the French DOC and from American and French physicians, they also learned through their own unique experiences. The nursing reputation of Sister Matilda and the SOC was well known by the Regular physicians, who worked closely with them. Dr. Stokes (1812–1893), the house physician for Mount Hope, wrote of the SOC in his report in 1851 the following:

> After an association of nine years with the Sisters of Charity in this work, we express but the settled conviction of our mind, when we say, that in vain would we seek elsewhere to find persons who would so zealously devote themselves to the welfare of the insane—who would practice such complete self-denial in laboring to benefit them—and who would watch, with such untiring patience, by night and by day, over these objects of their care.[76]

Sister Matilda was admired and considered an "oracle" by the physicians, who consulted her about their patients "as if she were an old professor."[77] The expertise of the SOC' nursing care of the insane stemmed from their spirituality and their community's guiding principles, such as charity. Sister Matilda instructed the sisters in their care of the mentally ill that "Now in this misery and despair, it is plain to be seen that the kindest, mildest persuasion is the only course to pursue. You cannot have greater objects for your charity. Let every attendant see in this poor creature a beloved Father or Brother, and act accordingly."[78]

The SOC's expertise also may have been a result of their interaction with a number of sources. In her instructions, Sister Matilda, while not revealing the texts she had read, mentioned that "the best writers on insanity say: that kindness is the main remedy."[79] The SOC also may have learned about the care of the insane from physicians such as Dr. Stokes, who had traveled abroad before working with the SOC to visit "reputable" mental institutions.[80] Dr. Stokes may have visited a Quaker institution in Britain, called the "York Retreat," which was renowned for its use of a treatment for the mentally ill known as "moral treatment." The focus of this treatment was on providing a therapeutic environment, occupational therapy, and a social milieu,[81] a practice similar to that implemented by the SOC. The SOC's therapeutic interventions included patients accompanying them on shopping trips, entertainment such as chess, sewing parties and music, and elevation of patients' self-esteem through encouragement. The SOC took meals with the patients and regulated each patient's diet individually under the guidance of a physician.[82]

In the mid-nineteenth century, the American hospitals for the care of the mentally ill came under scrutiny to assess the validity of accusations of brutality to patients. Mr. W. G. Read, commissioned by the New York State Legislature to visit and report on "institutions managing lunatics" wrote in his report of the Mount St. Vincent Institution (later Mount Hope Retreat) in 1841, after the Retreat had been functioning for two years, that he had had "a very interesting conversation with the Sister who is charged with the direction of the establishment."[83] He outlined the sisters' care of the mentally ill and underlined in his notes his observation that they did not harm their patients or use the more common forms of restraint. He reported that the SOC used a different form of restraint. They preferred, "as far as their circumstances permit, the restraint of their own presence and intercourse to actual bonds."[84] He noted that at times the SOC used a "sleeve" that they had invented to provide gentle restraint for patients, however, that they were trained to dialog with patients as though the patients were "rational beings."[85] Sister Matilda's instructions to the SOC when they had to restrain a patient included "saying to the patient kindly: My dear friend, do not be angry with us for this, you are so out of humour that we are obliged to do this. When you are better, all will be right again. You have fever, makes you do as you do. . . . If you were my own dear Brother, I could not grant it [removing the restraint]—It is because we love and respect you, that we refuse you now."[86]

The SOC were recognized experts in psychiatric nursing in the mid-nineteenth century. In his book on mental illness during the period 1875–1940, Grob stated that the psychiatric nursing of the period he examined was "of course, an example of a specialty that was not especially successful in creating a specific self-identity. This was so partly because of the generalized nature of the work, the inability to define a body of data whose mastery would become a precondition for a specialty, and the female nature of nursing."[87] Perhaps this was true of the late nineteenth century, but it certainly was not the case with the mental health nursing provided by the SOC during the mid-nineteenth century. The SOC, under the guidance of Sister Matilda, provided expert, specialized, and compassionate nursing services.

Mother Mary Xavier Clark (1776-1855)

In addition to Matilda Coskery's *Advices,* evidence of the formal instruction given to sister-nurses can be found in the Marillac Provincial House Archives in St. Louis, Missouri, in a handwritten, pocket-size booklet containing two parts on what appear to be two sets of copied instructions. The first part includes instructions in French, *Instruction pour les Filles de la Charite et les autres Religieuses Hospitalieres en 1796,* followed by the English translation. This was the spiritual instruction that the DOC were allowed to give to the public in France during the French Revolution, when the priests were forbidden to perform their usual duties. The responsibility for ministering to and "instructing" the sick poor fell to the DOC. For example, the booklet contains a copy of the French instructions for the nurse on how to teach the patient to make "good use of his suffering," and how the nurse should instruct the patient in a way so as not to cool his or her spiritual fervor or somehow cause him or her to fall deeper into despair.[88]

The second part of the booklet is entitled "Instruction on the care of the sick. By M. X.," presumably Mother M. Xavier Clark, with the final page dated October 26, 1846.[89] Mother M. Xavier's instruction begins on page thirty-two, with the spiritual instruction that SOC nurses not try to convert patients to Catholicism. Nurses were not to show preference for Catholic patients, and they were not to proselytize. She is quoted as teaching "Her charity towards the body will more easily gain the soul than pressing exhortations."[90] Mother M. Xavier taught the nurses that they should even be careful with confirmed Catholics, because "There are some Catholics who are even worse than infidels and heretics; therefore, an imprudent urging to go to confession might put the person in a passion and even draw from him words of imprecation & blasphemy . . . remember one thing—never begin to speak of religion before you have afforded them all the little relief & comforts you can to the poor body: by these you will find the way to the soul. Your charity to their bodies will aid them to raise their minds to God."[91]

Mother M. Xavier's book also included a reference to the importance of proper preparation and distribution of "remedies." She specifically mentions her personal experience of observing a nurse who misread the label on a bottle of medicine and gave a patient calomel instead of magnesia.[92] She instructed the nurses to purchase "the best" and never get "indifferent things because they are cheap: nor even when given them free cost"[93] when preparing remedies. Mother M. Xavier was known to "go herself to the kitchen to show the Sisters how to prepare little delicacies for the weak and infirm."[94]

There is one reference to the use of botanicals recorded in the booklet. The section in which Mother M. Xavier discusses preparing proper nourishment for the sick poor includes: "I have seen 'tisanes' and other drinks so thick, that it was a real task to take such, especially for a weak stomach."[95] A tisane is "an infusion (as of dried herbs) used as a beverage or for medicinal effects."[96] Like Sister Matilda, Mother M. Xavier is most likely concerned about the proper preparation of the herbal tisanes made by the sister-nurses in the routine care of patients. No specific herbs are mentioned in regard to the tisane preparation, however.

The Health Beliefs of the American Sisters of Charity Nurses

There is evidence in her *Advices* that Sister Matilda supported the use of botanical therapies in the care of patients. But there is no direct evidence that the community as a whole believed that botanical therapies should or should not be used in nursing care during the years of the Botanical Medical Movement, as is found among French DOC records. The health beliefs and nursing practices of the SOC were intimately linked to the spiritual teachings they followed in all aspects of their lives, thus one can only wonder what role herbs might have played given the guidelines, rules, and philosophy the SOC were following in their care. As mentioned, Mother Seton and the American SOC had adopted a modification of the *Common Rules* of the French DOC, which were based on the teachings of Vincent de Paul. Vincent de Paul's early health-related teachings to the DOC nurses were documented in the conference on March 16, 1642, "How to Nurse the Sick."[97] These teachings included foundational health beliefs that were to guide the service of the sister-nurses. First, the DOC believed that in caring for the sick poor they were serving Christ. "The thought that the poor are the members of Jesus Christ was a powerful motive for all to serve them with greater attention and charity than they had hitherto done."[98] The sisters' nursing actions, as demonstrated in Sister Matilda's and Mother M. Xavier's instructions, were guided by their Christian beliefs.

In terms of their own health practices, the sisters also were cautioned against "too much tenderness for self" and mentioning their own infirmities to the physicians of the poor, with whom those with a nursing mission would be working. The rationale for not discussing their ailments with a physician was related to a belief that medical doctors overprescribed. "To mention their slight indispositions to the physician of the poor, and who, by being too ready to give them remedies, might expose them to the danger of ruining their health instead of improving it. They shall not take any medicine, be bled, or consult a physician or any other person of similar profession for this purpose, without the permission of the superioress."[99] Sister Matilda may have been describing the sister-nurses' contribution to physician overprescription when she wrote that a physician, when faced with an adverse reaction of a patient to a tea, quickly changed the prescription for something stronger, "brandy or some other thing that does real harm,"[100] rather than looking into the situation and finding that the nurse had spoiled the tea that had caused the untoward reaction.

The SOC were required by their *Common Rules* not to be eager to put their lives in the hands of the physician who might make their health worse. They also believed that the "health" of the soul was more important than the health of the body, and that illness and suffering were not necessarily bad things for which one needed to seek out the services of a physician. While the purpose of the Regular had historically been to remove a person's illness, the SOC followed the tradition of Vincent de Paul that taught them that "God sometimes sends illness to punish us for our sins and occasionally to afford us an opportunity of showing Him our love . . . God has allowed your body to be ill in order to cure your soul."[101] With this health belief, one would not be as inclined to rush to a physician for fear of illness. The sisters might even have welcomed the spiritual opportunity inherent in illness as a means of atonement.

The DOC and SOC believed that suffering was not necessarily

bad. In a letter to an ailing Vincent de Paul, Louise de Marillac wrote: "I ask your charity to let me know if there is anything else I should do in this matter other than to admire the workings of Providence; to try to make known Its goodness and power; and to believe that it is a good thing to suffer and to await patiently the hour of God in very difficult circumstances."[102] The SOC certainly believed that sickness in someone's life was a teachable moment when the afflicted could be brought to God. "A patient should be able to say, when a Sister leaves his bed side, 'That Sister is more like an angel than a human being: the very sight of her makes me think of God and love him.' A few words of instruction and encouragement said with piety and in a proper manner, will help a poor sick person to bear patiently with his miseries, and bring him perhaps to his duty towards God."[103]

Measured Obedience

In serving the sick poor, the SOC were to minister to the body as well as to the spirit and to "value the salvation of the soul above all earthly things."[104] Therefore, the spiritual guidance of Vincent de Paul and Louise de Marillac, as documented in the *Common Rules of the Daughters of Charity,* was very important to the missions of the American SOC. One of the main rules governing the sister-nurses' care of the sick poor was their vow of obedience. "The rules summoned the Sisters to imitate Jesus in his mysteries, but also to minister to him in others, particularly in the poor. So unified was this world view that to obey superiors was to obey God; to leave scheduled prayers or other activities to serve the poor was, in a memorable phrase, to 'leave God for God'. The means to serve others was principally efficient spiritual and physical service, done with a view to one's own perfection in accomplishing the will of God."[105] Vincent de Paul admonished the sisters: "The principal end of your obedience, my dear Sisters, should be to please God."[106] He taught the sisters that their obedience to their superiors, their rules, and Divine Providence would ensure that they went "straight to God."[107]

While the SOC of the nineteenth century understood the vow of obedience to their superiors, outlined in the *Common Rules* governing their order, which specifically included hospital administrators and physicians, they also knew that they were obedient to God first. Clearly stated in the SOC's Common Rules was that the sisters' obedience to others was secondary to their obedience to God and their vows. Article III of the Regulations for the Society of SOC on obedience stated that the SOC would be

> submitting to their [local priests] orders and advice in everything that is not sinful nor contrary to the rules and practices of the society or to the intentions of their Superiors. . . They will also pay respect and obedience in what concerns the service of the poor to the administrators of the hospitals which may be entrusted to their immediate management hereafter, [and] physicians or other persons who, by their office or out of charity may be concerned in the service of the poor and as nurses, as well as if they are sick themselves. They shall punctually obey, for others as well as for themselves, the prescriptions of the physician in every thing proper to his office *and not contrary to their rules*. They shall also obey in the same manner the infirmarian or nurses given to them, according to the extent of authority given to them by their office or their Superiors.[108]

At times the passion of the sister-nurses in carrying out their mission of caring for the sick poor generated a desire for a level of scientific accuracy and a set of caring ethics that superceded all instruction of and obedience to physicians. One of the most noted examples occurred in 1840 at the Maryland Hospital.

The SOC resigned from their post at the Maryland Hospital and subsequently purchased Mount Hope to begin their own hospital for the mentally ill because of differences with the resident physician of the Maryland Hospital, Dr. Steuart, over the way the hospital was being administrated. "Control of the Institution" had been in the SOC's agreement, and they ultimately became frustrated that they were not allowed to run the daily activities of the hospital in the way they needed to fulfill their spiritual mission. For example, Sister Mary Olympia, Sister Servant of the Maryland Hospital at the time of the resignation, wrote: "We are subjected to much inconvenience from the Patients, without having the Doctor to contend with & if Drunkards can go in & out without the Sister's permission, I think it a very improper place for us to be."[109] Dr. Steuart and the Maryland Hospital administrators refused to allow the SOC the authority they needed to make sure that the hospital was safe and proper for the Sisters and patients. Dr. Steuart's letter, which he wrote to Father Deluol, the negotiator on behalf of the SOC, is a notable representation of the culture of medical dominance that existed in the hospitals in the public sphere in 1840.

> You remark that when the Sisters took charge of the hospital, I promised you that they should have entire control of the Institution. Now, sir, allow me to say, with every feeling of respect for you and for them that I never did make such a concession, it was not in the nature of things to do so, and I do assure you that the Sisters have never laid claim to any such extent of power, & I believe would not accept, if offered to them. "To have entire control over the Institution" would be to dispense with the Board, the Priest, and the Physician, which would be an absurdity—I promised (and to the letter have I fulfilled my promise) that they would have entire control in the Domestick affairs of the House, and should participate largely in the moral management of the patients, in fact exercising any degree of moral influence that did not directly conflict with medical principles which of course must always have precedence; when the Sisters came to the Hospital, they were as children, unacquainted with everything relating to lunacy, and were of course guided by myself and the medical gentlemen who assisted me at the time. As they grew more experi-

> enced, I allowed them and encouraged them to exercise more moral management. It was then for the first time I discovered that difficulties would occur between them and the Regular Physician of the house, and I said how difficult it would be to arrange to the satisfaction of both parties this matter—they "even the best of nurses and attendants," and yet a medical man's services could not be dispensed with; medical dignity requires certain privileges and no medical man of character will dispense with these rights—difficult however as the last is, I have endeavored to meet it, scrupulously. As regards my promise to you when they came to us, and correctly as it regards what I think due to Science and humanity, which last has always been the end and aim of my efforts.[110]

It is interesting that Dr. Steuart referred to the early sister-nurses who began the work at the hospital in 1823 as "children" instead of novice nurses. He used a paternalistic approach in the negotiation process and also clearly took the credit for having trained the SOC. By 1840, the SOC were not novice nurses. At the time of the writing of the letter, they had been a presence at the Maryland Hospital for seventeen years.

By the 1840s, the SOC were gaining the public's trust, and their reputation for their nursing skills and compassion was growing quickly. When they left Maryland Hospital, many of their patients followed them. Hannefin wrote: "The withdrawal of the sisters from Maryland General Hospital in 1840, to form a psychiatric hospital of their own in which they could determine policy, marked a turning point in the history of hospitals in the United States."[111]

The Reputation of the Sisters of Charity

The SOC's reputation grew rapidly during the mid-nineteenth century. The skills and courage of the American SOC were first recognized nationally during the cholera epidemic of 1832. William

Stewart, the mayor of Baltimore, wrote of the SOC who served in the hospitals during the cholera epidemic: "To those invaluable Sisters of Charity, whose benevolent conduct has been of such essential utility in alleviating the horrors incident to the fatal epidemic, which a short period since, raged in our city . . . in behalf of the citizens of Baltimore, to express our warmest gratitude and deepest sense of obligation for those services which were given without compensation—thereby leaving us doubly your debtors."[112] In his letter, published in the local newspapers, Mayor Stewart acknowledged each of the Sister-nurses who had served in the temporary cholera hospitals by name. He also set aside $600 to create a monument to commemorate two of the SOC, Mary George Smith and Mary Frances Boarman, who died during their service in Cholera Hospital Number 3.[113]

During the Civil War, the SOC became highly favored as experienced nurses who served both Union and Confederate wounded soldiers. Physicians, wounded patients, government officials, and growing members of society moved beyond their prejudices and fears of Catholicism after witnessing the charitable works of the SOC. By 1869, Beecher and Stowe, in their very popular advice book *The American Woman's Home*, wrote:

> Are the Sisters of Charity really better nurses than most other women? I asked an intelligent lady who had seen much of our military hospitals. Yes they are, was her reply. Why should it be so? I think it is because with them it is a work of self-abnegation, and of duty to God, and they are so quiet and self-forgetful in its exercise that they do it better, while many other women show such self-consciousness and are so fussy! Is there any reason why every Protestant woman should not be trained for this self-denying office as a *duty owed to God?*[114]

Protestant female nurses, such as those under the supervision of Dorothea Dix, a health care reformer, had "little or no experience, were disorganized, or were too regulated by Dorothea Dix."[115] Dix, in the 1840s, conducted surveys of the treatment of the mentally ill in hospitals, jails, and almshouses in the United States, and she was subsequently commissioned to be superintendent of army nurses in 1861. She was known to have "a deeply religious nature, increasingly influenced by Unitarianism."[116] She spent eighteen months in the home of a wealthy Unitarian merchant in England while she recuperated from a severe illness and had even been a governess in the 1820s for Unitarian leader William Channing. She conducted her surveys of the neglect of the mentally ill with the "blessing of Channing."[117]

Dix knew Dr. Stokes and knew of the work of the SOC at Mount Hope. She included Mount Hope as one of two successful facilities in her report of the treatment of the mentally ill in the state of Maryland;[118] however, she was notably anti-Catholic. A huge "controversy erupted when she refused to accept qualified nuns and other members of religious sisterhoods"[119] as army nurses. By the 1860s the reputation of the SOC was well known, especially among physicians and surgeons. Doctors in the field wanted the SOC and others to serve with them, and so they complained. In 1863, the secretary of war granted the surgeon general the power to appoint nurses as well as Dix.

Dix perceived the physicians' support of the SOC as the result of the SOC's behavior toward the physicians. Nelson wrote: "Paradoxically, nursing nuns were criticized by Dorothea Dix and her nurses for kowtowing to medicine, whereas they were opposed in France for refusing to recognize medical authority as supreme."[120] Nurse Mary Livermore wrote in her personal narrative of the Civil War that a surgeon told her the reason for requesting Catholic nurses was that "Your Protestant nurses are always finding some mare's-nest or other that they can't let alone. They all write for the papers . . . and directly we are in hot water."[121] The surgeons liked the Sister-nurses because they did not report problems with the care of the soldiers to the papers. While the American SOC tried to build and maintain relations with physicians, they did not "kowtow" to them. While Dix and others may have known of the SOC's vow of obedience to their superiors, including physicians, they did not seem to understand that their obedience only went so far.

Partnering with Regulars

During the life of Mother Seton, the SOC visited the sick poor in their homes as needed. Mother Seton wrote to her friend, Eliza Sadler, in 1810 that "every occasion to visit the sick is embraced, but the Villages round us are not very extensive."[122] However, the majority of the American SOC's early nursing work took place in the hospital or institutional setting. Because the hospitals were not only physician-dominated cultures but also were dominated by Protestant administrators, the SOC would have had to have been especially tactful upon their entry into the public domain of the hospitals. There is no specific indication in the archives that the SOC made a decision to partner closely with the Regulars; however, it is remarkable that there is no mention in all of the SOC documents reviewed for this study, of the use of, or interaction with, any health care provider other than a Regular physician. There is no mention of water cure physicians, midwives, or botanical practitioners by Mother Seton, her family, or the SOC and their patients. There is evidence in Thomsonian records that Thomsonianism was not foreign to Baltimore, however. In 1834, at the third national Thomsonian convention, held in Baltimore, a resolution was passed "boycotting regular drug and apothecary stores."[123] It is quite possible that the SOC nurses, who would have frequented apothecaries for the medicines needed in their work, might have, at the very least, been aware of the work of the Thomsonians.

The SOC supported the work of the Regulars in return for a place to carry out their mission, which historically had been linked to hospital care. This was demonstrated in 1849, when the Sisters opened a hospital in Buffalo, New York. The regulations for the hospital, published in a New York City paper, included: "No questions shall be made as to what the applicant believes on matters of religion. . . . For the sick who can pay, and desire private rooms, the charge will be $4.00 per week; moderate extras would be required for extraordinary attendance, or costly prescriptions. This class of persons may select any *regular* physician to attend: in conjunction with the attendance they will pay their physicians according to the rules of practice."[124] And of the new St. John's Hospital in Milwaukee, Wisconsin, the

Catholic Almanac recorded: "As the Sisters of Charity are to be the only nurses and attendants in the house, none need fear the absence of sympathy and eager vigilance. . . . Patients may call in any *duly authorized medical man* they please, but all food and medicine must be administered by the sisters."[125] This statement leaves it open to interpretation as to whether they meant any male Regular physician or only in this specific context.

Did Mother Seton's health beliefs in the use of the Regulars, as demonstrated by her personal health choices and close friendships, influence the health practices of her followers? There seems to have been some incongruity in the messages given the SOC about their relationship with the Regulars. On the one hand, the SOC's *Regulations* stated that they should avoid the Regulars for their own care, because they may cause more harm, and yet they worked closely with them, and the evidence is equivocal about whether they used the services of different types of healers. It seems likely that the SOC chose to work within the public sphere of the Regulars to introduce their mission to the public and to use an integrative approach to choosing modalities that was perhaps so subtle (as demonstrated in Sister Matilda's writings) so as not to concern their physician colleagues. Understanding and diplomatically respecting professional boundaries as mentioned previously, had been part of the nursing education and professional culture of the SOC and DOC, beginning with Louise de Marillac.

Sister Matilda, who held botanical knowledge, did not align herself with the Botanical Medical Movement. It would have been out of character for an Emmitsburg Sister-nurse to purchase a Thomsonian patent the way nurses in the Latter-day Saints or Shaker communities did. However, the records demonstrate that making a simple herb tea or a poultice was an acceptable practice for an SOC nurse. It was in fact a part of the nursing tradition of the SOC, the DOC, and the Ladies of Charity. Perhaps the SOC, whose focus was first and foremost their spiritual mission, believed that the integrative, culturally diplomatic course to follow, especially since their desire was to work in hospitals, as had the French DOC, was their rule of obedience to physicians and administrators as closely as possible, and with the discretion as taught by Sister Servants such as Sister Matilda, to use their knowledge of herbs and diet dating back to Louise de Marillac to help patients when they knew that they would benefit from the SOC's modality.

The patients, the sick poor, were the focus of the SOC's mission. While they supported, served, taught, and even hired the Regulars, they also knew very well from listening to their patients and from their own keen observations that the quality of the Regulars' practice of medicine at the time was less than desirable. The following account from the SOC's work during the Civil War not only includes evidence about the sentiment of the public toward the Regulars and the SOC but also demonstrates that the threads of evidence that the SOC used botanical therapies continued at least into the late nineteenth century. Again, the herb hops is at the center of the story. Sister M. Florence O'Hara (1827–1906) of St. Louis reported the following:

> I was accustomed to visit every evening a tent, that was a few yards' distance from the Hospital, where the gangrene and worst wounded cases were put_ One evening I found a poor man (whose hand from the wrist had been amputated) suffering very much, the arm being somewhat inflamed __ he complained to me that the Doctor had that morning ordered a hop poultice, and that he did not get it __ I called the nurse and wound dresser, to inquire why the Doctor's orders had not been attended to __ They told me that there were none in the Hospital __ that the steward had gone to town that morning before they knew it, and that there was no other opportunity of sending to town that day __ I immediately sent across the yard to the Bakery and got some hops and had the poultice put on. The poor man was surprised—the Sisters he said, found ways and means of relieving every one __ and those who made profession of the business, did not even know where to look for them. They would rather apply to the Sisters in cases where they could do so, than to

> the Doctors __ so that we had to encourage them to have confidence in the Doctors.[126]

Patients' preferences for the SOC were nothing new. In 1832, Rosina Quinn, an SOC, wrote of the cholera epidemic that poor people attacked by cholera "begged to be taken to the Sisters, as they thought they would prevent the Doctors from trying experiments on them."[127] By the time of the Civil War, the SOC had achieved their goal of finding ways to nurse the sick poor in America—their work and reputation had become linked in the minds of Americans to the care of the poor.

Nursing the Sick Poor

The spiritual mission of the DOC and the SOC, since the inception of the community by Vincent de Paul, was serving the poor. When the DOC began their mission in France, the *Common Rules* were explicit; the Ladies of Charity and Daughters of Charity were not allowed by law to care for the rich, because they would be interfering with the livelihood of the physicians and surgeons who worked with those who could pay. The *Common Rules* did state the following exception: "If, however, in pressing need, a physician or surgeon cannot be found in the place, they [the DOC] may bestow even on rich persons the usual relief which they give to others, provided however, the poor be first served."[128] While the SOC's nursing service may have been rendered at no charge, their modest living expenses and supplies and medicines had to be paid. Yet the missions suffered, because unlike the education missions, where tuitions were expected, when payment was requested for nursing care, the SOC's motives often were scrutinized and criticized.[129]

The SOC themselves took a vow of poverty. Their *Common Rules* included spiritual guidelines to be followed when they were sick. "The Servants of the Poor ought not to be better attended than their masters, and that it is a great blessing to suffer something for the love of God, who deigns to try their patience in order to increase their merit."[130] The type of health care one received in France and in the

United States was becoming more and more associated with one's economic status, with attendance by the Regulars when one was sick being associated with wealth; therefore, because the sisters had vowed poverty, they were to content themselves when they were sick with the common treatments rendered to the poor. This was yet another reason for the Sisters to avoid the use of a physician. It is not exactly clear how the SOC defined "common treatments." There is no delineation in either of the two instruction books by Coskery or M. Xavier Clark. Could the common treatments the American poor received have routinely included botanical therapies, such as a hops poultice, concocted by the SOC in their pharmacies and kitchens the way their French counterparts had done? Did the SOC and their patients think of herbalism as a lesser form of medicine used only by the poor? In addition to their French-based botanical instruction, did any of the Sister-nurses ever have cause or opportunity to learn botanical healing from American Indians, as did the Shaker and Mormon nurses?

No records were found in the Emmitsburg archives that could answer these questions or describe the relationship between the SOC and the American Indians, perhaps because many of the Indians had already moved out of the Baltimore area or had intermarried. One source said that, in general, Sisters of the religious orders, "despite their intention to work among native non-Christians, all too often ended up serving white settlers in America, Africa, Asia, and the Pacific Islands."[131] However, later in the nineteenth century, in 1858, Mother Xavier Ross, of a separate community of Sisters of Charity, met a Jesuit missionary, Father Peter DeSmet, who arranged for fourteen sisters to relocate to Leavenworth, Kansas, to work among the Indians.[132] There may be additional records of botanical or health-related exchanges between the SOC and the American Indians after the period studied here.

Integration of Remedies

The pioneer work of the early SOC nurses was by no means easy, but the nurses' spirituality sustained them. Sister of Charity Juliana Chatard (the granddaughter of Dr. Pierre Chatard) recorded:

"Our Hospitals were often also extremely scarce of the necessaries of life, but we thanked our dear Lord that our Sisters seemed not to feel their own privations if they could obtain something for the sick, wounded, and starving members of our Jesus. . . . For our own table, rough corn bread & strong fat bacon were luxuries provided the dear sufferers were better served. As for beverage, we could not always tell what they gave us for coffee or tea, for, at one time it would be sage or some other herb, roots, beans &-e [& etc.] &-e [& etc.].[133] Their spirituality also sustained numerous patients. An account of a male patient who came to Mount Hope for help demonstrates the effects of the ministry of the sister-nurses. The patient was Catholic but had not received the Sacraments for seven years. Nothing the doctors did to try to save the man's life helped him. One of the sisters (most likely Sister Servant Matilda Coskery) is recorded as having said to him: "Then it is no wonder that you cannot be cured, for in some cases, the peace of the Soul is absolutely necessary for the welfare of the body."[134] After the rebuke, the man resumed his spiritual practice and is said to have lived, mystifying his physicians.

The American SOC nurses played an important role in saving the lives and promoting the health of mid-nineteenth-century Americans. They used a subtle and an integrated, diplomatic approach in their caregiving, working with the remedies of the Regulars as well as with the simple remedies, such as herbal teas and topical remedies passed down to them through their women's cultural network, which included nursing traditions, education, and spiritual writings. Sister Matilda led the way in carving out the autonomous practice for which the SOC became well known. She and the other SOC wove their own spiritual healing tapestry. For example, while both American Regular and Botanic physicians favored the use of emetics in the nineteenth century, Sister Matilda disagreed. She wrote: "Fevers of all kinds frequently are attended by sick stomach, or even vomiting, and the nurse too often gives an emetic as the cure, which nearly always does great harm to the sick."[135] She wrote about the "abuses" of sweating, a common remedy of Thomsonians and health care reformers, for the cure of fever, and she recommended that the SOC nurses "avoid having sweating and purging at the same time."[136] She was just as likely to instruct her students to use small amounts of calomel or to apply leeches as she was to recommend purgatives, hops tea, or mustard plasters.

The focus of the SOC was primarily their spiritual mission rather than the modus operandi and the politicking and positioning of medical sects during the American Botanical Medical Movement. Louise de Marillac summed up the goal of the Daughters of Charity in their care of the sick in her statement: "Nevertheless, my dear Sister, we are obliged to satisfy everyone. . . . We must respect and honor everyone."[137] While she was referring to honoring the rich and the poor, her philosophy was clearly emulated in many aspects of the DOC's and the SOC's spiritual lives, including their work in nursing. The American SOC were concerned with serving God in the sick poor, and if herbs could help them provide a better service, then they used them. However, nothing, including herbs, was as important to the Sister-nurses as fulfilling their underlying mission of charity. Matilda Coskery exemplified this in her instruction to her nursing students when she wrote: "The great St. Francis de Sales cured the most violent, by patience, kindness, and prayer. . . . We see the fruits of kindness, for (it) is, and forever will be, the remedy of remedies."[138]

HARVESTING HISTORY—STAGE III

PROCESSING

In many ways, the success of women nurses entering hospital work in the late nineteenth century, and to a degree gaining authority in this one sector of the public sphere, can be attributed to the success of the American Sisters of Charity (SOC) as well as other religious orders. The culture of nursing in America has since the late nineteenth century become intertwined with the hospital culture that historically was the domain of the Regulars and administrators. The most common workplace for nurses in the twentieth and twenty-first centuries has been the hospital. Nurses are usually portrayed by the media as hospital workers rather than as practitioners in private practice, community caregivers, or health care leaders and policy makers. Many nurses realize these roles, and yet the present perception of the professional nurse remains that of being an assistant to a physician or hospital worker.

The first step in processing any history of women nurses in the mid-nineteenth century is to shift one's cultural perception of nurses and nursing care to the sociocultural context of mid-nineteenth-century America. The mid-nineteenth-century hospital was not the focus of nursing care during the period. Health care and nursing were still very much a fundamental part of community culture. The history of the contribution of women nurses to the Botanical Medical Movement in the mid-nineteenth century must be processed or reviewed through the cultural context of the communities and individuals served. The contribution of the women nurses is found in the role they played in relationship to others who together ultimately created and defined the cultural phenomenon now known as the "Botanical Medical Movement." Their botanical contribution also can be assessed in terms of the commitment to and expression of herbalism found in the stories of individual women and communities.

Sifting and sorting through the history harvested from the records of women nurses, such as the Shakers, the Latter-day Saints, and the Sisters of Charity, we find some similarities and differences in terms of participation in what has been already historically defined in the history of the mid-nineteenth-century public sphere as the "Botanical Medical Movement." Similarities and differences also occur in the expression of herbalism when comparing nurse group to nurse group and nurse group to Regulars and Empirics. In essence the nurses of the mid-nineteenth century were themselves Empirics. After reviewing the histories presented here, they also perhaps fit the definition of their own sect of health care as well, which would have been perceived as an anathema by anyone who believed that the Regulars should have social and cultural authority and economic monopoly.

Few histories of women sectarian groups of the early and mid-nineteenth century had been researched until the last decade or so. In an extensive historical survey of women in health care and medicine in the United States, Naomi Rogers wrote: "Women sectarians'stories have been mostly left out of women's medical history, even by feminist historians anxious to show how women's rights activists supported women's medical education"[1] in the public sphere. There is a historical pattern of equating sectarians, especially Botanics or herbalists, with the "unorthodox," the "Empirics," the "others," "witchcraft," and even "quackery," therefore, rising health professionals often have attempted to put historical distance between themselves and those of perceived lesser authority, power, and knowledge. The sociocultural tension between the orthodoxy and sectarians has not abated, even to the present day. Occasional remnants of the alleged connection between the use of herbs and witchcraft can be found in current American health care literature.[2] The power of the mid-nineteenth-century orthodox or Regular physicians, however, was a function of the culture of the public sphere. And it is the public sphere of which so much health care history has been produced.

If one studies the health care culture of the domestic sphere, then one is, in essence, associating with the unorthodox. Feminist historians who have studied forgotten women healers who have broadened the definitions of health and healing to be able to include the stories of women in the domestic sphere have been described as taking an "antiestablishment position."[3] Regarding this feminist position of studying the past, Rogers wrote: "Sectarians and critics of regular medicine became not cranks or quacks but insightful critics of the relations between medicine and society, medical therapy and science."[4] This examination of health care in the domestic sphere, specifically the use of botanical therapies by women nurses, is a study of just one aspect of an emerging American health care culture. The stories of the women are best processed within their cultural context when the biomedical culture that today represents the "establishment" was forming and, therefore, had a different meaning for the nurses.

The themes that have come to light as a result of the sifting and sorting of the contribution of mid-nineteenth-century nurses to the American Botanical Medical Movement, described in Stage II, are processed in this final stage of the historical harvest from the cultural perspective of the American women of the period. Just as an herb is processed according to its constitution, so too, shall the women nurses' stories be treated here. In processing the calendula flower, the delicate petals of the flower head are dried whole on an open rack in a quiet, dark room where they will not be blown away by a sudden breeze. Hefty horseradish roots are washed, scrubbed as one would scrub a carrot, cut into small pieces, and dried in an oven to facilitate uniform drying. Like herbs, the processing of women nurses' history must take place in accordance with the historical constitution, in this case, the appropriate cultural context.

CHAPTER 8

THE INTEGRATION OF THE SPHERES

Science now declares the feminine principle to inhere in plants, rocks, gems, and even in the minutest atoms.[1]

—Matilda Joslyn Gage, in Donovan, *Feminist Theory*

The nursing histories of the American Sisters of Charity, the Latter-day Saints, and the Shakers, indicate that women, in particular, nurses, played an important role during the Botanical Medical Movement of the mid-nineteenth century. Their roles, like their medical colleagues, were in no way uniform and were influenced by the culture and health beliefs of their local communities as well as their religious practices. It was not only the public sphere leadership of the Regulars and the Botanics, such as Thomson and Beach, and health care reformers that influenced the health beliefs and practices of American citizens. The industrialization and urbanization of the United States contributed significantly to the changing health beliefs and practices of Americans about whether they rejected the emerging practices of the Regulars' medicine or integrated the Regulars' health beliefs and practices with traditional healing practices, such as botanical therapies. American industrialization during the mid-nineteenth century took its toll on the physical constitutions of its citizens. Volume 5 of the *Medical and Surgical Report of 1860* concluded that "factory conditions, rapid growth of urban populations, and the increased tempo of industrial life" had a detrimental effect on the constitutions of many Americans, causing them to be no longer able to "withstand the former heroic medication."[2]

In addition, local leadership of the nurses within the broader domestic sphere also influenced peoples' health care decisions, beliefs, and practices and was ultimately critical to the success of the Botanical Medical Movement and other health care reform during this period. Within the history of nurse herbalism, explicit examples of the scope of herbal integration exhibited by the women nurses of the period can be found. The mid-nineteenth-century professional nurses presented here not only exemplified the way to integrate multiple health modalities, including herbs, but they also exemplified how, as women and as cultural-herbal diplomats, they could move within and among the cultures of the public and domestic spheres to sustain and promote cultural understandings related to health, caring, and nursing. Their ability as herbal diplomats typifies the activities of the larger movement of cultural feminism of the period.

The way in which each group of women nurses served its communities, and how each group demonstrated its herbal diplomacy, was unique. This chapter compares the histories of the three groups of nurses and their practice of herbal integration during the Botanical Medical Movement. Ample historical evidence exists of these American women's significant contributions to the Botanical Medical Movement during the period 1830–1860. The nature of that contribution, which goes beyond the simple task of using herbs or applying botanical systems, such as Thomsonianism, in the care of patients, is reviewed in this chapter based on five themes: botanical expertise, herbal diplomacy, the healing network, nurse autonomy, and the integration of the spheres.

Nurse-Herbalists' Expertise

From personal diaries, ladies' journals, newspapers, advice books, and, most importantly, from receipt books, it is clear that the women of the period had knowledge of the use of herbs in promoting health and healing. It also is evident that they were familiar with the philosophies and practices of health care reformers and sects such as water cure, Grahamism, and Thomsonianism. In addition, from Shaker infirmary records and the nursing instruction manuscripts of the Shakers and the Sisters of Charity, we also find that the women nurses expanded upon the "normal" domestic role of women as sickroom manager, family caregiver, and herbal medicine maker to that of identified community healing expert, whose instruments of caring most often included botanical therapies, though not exclusively.

How representative the sample of nurses studied here is of all the nurses of the period regarding their botanical expertise is unclear. In light of the evidence from the Sisters of Charity archives, that nurse herbalism extended back to the seventeenth century, it is probable that many, if not all, European-American nurses of the period 1830–1860s used herbs in their service. It also is likely that nurses in the more rural areas of the northeastern United States, such as the Shakers, had greater access to herbs and, therefore, may have been more inclined to use plants found in their local environments for healing work in their communities.

The three groups of nurses reviewed here are community-focused caregivers—community health leaders, educators, health facility managers, and healers, who often were "set apart" in their calling to serve humanity. Their service was not just an extension of their roles as wives and mothers, as some historians have speculated of nurses preceding the influence of Florence Nightingale and the institutionalization of American nursing education in 1873. In fact, after joining their communities, the Shaker and Sisters of Charity nurses were neither wives nor mothers. The women described here were, by the definition put forward here, "nurses." They were dedicated professional caregivers, recognized by their nineteenth-century communities as experts in caregiving, many of whom also had expertise in the application of botanical therapies. This expertise is explicitly revealed in the writings of Shaker nurse Prudence Morrell, Sisters of Charity nurse, Matilda Coskery, and LDS midwife, Patty Sessions.

Receipt and instruction manuscripts, histories, and diaries of the three communities during midcentury show that the knowledge of botanicals used in domestic practice by these American women was not marginalized by the nurse experts in order to identify themselves as "professionals," as had occurred with Regular physicians. The nurses continued to use remedies, even simples such as onion poultices prepared in their kitchens, to help their patients. No specific record exists of a decision per se to use herbs in nursing. It is clear, however, that the nurses studied here not only used herbs in caregiving but were recognized for their expert understanding and experience in the use of herbs.

An expert in nursing is defined by nurse theorist Patricia Benner as one who has much experience, has an "intuitive grasp" of how to act in a particular situation, and demonstrates a proficiency that is fluid and flexible.[3] There are any number of examples in the Shaker infirmary records, the LDS nurse diaries, and the Sisters of Charity instruction manuscripts in which the nurses demonstrate, or are encouraged to demonstrate, an intuitive, expert approach in the choice and use of herbs. One of the clearest examples is the excerpt in Sister Matilda's *Advices*, in which she admonishes the nurse to use hops tea instead of opiates or spirits[4] when she thinks it necessary. The SOC also used hops in poultices, demonstrating the expert knowledge and flexibility of using one plant in multiple ways. It is not uncommon for knowledgeable experts in herbalism to be able to use a single plant in multiple ways for different health concerns such as these nurses did. As experts, the nurses had an intuitive grasp of the process of the application of herbs and a larger caring repertoire from which to draw because of their ongoing dedication to improved health in their communities. These women nurses had wisdom and experience in the integration of herbs in their care of patients and demonstrated their expertise even when using common remedies also used by housewives.

To the present day, historians at times diminish the importance of nineteenth-century women's use of botanical therapies in self-care and domestic care as demonstrated in statements such as, "As can be seen from the kinds of herbs used, most remedies could neither help nor hurt the patient."[5] This statement not only underestimates the herbal expertise of women and nurses, it also is incorrect. Even the simplest of remedies, if used incorrectly or inappropriately, could harm, and the nurses knew it. Nurses and housewives also knew that the herbal remedies used in domestic care were very helpful. These remedies supported, if not extended, the lives of many nineteenth-century Americans, even those who were reluctant to subject themselves to heroic therapies and would have continued to suffer adverse effects had it not been for the restorative benefits of botanical therapies.

In addition to herbal applications, the Shaker nurses also showed their unique herbal expertise in the production of remedies of exceptional quality for the public market. Their expertise in using their own products for therapeutic applications with their patients was referenced by the brethren in the marketing of Shaker herbal products. The LDS midwives, with their years of expertise in nursing and herbalism, held positions of authority next to their Thomsonian physician colleagues in the Council of Health. And while it is not entirely clear as to the depth of application the SOC made in regard to botanicals, they had access to their French Sisters' centuries of herbal expertise, and they did use that expertise, herbal teas in particular, in the care of patients. Given the SOC's humility and obedience, and given the possible biases against botanicism by the Regulars administering the institutions in which Sisters of Charity nurses served the sick poor, it is possible that the American SOC, even if they possessed as much botanical knowledge as their French counterparts, would not necessarily have spoken freely of it. The SOC, since the time of Louise de Marillac, had been cautioned not to upstage the physicians with whom they worked.

The nurses' expert use of botanicals was supported by their communities and their religious beliefs and practices. The most striking example is the *Doctrine and Covenants* of the LDS nurses, in which it is specifically stated that herbs should be used by the LDS nurses, and that the nurses and midwives set aside by the prophet, Joseph Smith, should nurse the community with herbs. The Shakers were chastised for their overreliance on any treatment outside of faith healing, but plants were accepted for their utilitarian value, and, therefore, herbs, as mild medicines, were accepted more often than the medicines of the Regulars. The SOC were avowed to a life of poverty and were to receive no better health care than their patients, thus it would seem probable that herbs, identified by the French DOC as medicine for the sick poor, would have been good enough both for the American SOC and their patients. All in all, however, all three groups clearly put their faith in their spiritual practices before any healing modality, including herbs.

The three histories of nurses presented here were also, in some cases, histories of religious community life. Women involved in churches in the nineteenth century were encouraged to perform benevolent nursing services for the sick poor. The women in the LDS and SOC communities were no exception. The Shaker nurses, however, tended their own communities, and no records were found regarding the provision of services for those of the "world." In some instances, there was a direct overlap between herbalism and religious culture in the communities. For example, the LDS nurses used blessed olive oil in anointing the sick. All three groups used prayer in their nursing interventions, thus it would be interesting to explore whether herbs were considered by the nurses and patients more powerful when used in conjunction with prayer.

The nurses, perhaps unintentionally, or perhaps because of their devotion to their spiritual missions as the primary focus of their lives, were able to act as integrators, forging the amalgamation between the domestic and public spheres in the realm of healing. They also were herbal diplomats who navigated the sociopolitical conflicts that were peaking in the field of medicine between the Regulars and the Botanics, often integrating interventions from both medical philosophies prevalent in the public sphere, as well as the common interventions from the domestic sphere in order to bring the best care to their patients.

Herbal Diplomacy

In all three nurse groups a strikingly similar "message" was found, cautioning against reliance upon the medicine of the Regulars. Historians have recognized that public confidence in the medical practices of the period was low, thus preparing the environment for the introduction to both the public and domestic spheres of new sects of health care, such as Thomsonianism. However, if the three church leaderships in the case studies felt it important to so often instruct and even rebuke their followers to not rely upon the Regulars, then people must have continued to do so. But why did the people still use the services and philosophies of the Regulars if they were so disgruntled?

I think the reasons are related to historical evidence that nineteenth-century Americans had an eclectic approach to health care. Some people may still have held the belief that illness and disease were penance for sin and, therefore, hoped for deliverance through powerful heroics. Others may have wanted to believe that the "active therapies," the heroic therapies of the Regulars, were creating dramatic responses in the body that would affect spiritual and physical health. The belief in the Regulars' medicine went only so far though. Americans drew the line when the Regulars tried to monopolize health care as well as medicine and encroach upon their health freedoms. They wanted heroic therapies and the emerging technology of medicine with its smallpox vaccinations, new patented medicines, surgical techniques, and instruments such as forceps, but not at the expense of their freedom to choose their medicine and the freedom and empowerment to care for self and family. They may have wanted to believe in a system of newer and improved remedies, but not to the exclusion of the simple remedies used in domestic self-care that had been passed down from generation to generation.

In the mid-nineteenth century, Americans wanted to continue to be free to explore self-care. The sectarian leaders and health care reformers who rose to prominence during this period did not criticize the traditional healing practices of the people, as did many Regulars. They did the opposite. Leaders such as Samuel Thomson encouraged self-care among Americans, and they specifically structured their role as health expert educators and guides. In addition, religious leaders, such as those among the Shakers, the LDS, and the SOC, often served as the conscience of the people, reminding their followers that they had the power within them to heal themselves. Their message was one of faith and belief, not only in the methods of healing, whether botanical or heroic, but in the message of self-healing. If the history of medicine is explored from the perspective of a male-dominated public sphere, then a "war" between the medical sects of the period is often identified as the root cause of the conflict in medicine at the time. The history of health care in the domestic sphere reveals that the conflict was perhaps more complex than a war or struggle for power between medical philosophies. The origin of the nineteenth-century conflict was indeed spiritual, for it was a question of belief in self-care.

Ethnographers and folklorists have demonstrated that health beliefs are the foundation of health and healing cultures,[6] from the creation of individual health decisions and the power of placebos to the construction of entire health systems. One reason the Botanical Medical Movement, in particular, the Thomsonianism system, was so successful in the mid-nineteenth century is that belief in the power of self-care with herbs was promoted. Thomson's message was well received by the women of the domestic sphere, especially where self-care was a central value and the medical or nurse expert was welcomed as a guide.

It was in the domestic sphere of the community that nurses found their talents and expertise recognized and utilized. The nurses, like Thomson, supported the ongoing role of self-care in the health of their communities. For example, the LDS's Council of Health and *Doctrines and Covenants* outlined the importance of self-care, hygiene, and lifestyle practices, such as abstention from meat and the use of gentle foods and herbs as medicine. The SOC encouraged self-care in the act of prayer, and the Shakers encouraged herbs, diet, and exercise as the mainstays of good health.

Thomson's patented series of remedies was integrated by nurses into their patient care. The Shaker nurses added his botanical remedies to their infirmary repertoire. The LDS nurses and midwives were very influenced by Thomson's system and the Thomsonian physicians of their community. Midwives such as Patty Sessions also integrated Wooster Beach's philosophies and practices, botanical and otherwise, into their work. The Shaker and LDS nurses welcomed the practices of both the Regulars and Botanics in their work. They integrated the interventions from both sides of the sociocultural conflict of the public sphere, ultimately establishing themselves as herbal diplomats. The Shaker and LDS nurses exemplified the tactful, negotiating strategies of a cultural diplomat in their consideration and examination of the philosophies and practices of the health care leaders of both sides of the public sphere debate, ultimately integrating that philosophy and practice into that which they were already doing in the domestic sphere of local community, home care, and infirmary practice.

The SOC, however, practiced a different type of herbal diplomacy. With their French historical tradition of nurse herbalism, they took their knowledge of herbs to the public sphere of male, medically dominated hospitals. No evidence exists that the SOC had any knowledge of or specific interaction with Botanic health care reformers such as Thomson. But if their role was to bring the knowledge and values of the domestic sphere, such as compassionate caring or even herbalism, to the public sphere, then they would most likely have needed to avoid taking sides in the conflict. This is indeed what is found in the records of the SOC. While they do record relationships with the Regulars, these were business, not necessarily philosophical, alliances. There is evidence that the SOC removed their services from institutions where their alliance, which was to their spiritual mission and orders, was not supported. While they worked side by side with the Regulars rather than the Botanics, it is clear that they "sided" with their spiritual mission and no other. All three communities of nurses served as cultural integrators and cultural, herbal diplomats, moving between the spheres, often seamlessly, to achieve the greater national goal identified by nineteenth-century American women themselves, the enjoyment of greater health and longevity by the nation's people.

Rational Health Care

Health beliefs provide the cultural structure for a community's health choices and systems. The meaning of science in general is a cultural creation that provides structure for those health beliefs. Ludwik Fleck, a physician and philosopher, wrote that scientific knowledge is constructed as a result of a social process[7] in which the scientist's training, preconceived ideas, and anticipations play a role in the development of the resulting "knowledge" or scientific "fact." These facts are organized and shared by groups of individuals with similar thought "styles."[8] Fleck found that different thought styles can coexist within the same culture, such as is found in the health beliefs or thought styles of the nineteenth-century nurses studied. The nurses' culture employed helpful applications from different, and sometimes seemingly divergent, health care philosophies.

Fleck primarily studied the influence that society had on the formation of medical "fact." He developed a "highly dynamic vision of the formation of medical knowledge, in which expert knowledge was influenced by popular knowledge and then influences it in turn."[9] The circulation and intercollective exchange of ideas from various thought styles "always results in a shift or a change in the currency of thought,"[10] which leads to the creation and innovation, that is, the emergence of new "truths." In addition to Fleck, other scholars such as Ronald Barnett, in his writings on higher education, have written about societal influences regarding what is deemed "rational." "Societies develop their own ideas as to what is to count as rationality. Our ideas about rationality, within a pluralistic society, are bound to be complex and fuzzy, but even so we can readily see that certain kinds of rationality are dominant."[11]

In a pluralistic society, rationality involves the ability to hold that there is more than one reason or reality. Often it is "science" and technology, with physicians as the gatekeepers, that is viewed by Western cultures as the epitome of rationality. Often the ideology of those working in the fields related to science and technology is the concept of one reality, or the possibility of a single "truth" regarding a scientific question, and that that truth is best sought objectively. This is known as the "received view." In nursing science today, as in the nineteenth century, the perceived view that multiple realities exist, and that "truth" is determined by the individual or cultural group, also is valued. Nurses demonstrate rationality by being able and willing to hold seemingly opposing realities, the perceived and received views, as valid for reflection and discussion.

Yet the scientific and integrative ways in which women nurses have historically allowed for the entertainment of differing health opinions and choices have been diminished as "soft" science by some. Perhaps this integrative approach to science is due to women's ability to construct relationships not only among people in their communities and with their patients but in their minds as a scientific process.

Research has shown that women have distinctive ways of knowing, including "constructed knowledge," where they integrate knowledge learned from others.[12] This was clearly evident in nineteenth-century women's actions in dealing with the conflict during the Botanical Medical Movement. For example, the leaders of the Ladies Physiological Institute, who in hiring speakers from both the Regulars and Empirics camps, were able to explore and reasonably conclude that they could learn from Botanics *and* Regulars. They integrated what they had learned in a constructivist process to ultimately create a knowledge base of their own. Contemporary research by Pill and Stott has shown that the Welsh mothers they studied were capable of holding "apparently contradictory theories of health and illness causation at the same time."[13] The study showed that it is "clearly misleading to think in terms of two polar groups—the Fatalists stressing external factors and the Lifestylists with their emphasis on the importance of individual choices in diet, exercise, smoking and drinking."[14] From the receipt books and behaviors of the nineteenth-century nurses, it also is apparent that women of that period were able to recognize and validate opposing health and medical philosophies, theories, and practices and utilize them based on need and context.

Nineteenth-century women, through their support networks of benevolent societies, receipt exchanges, and ladies' journals, created a rational culture of health care that was pluralistic and integrative in scope. Because of their ability to reason and because of a desire to create changes in health care, new solutions were generated. The Shaker, LDS, and SOC nurses were rational scientists who demonstrated that they were capable of holding different and even opposing health beliefs and theories while forging a path of the study and observation of human health behavior that supported their caring practices. These groups, each in their own way, carved out an integrative structure that worked for them and their patients. The nature of that integration, in particular, herbal integration, is evident in their nursing actions. This integrative structure contributed to the ultimate goal of Americans to preserve their medical freedoms.

American nurses could not have accomplished what they did without the support of the public. Florence Nightingale once said that

"Jesus Christ raised women above the conditions of mere slaves, mere ministers to the passions of man, raised them by his sympathy, to be ministers of God. He gave them moral activity. But the Age, the World, Humanity, must give them the means to exercise this moral activity, must give them intellectual cultivation, spheres of action."[15] Nineteenth-century women nurses were successful health care experts, advocates, integrators, and leaders, as well as herbal diplomats, because humanity, their communities and their patients supported them.

Patient Self-Care in the Domestic Sphere

Did nineteenth-century American women throw away their receipt books when they purchased the newest domestic guide by Dr. Gunn or heard of a new heroic cure of the Regulars? The health belief in "one cause, one cure," constructed and promoted by Regulars such as Benjamin Rush, was the dominant belief of the Regulars in the early and mid-nineteenth century but not necessarily the public. Nineteenth-century women, in their integrative process, did not necessarily throw away their old receipt books to be replaced by domestic medicine guides that provided more "professional, if not more valid, advice" as one historian suggests.[16] Evidence from the case studies presented here supports the fact that American women and nurses, as well as other healers in communities where self-care played an important role in the support of the overall system of national health care, did not discard one theory for another, or one book for another.

Many women health care leaders, such as nurses and midwives, led their communities to a greater realization of the benefits of the practice of integration, gleaning the best from technological advancement in medicine and pharmacy and healing in the use of traditional time-honored methods such as herbs. The mid-nineteenth-century nurse-herbalists led their communities in establishing a domestic culture accepting of health pluralism as a basis for individual health choices. In addition to serving as integrators of the health care beliefs, philosophies, and practices of the public and domestic spheres, the nurses demonstrated that they served as supporters of their patients' self-care practices within the domestic sphere. They often communicated the importance and the effects of self-care practices to leaders in the public sphere. This was especially apparent in the work of the LDS nurses and midwives in their work with the Council of Health. As discussed in chapter 4, self-care, sharing health-related advice, and health networking were foundational to the success of the health care reforms of the period. The domestic health belief was founded on the greater social belief in the noble purpose of taking responsibility for one's health as a way of affecting the overall health of the nation.

Historically, nurses' service included being available for any need twenty-four hours a day. The work of the nurses often was to assist people in helping and healing themselves. Florence Nightingale, in a discussion with her father on social issues in which he told her that he believed in the doctrine of laissez-faire in health care, and that people should be *left* to help themselves, responded: "No, they must be taught to help themselves."[17] Her view was consistent with the work of mid-nineteenth-century American nurses. Nurses' roles have historically been one of helping people to help themselves.

Self-care is a value of the discipline of nursing documented in contemporary nursing theories, most prominently the self-care theory of Dorothea Orem. She wrote that self-care has a purpose. It "contributes in specific ways to human structured integrity, human functioning, and human development," and it is the action of "mature and maturing persons."[18] Nurses and their promotion of self-care have historically been a tightly woven part of the health care fabric of a community. Nurses have acted as integrators between the domestic and public spheres, promoting the value of self-care in society to both patients and practitioners alike.

The roots of self-care in the community are historically related to people's health beliefs, not only in shoring up their communities and their nation but also in bearing their own burden. Nineteenth-century Americans, as mentioned previously, were conflicted over the desire to bear the burden of their illnesses themselves or to employ the services of the Regulars, with their claims of the knowledge and experience to share their burden at the very least and at the most take the burden away completely. This psycho-spiritual dilemma is still present in the American culture and health care system today. Recent studies have shown that Americans now resolve this dilemma much the way nineteenth-century nurses and their patients did, by integrating the beliefs and practices of physicians and other practitioners of the biomedical world and self-care practices into their lives.[19]

In modern America, self-care has not been rejected but has faded into the backdrop of the community.[20] It has been called the "hidden health care system."[21] While some nineteenth-century Regulars joined health care reformers and used their skills to educate and support the public's self-care practices, the Regulars, for the most part, pulled their support away from self-care promotion later in the nineteenth century. Many physicians continue to question or oppose a major part of the public's self-care practices, the use of traditional healers and what are called in industrialized countries today "complementary therapies." The most common argument against people utilizing self-care and traditional and folk healers has been that there is significant risk involved in self-care, in particular, in the use of herbs. This is not a new concern. In the nineteenth century, Regulars emphasized the risk of self-care practices, such as Thomsonian herbal treatments, in delaying "proper treatment," and that the botanical treatments, at least the Empirics' treatments, were not founded upon sufficient theory and academic knowledge and, therefore, were not as "safe" as what the Regulars had to offer.

Over time, while people's affinity for self-care may not have changed, the conflict between the spheres has intensified. The tiered American system of health care pluralism, established as a result of botanical reformers' success in repealing medical licensure, what they believed to be the evidence of attempting medical monopoly in the 1830s, has been gradually leveled to a system of polarized camps.

A Tiered System of Health Care

Health care of the nineteenth century, at least from the view of nurses and patients, such as Homer Merriam's view, described in chapter 3, was structured as a tiered system. In resolving any health care issue, people usually believed that their self-care practices might be enough to help them. They often implemented healthy lifestyle practices such as dietary changes to promote well-being and prevent illness. If they needed help with disease or wellness issues, then they went to the next tier. They sought advice from family and friends or from the numerous advice books available to them. If they wanted more help, then they would go to the third tier, seeking the help of a local expert or an itinerant healer such as a nurse, midwife, or bonesetter. And, finally, if they still desired additional support, then they would seek out the services of a physician, whether Botanic, water cure, or Regular. This system, however, was not necessarily linear and perfectly "tiered" at all times. The healing trajectory of seekers, such as Homer Merriam, often included overlapping tiers. Nineteenth-century Americans believed that engaging the services of a physician, entering the fourth tier, was indeed something to be avoided if possible, and that reliance on the first three tiers was much more preferable for health issues ranging from physical concerns to health and spiritual beliefs.

While patients today may still consider all tiers important to their health and well-being, health professionals do not often agree. Levin wrote: "So-called primitive and folk health practices have been elaborately described by anthropologists, defended through testimonials, rationalized, and codified, or criticized as dangerous, ineffective, placebo, or nuisance (delaying seeking professional care or interfering with professional advice). . . . Each system of practice has its own criteria for judging effectiveness; yet the validation criteria of allopathic medicine [orthodox medicine] have been universally applied."[22] Over the past century, the health beliefs and practices of the Regulars have steadily risen to the level of the monopoly so feared by nineteenth-century Americans and health care reformers, such as Samuel Thomson. In order to attain monopoly, the public would have needed to believe that the offering of the Regulars was medically "safer." This change in culture, in health belief, was perhaps achieved by linking the term *progress* to technology and technology to health care in a concerted effort to move the focus of health care away from self-care and healing traditions and toward reliance upon an emerging medical industry.

The concept of health risk was not new to nineteenth-century Americans. They often heard not only about the ill effects of the

Regulars' heroic treatments from health care reformers but they also heard from many Regulars about the problems of relying on traditional healing methods that were not supported by education and medical knowledge. Through various media and public education campaigns, academically based medicine became linked to progress, the "new." The "risks" of traditional healing practices and self-care were then directly and indirectly linked to the old, the uncultured, the uncivilized, and the crude. As society became more industrialized, so did health care. Progress and technology were inextricably linked and were proclaimed and believed to provide greater safety and efficacy in medical care. For example, by the twentieth century, women believed that it was safer and healthier to give birth in a hospital than at home.

Women's authority over childbirth was gradually "eroded by the promises of safety offered through applying medical answers to birth's traditional uncertainties."[23] The safety of childbirth became linked to technology such as forceps and intrauterine monitoring. That technology also was linked to the hospital in the public sphere. Therefore, women not only left their homes, they left their traditional sphere of influence to birth their babies in the public sphere. Some historians have written that the medicalization of childbirth led to the loss of control of a woman's own "natural sphere" of reproduction[24] and to the empowerment of physicians seeking the elimination of midwives.[25]

Since the days of the entry of the SOC into the public hospitals, women and nurses have continued to bring their values to the public sphere. The SOC nurses did not expect to be nurtured and cared for by hospital administrators or physicians. Their only expectation was that they would receive fulfillment of the terms of their contract to receive room and board, clothing, and the ability to work according to their vows in serving the sick poor. They modeled a way of existing in the public sphere by mentoring and supporting each other and demonstrating the values of the domestic sphere, such as caring for others. They exemplified the power that women could express in the public sphere while staying firmly rooted in the caring *network* of the domestic sphere which, for the SOC, was their apostolic community.

Healing Networks

The third theme that emerges from the histories of mid-nineteenth-century nurses is that of their extensive participation in women's social networks. The nurses expanded the nature and influence of the networks by creating *healing networks*. These community-based healing networks not only supported the public but were the support system for those women called to nursing as a service to humanity. The nurses of the various community healing networks explored here mentored and supported each other with their instruction manuals. The LDS network was utilized by those pioneer women crossing the plains to Utah, where they built their new church headquarters. The SOC were mentored by their Sister Servants, and the Shaker infirmary nurses used the instruction manuals that circulated among their communities to help patients and support the Shaker herb industry. The education, mentoring, and support that these women gave to each other may not have been "formal" by contemporary nursing education standards but, nevertheless, the nurses' networks were well-organized, trusted, and influential resources in the development of community health practices.

The nurses of the mid-nineteenth century designed and participated in healing network events such as health care education. The records of the Ladies Physiological Institute, for example, show that nurses were among their membership who received a formal curriculum of lectures in anatomy and health topics, not unlike what might be present in nursing education today. The LDS nurses and midwives created their own resource and education network, called the "Women's Council of Health," to guide their community in health practices. While facing some extreme social challenges associated with religious community and nation building, these nurses successfully educated each other, supported each other, and healed each other using the resources and communication strategies they knew best. Mid-nineteenth-century nurses gathered together and shared their healing experiences and information.

Present-day women scientists continue to be fascinated by women's tendency to gather. Current research of this phenomenon, recently referred to as the "tend and befriend"[26] stress response, has shown preliminarily that rather than the oft-cited fight-or-flight stress response, women, perhaps as a result of the production of the hormone oxytocin, actually relieve their stress through the development of social networks for the purpose of exchanging resources and responsibilities. The researchers suggest that women respond to stress by tending, "nurturing offspring, exhibiting behaviors that protect them from harm . . . and by befriending, namely, affiliating with social groups to reduce risk."[27] The rapid changes of the mid-nineteenth century were stressful for many Americans. It is not surprising that mid-nineteenth-century women turned their focus to their women peer relationships for comfort and care. Nineteenth-century nurses' healing networks were the early American "nursing schools" and community health systems where women could receive and give tending and befriending.

European-American and American Indian Relations

Did the healing network of the European-American nurses include American Indian women healers, and did the values of sharing and support found in the nurses' networks extend to American Indians? Answering this question is somewhat difficult for a number of reasons. First, while identification from historical archives of the presence of relationships between people of different cultures may not be especially difficult, reconstructing an accurate historical understanding of the nature of those human relationships is altogether different. Creating an accurate interpretation of the relationship between European-Americans and American Indians who had been in a difficult invader-colonized relationship for more than 200 years is not only part of an ongoing historical process, it is part of the ongoing diplomatic process of relationship repair. This process needed to be approached with sensitivity.

Second, when evaluating historical relationships, both parties in the relationship must be represented for the historical report to be complete and accurate. American Indian history, recorded from the perspective of Indians, not from those of European descent, is sparse at best.[28] Most of the history presented here and in the case studies of the three groups of women nurses was gleaned from European-American archives. Third, the period in question, 1830–1860, was a dire time for American Indians, when the federal government was relocating whole Indian nations, and huge numbers of Indians were dying.

The media and literature of the period are replete with myths relating to the character and lives of American Indians, whites of European descent, and the relationship between the two. Perhaps one of the most prominent examples is the myth of the superiority and civility of the English to the Indians, exemplified in the writings of James Fenimore Cooper.[29] Historian Glenda Riley has concluded from her research of hundreds of diary accounts (1825–1915) of frontier women in particular and a substantial survey of the literature of the period that "Myth and the media have continued to promote the idea that white women and American Indians were at loggerheads more often than not. Violent confrontations that did harm to frontier women have been emphasized, and Indians have too often been portrayed as barbarous natives who pillaged, burned, and raped whenever possible."[30]

What Riley demonstrates is that like all historical relationships, gross historical generalizations have been made. When looking more directly at the personal, day-to-day experiences documented in the histories of people in communities, one quickly finds that the black-and-white descriptions of historical relationships, such as have been portrayed of whites and Indians during the nineteenth century, are virtually unsupported. Relationships are complex and have many influencing variables. Therefore, what is presented here are only preliminary and tentative conclusions about the character of mid-nineteenth-century white-Indian relations, specifically of the women, from a Euro-American perspective.

By 1830, European-Americans and American Indians had already endured numerous conflicts and wars. Under the Jackson presidency, the American Congress passed the Indian Removal Act, which led to the "resettlement" or segregation of many native peoples to the state known as Oklahoma today. Much of the European-American history of relations with American Indian nations has reflected the activities, values, and perspective of the public sphere with its wars and conflict and does not necessarily represent the history of which relationships were taking place in the domestic sphere. The histories of women nurses in the Shaker and LDS communities suggest that there may have actually been respectful and even friendly relationships between whites and Indians in the domestic sphere. There was no mention in the main SOC archives in Emmitsburg of Indian relations with the early SOC. In the later part of the nineteenth century, the Leavenworth SOC expanded their missions to the West and worked with Indians.

There is some evidence that the Shakers, as mentioned in chapter 5, did have relationships with Indians and may have shared botanical remedies information through various channels, such as through members who had lived among the Indians, through herb trade, and through visits to Indian healers. The LDS records, however, provided the most evidence of relationship with the Indians. The LDS not only shared botanical information and healing experiences, European-Americans to American Indians, and vice versa, bought land from the Indians to build their Utah community, and defended the Indians against government encroachment, but they also had a church teaching about the Indians that guided their behaviors toward the Indians. The LDS helped the Indians, but like many other European-Americans, for the most part they expressed their caring for the Indians using a parental approach. For example, the LDS, like other Christians, sought to convert the Indians. The cultural conflict between the European-Americans and the American Indians regarding who was "civilized" and who was "savage" was often a central issue of the relationship. At the heart of the issue for many European-Americans was the doctrine and dogma of the Christian faith.

Many American Indians who did become Christians demonstrated the values and beliefs of the religion, including the belief in ministering to the sick poor. For example, one colonial manuscript described the lives of Indian women, who lived on Martha's Vineyard, Massachusetts, who became Christians and ministered to the sick poor. Assannooshque, who also was known by the English name Sarah (d. 1708), was recorded as a "person of great industry who kept her wigwam in very good repair . . . who was very observable for her charity and compassion to the poor, which she manifested by feeding them when they were hungry, visiting them when they were sick."[31] Another pious Indian woman was Nattootumau Nahnosoo, the daughter of an Indian Sachem, called "Cheshchaaamog." Nattootumau, or Hannah (d. 1716), had herbal knowledge that she not only used to help her sick Indian neighbors. She also was "employed" by the English to heal the sick.[32]

Whether or not these women held a belief in the benevolent service to the sick before their conversion is unknown. These accounts, as well as the histories of the Shaker and LDS nurses, do suggest, however, that European-American and American Indian women did network and share botanical knowledge. Their cultural exchanges may have occurred because of a desire to learn about each other, and perhaps even a desire to live peacefully side by side, as originally hoped by the Indian nations when they sold some of their lands to the first settlers. Their desire for networking most likely grew out of sheer necessity and the desire to survive, especially among those who lived on the Western frontier.

Women's Domestic Diplomacy

Because of forced removal, many of the Indians were in a cultural state similar to recently immigrated Europeans and those who were pioneering the Western frontier after living in the East. Extreme change, such as that which occurs during a move to a new home or a culture that is entirely different from one's homeland, can be unsettling. It is in times of hardship, such as the struggle for survival on the Western frontier, that people rely on each other for comfort, support, and healing. Historical studies show that pioneer women routinely "bartered, traded, and entered into acts of mutual assistance. In other words, in their attempts to provide food, clothing, and other commodities for those people who depended upon them for succor, women often formed relationships for mutual support with the Indians."[33] Evidence from diary accounts supports that European-American women, in a spirit of "gentleness and fairness," entered into close relationships with Indian women. "Women began to visit them in their homes and attend their celebrations and ceremonies."[34] For example, one woman, Caroline Phelps, not only attended Indian dances and ceremonies, but she also called upon a community Indian doctor for help and hired a male Indian nurse for her children.[35]

American Indian and European-American women networked and shared their cultures, including their healing knowledge. There is evidence that they shared botanical remedies. In one oral history of Indian women healers of the twentieth century, Dhyani Ywahoo, Keeper of the Priestcraft of the Cherokee Nation, teaches that when the first Anglo settlers came to America, "the traditions of healing with herbs, just sharing the natural gifts that the earth has to offer, [were] very readily shared with whoever asked for it."[36] This was at least true in the Cherokee tribe. Botanical healing knowledge traditionally held by certain members of the different Indian nations is inseparable from spiritual belief. The Cherokees' sharing of cultural knowledge was based on their belief that all are in communion with the universe, and that every part of life is related, including plants, trees, animals, and human beings.

While there may have been some exchange, networking, and healing between Indian and white people from 1830 to 1860, for the most part, due to cultural upheaval, it is highly doubtful that anything more than herbs passing from hand to hand and plant information being shared occurred. While whites may have shared their healing beliefs founded in their Christian tradition perhaps in hope of converting an Indian, the deeper spiritual healing traditions of the Indians that were the foundation and source of botanical knowledge and wisdom were most likely not shared during this period in American history.

Nurse Autonomy

Sharing and networking about health and healing ideas and remedies were foundational parts of the culture of the American nurse of the mid-nineteenth century. The healing networks provided the education and support for the nurses' healing acts. Although nurses took suggestions, advice, support, and even orders from others in regard to patient care, the case histories indicate that the nurses of the mid-nineteenth century practiced autonomously, though not in isolation. Their decisions were their own. They were responsible for the care they provided. They were the ones set aside to heal. Their decision about whether to use or not use botanical therapies also was their own.

The records of the SOC, Shaker, and LDS nurses demonstrate that women nurses from the 1830s to the 1860s had autonomy in their caregiving practice. Even with their vows of obedience, the SOC, who worked for hospitals where they submitted to the authority of physicians and Protestant administrators, retained the ability to make decisions about patient care that might at times contradict their superiors. The Shaker and LDS nurses provided health care for their communities often without the support of a physician.

I would suggest that one of the reasons nineteenth-century nurses were so successful in establishing their autonomous practice was that they were not relegated to either the domestic or public sphere but lived their lives in both. They became part of the social "borderland . . . a positive place for women to colonise."[37] The nineteenth-century borderland represented a place that was neutral, neither completely domestic nor public in scope. It was from their position in the borderland that the nurses were able to establish what Marshall and Wall have identified as "carefully crafted relationships of mutual dependency"[38] with stakeholders of the public sphere. It was from the borderland that the SOC, who also worked physically in the public sphere (the hospital), exercised their skills as herbal diplomats and created mutually dependent relationships with Protestant male physicians. The nurses used the support of their networks and communities to maintain an autonomous practice in a period of history when women's roles were still primarily in the domestic sphere.

The borderland for nurses had been in place at least since the establishment of the Ladies of Charity by Vincent de Paul in France. Marshall and Wall stated that religious nurses were not allowed total control of their practice in the public sphere because society perceived them as weak and subordinate. However, American religious nurses of the mid-nineteenth century were not perceived as "weak and subordinate." They were able to enter the public sphere because they were not perceived as a threat to the powers that be. For example, the SOC accepted the rule that male Catholic priests and bishops would negotiate all contracts with male leaders in the public sphere. They were not threats, because they had successfully demonstrated that they could walk between the spheres neither sufficiently challenging the Regulars nor forsaking their bond to the domestic sphere, their networks, and their patients.

The religious devotion of the nurses in these case histories also was a factor in their acceptance as autonomous nurses in their communities. I do not think that the nursing work of the Shakers and the SOC, for example, was accepted because the Shakers' and the SOC's celibate practice "wiped out gender differences," and, therefore, they were accepted into a "separate space,"[39] as it has been hypothesized. Rather than explaining the women nurses' acceptance from what may be an essentialist viewpoint, that is, that they were just accepted because they were celibate, I would suggest that their acceptance was due to the broader historical, social, and cultural context in which they worked and lived.

The "separate space" in which historians witness women of the nineteenth century finding their place is the "borderland," a place not reserved for celibate women alone. From the experiences of the SOC at the Maryland Hospital, it is clear that even celibate sisters stood the risk of crossing social borders "too obviously or prematurely" and incurring "social stigma or social costs."[40] In the mid-nineteenth century, from the perspective of those in the public sphere, women were women, regardless of their vocation, religion, or race, and they were meant for the domestic sphere. This may have been the nature of their oppression, but the knowledge of this perspective also may have provided a source of strength for their identities as they ventured into the borderland, creating cultural change and achieving a more public presence.

The nineteenth-century nurses were autonomous in terms of their choices about whether or not to use botanical therapies. Some nurses chose to implement Thomsonian herbalism and some chose Beach's philosophy and practice. They chose when, where, and whether they would give patients emetics and tonic teas. They changed poultices when they felt their observed results demonstrated that one was better than another for the patient. In botanical practice, they were ingenious, creative, and empowered. During the Botanical Medical Movement, herbs were part of the historical healing traditions of all three groups. Each group was selective, however, about how and when they used herbs in the public sphere. For example, Matilda Coskery only suggested hops tea for a psychiatric patient after the physician-prescribed opiate had proven not to be beneficial. This was an example of an informed, reflective decision from the borderland.

The three groups of nurses retained enough autonomy in practice to choose to continue to use herbs even as newer treatments and chemical drugs were introduced by the Regulars. The women used the support of their social networks in the borderland and their diplomatic skill to carve out their healing missions, which included botanical therapies as they were needed. It was late in the nineteenth century when nurses left the borderland to fully engage in their work in the hospitals of the public sphere and to follow a vision of a professional status similar to physicians, that the inclusion of botanical therapies in American nursing care would change. By working for hospital physicians and administrators and by more closely patterning the evolution of their profession after the Regulars instead of the traditions established by early American nurses such as the SOC, nurses found themselves abdicating the autonomy that they had known for centuries.

It was during the late nineteenth century that the work of Protestant Florence Nightingale was brought as a standard in nursing care from Great Britain by American deaconess women to be utilized in American, hospital-based schools of nursing. It is noteworthy that Nightingale's work was significantly influenced by the DOC as well as by the work of Kaiserwerth in Germany. In the early 1850s, Nightingale wrote:

> You do not know now, with all its faults, what a home the Catholic Church is . . . no man can tell what she is to women—their training, their discipline, their hope their home—to women because they are wholly

> uncared-for while men are not. . . . There is nothing like the training (in these days) which the Sacred Heart or the Order of St. Vincent gives to women.[41] The daughters of St. Vincent would open their arms to me. They have already done so, and what should I find there. My work already laid out for me instead of seeking it to and fro and finding none; my home, sympathy, human and divine.[42]

While American and British nurses were quickly modeling a new profession after the values of the public sphere, Nightingale struggled to keep nurses true to their heritage of autonomy and healing service. Much like Samuel Thomson, she opposed licensure, in this case of nurses, (called "certificates of proficiency" by the British General Medical Council, which issued them) on the grounds that nursing should not be examined by a medical body. She also opposed licensure in the public sphere on the principle that "Nursing is not only an art but a character, and how can that be arrived at by examination?"[43] She was concerned that certification could lead to a decrease in progress, and that in her experience "nursing and medicine must never be mixed up. It spoils both. If the enemy wishes to ruin our nurses in training at St. Thomas's it would be by persuading me to accept your noble offer of a female special certificate (or any degree) for them."[44]

She also stated in numerous letters, including one to *The Times* on April 14, 1876, her view that "Hospitals are but an intermediate stage of civilization. At present hospitals are the only place where the sick poor can be nursed, or indeed, often the sick rich. But the ultimate object is to nurse all sick at home."[45] Nightingale seemed to have recognized the history of women's power in providing nursing care in the domestic sphere. She herself spent a good portion of her life epitomizing the life of a nineteenth-century woman, as an invalid in her own home.

Harriet Austin, in the *Water Cure Journal*, wrote of women: "It is her sphere to do what she desires to do. When conscious of the divinity within her and of the mightiness of her power she determines to elevate, not only her sex, but humanity, this too will be her sphere."[46]

The lives of nineteenth-century women spanned the gamut of the spheres, from full connection with the domestic or private sphere, to borderland diplomacy, and then to full entry into the public sphere, where they would seek to elevate men, women, and children. Perhaps the next step, the future of women nurses' diplomacy, including herbal integration, is the continued pursuit of this integration of the spheres.

Chapter 9

Conclusion:
The Future of Herbal Diplomacy

Nursing care is culturally derived.[1] Nurses from different cultures express caring through different modalities and processes. Whether or not herbal remedies are given to a patient in America as an option to be integrated into a plan of care is up to American nurses. This was true in the mid-nineteenth century, and it still holds true today. According to research by Dr. Madeleine Leininger, a transcultural nurse theorist, contemporary nurses tend to marginalize folk or healing traditions, such as botanical therapies, because of conflicts with the orthodox biomedical culture with which they have become closely identified.[2] This chapter addresses the potential cultural challenges that the nurse who seeks to utilize the evidence from the history presented here may encounter when exploring herbal integration into the nursing practices in the twenty-first century.

The Integrated "Turtle Mind"

Historians of the nineteenth century often reflect on the dualism, in particular, the gender dualism, of the public and domestic spheres existing in society during the period. As historian Anne Digby pointed out, the focus on the duality of the spheres may be "empirical over-simplification,"[3] when in fact many women of the period, as demonstrated in these histories, did inhabit the borderland, the integrative zone, between the spheres. The women who explored their power in the borderland developed the ability to integrate. It was the nature of the borderland that women, such as those living on the frontier, held opposing thoughts and emotions regarding cultural stances on health and illness that represented the best of both spheres. This ability to "walk between the spheres" or cultures, to walk between the social, political, and medical dualities that had been created by society, is not only the evidence of rationality but is the evidence of a spiritual process, a willingness of heart.[4] This willingness of heart can be the foundation for the exploration of integrative solutions rather than the exclusion that often results from a dualistic paradigm.

A willingness to seek integration of the spheres is not only helpful socially and medically. Cherokee Dhyani Ywahoo teaches the importance of the integration of the spheres, even the physical spheres of the brain, to the survival of the human race.

> It's just thought regenerating, bringing together the left, the right, and the middle brain. We call that snake or turtle mind. That's very important. That is the balance of our whole nature. In the creation process, we say it's the emptiness that everything comes from, and it manifests through three fires. One is will. One is wisdom. The other is active intelligence. [It] is for the human being to rebuild—the rebuilding of the rainbow bridges to make the connection between those hemispheres on the brain. And the foundation is the serpent's mind. Yes, the midbrain function is very significant to the survival of the species. It is the seat of survival.[5]

Integration in health care may be just as important to humanity as the integration of the spheres of the brain is to the survival of the species. In the nursing care and herbal practices of the nurses in the nineteenth century, we find evidence of integration as a means of sociocultural survival. The women nurses found a way to integrate their social and gender roles of the public and domestic spheres. In their roles as nurses, they integrated into their practice gentle and strong medicine. And in their role as community health leaders and herbal diplomats, they demonstrated integrative ability as they embraced healing traditions, such as herbs, as well as emerging medical inventions, theories, and practices. In light of the importance of integration, it seems imperative that nurses seek to explore what the future holds in terms of their history of valuing health care culture integration and herbal diplomacy. What is the future of nursing herbal diplomacy? Some answers may lie in the profession's interpretation of history, such as the relevance of the contribution of American nursing's foremothers during the Botanical Medical Movement 1830–1860 to contemporary practice, and in the historical clarification of what constitutes *progress* and *nostalgia* in nursing.

Progress

Research by medical anthropologists has shown that traditional healers, such as those who use botanical therapies, and "Western," biomedical," or "orthodox" medicine have competed against each other for decades. Today the biomedical culture often is perceived unquestioningly as being superior, not only by those who are part of that culture, such as physicians, but by the American public as well. Medical anthropologist David Landy argues that some, for the most part, traditional healers, have found ways to ease the sense of conflict by acting as "incorporating technocultural agents and creators of new technocultural syntheses."[6] The nineteenth-century equivalent of traditional healers would have been the Empirics, which includes the nurses, the Botanics, and the Indian healers. The nurses, as Landy says of traditional healers, most likely helped ease the tension of the cultural conflict in health care for patients during the mid-nineteenth century. Their diplomatic acts may or may not have been strategic. Nevertheless, the nurses were "culture brokers" in a difficult time. The culture broker concept, as defined by Digby and Sweet, has been used in recent times to describe the work of nurses who act as "bridges between the 'modern' western model of their training and the 'traditional' medicine of their patients"[7] and other community healers. In many ways, both "diplomat" and "culture broker" appropriately describe the bridging and intermediary work of the mid-nineteenth-century nurses who often did, although perhaps not overtly conscious of the fact, advocate for exploring multiple forms of healing, including botanical therapies.

While traditional healers and nurses may seek to integrate biomedical culture into what they do, biomedical practitioners, while adopting the remedies of the traditional healer, rarely adopt or integrate the values or beliefs of the traditional culture that serve as the foundational context for the proper use of the remedy. For example, American physicians and nurses can now take a brief, weeklong continuing education course in "medical acupuncture," whereas traditional Chinese physicians who use acupuncture as one modality spend up to a decade or more studying foundational theory and technique.

Regular physicians of the mid-nineteenth century, often of European descent and educated in Europe, had brought with them to the United States a cultural bias for their own medicine. While they still used herbs, their chosen remedies, such as jalap, were more often closer in power and operation to that of their preferred chemical drug armamentarium. While there is nothing inherently problematic in medical bias per se, many Regulars of the period sought to use their beliefs, values, and biases to seek control of others' health beliefs and practices. They often marginalized the beliefs and practices of traditional herbalism, American Indian and European based, as taught and used by the Thomsonians, eclectics, and nurses. They minimized the importance of herbs in domestic and self-care, which often included the use of simples by nurses in caregiving, as demonstrated in their receipt books.

American Indian culture, including healing traditions, was often perceived by European-American physicians as "uncivilized" and "uncultured," and they conversely perceived their own medical culture as "civilized" and "cultured." American Regulars believed that their European-based chemical medicine, most often derived from plants, was the prime example of a progressive and civilized culture. Many have adopted the term *modern* to describe the medicine, now often referred to as "Western" medicine, which has become synonymous with technology-based treatment. As the values of the medical profession became associated with industry and medicine as a commodity, the healing traditions of European-Americans and

American Indians were significantly, if not totally, excluded in the process. This was partially due to the public's desire for technology-based medicine, but also was due to the health beliefs and culture of the Regulars themselves. Self-care was considered inconsequential to patients' needs for medical care. The methods of healers following Indian historical traditions were deemed inferior. Ethnobotanists' research supports that historically Western medicine was regarded as "prima facie evidence of the intellectual and cultural superiority of Europeans; the figure of the medicine man or shaman was often viewed as inimical to social and cultural progress."[8]

Historically the American public has not always agreed that healing traditions, such as American Indian healing practices, were inferior to the medicine of the Regulars. As in Homer Merriam's stay with the Indian doctress or the Shakers who visited an Indian healer in Saratoga, some Americans have had positive, firsthand experience with the expertise of Indian traditional healers. For example, in the last part of the eighteenth century, a trader, James Adair, wrote that he would "prefer an old Indian before any chirurgeon (surgeon) whatsoever, in curing green wounds by bullets, arrows, &c. both for the certainty, ease, and speediness of cure. They bring the patient into a good temperament of body, by a decoction of proper herbs and roots."[9] It was in the mid- and late nineteenth century in particular that the reputation of Indian healers went far beyond the more rural areas of the country, where their expertise was welcomed. Some European-Americans began modeling their healing practices after the Indians. "It was the popular image of the Indian as healer which created in the nineteenth century the great success of the white "Indian doctors," the patent medicines of alleged Indian origin, and the "Indian" medicine shows."[10]

Botanical literature and receipt books of the nineteenth century hint at a connection to American Indian herbalism,[11] although more research is needed to determine whether or not the remedies listed are actually true to the cultural traditions of the Indian nations. In the process of integrating American Indian traditions and knowledge, it is highly probable that the European-Americans documenting the remedies would have recorded the information through their own eyes and would not necessarily have captured the essence or even the details of the Indian use of an herb. If, as Dhyani Ywahoo stated, spirituality (i.e. belief) is foundational to healing and if the recorder of the remedy were carrying a divergent set of beliefs, then it is quite likely that the remedy would lose much in the cultural translation. The foundation for the practice of herbalism in all cultures, including various European cultures, is not only the herbs used in healing but is also very much about the process of using herbs.[12] The Shaker, LDS, and SOC nurses had much in common with the Indians, in that they too, believed that the healing modality, herb or otherwise, was secondary to spiritual healing.

Biomedicine, with its claims to success in developing powerful technological instruments for the diagnosis and treatment of disease has won the favor of international leaders, policy makers, and the public. There is a difference between the public and political support, however. The public, as discussed previously, has continued in its private choices and practices to support the hidden health care system and traditional healers, known today as "complementary therapies" or "alternative medicine" practitioners. American political and economic support has, for the most part, been given to the biomedical culture. Nursing, which has directly aligned itself with the biomedical culture since the late nineteenth century, has consistently weaned itself from association with the sphere of traditional healing over the years.

Herbalism, which was once a common modality available to nurses up until the late nineteenth century, is now rarely, if ever, mentioned in nursing schools or texts. When herbs are discussed, it is usually in terms of the needs associated with the biomedical culture, such as whether or not herbal supplements interact with certain drugs or what the safe dose of an herbal supplement might be for a patient. Long gone in nursing is the understanding of healing plants and the full scope of nurse herbalism, with all of its whole plant poultices, compresses, teas, and floral waters. Nurses and physicians in the biomedical culture often perceive herbs as "crude" medicines used by those who cannot afford or do not have access to the best medical care (i.e., laboratory-produced drugs). Access to care, an important issue on the agenda for many nursing organizations, most often focuses on access to biomedical care rather than an integrative approach that would include less expensive healing traditions such as botanical therapies.[13] Contemporary nurses may want to take the opportunity to learn from the integrative, inclusive approach of the mid-nineteenth-century nurses when shaping policy and practice strategies intended to increase access to care.

Herbs, unless appearing in capsule or tablet form like pharmaceuticals, are not so welcome in a health culture that has "progressed." Progress, defined as "forward or onward movement or gradual betterment,"[14] has become culturally synonymous in American health care for practitioners and patients alike, with technology. The words "technology" and "modern" often are used together. Demonstrating the common belief that by definition modern or new things are better and improved. Technology is defined as the "practical application of knowledge"[15] but in the vernacular it has come to be associated with "things," human creations.[16] An object becomes "technological" when it is made or used in purposeful activity.

Sandelowski, who has written extensively on the concept of technology in nursing practice, said that technology functions as cultural artifact and even culture itself, is context dependent, and is "subject to historical change."[17] In recent history, Leonard, in evaluating society's belief in technology, wrote: "Progress is America's destiny and technology is the method and the evidence."[18] Science in American culture also has become synonymous with the scientific "method." Perhaps the most well-known example of the manifestation of the American values of progress as science and technology is the creation of the method of inquiry known as the randomized clinical trial (RCT).

Looking closely at the health beliefs of the biomedical culture that has permeated American culture since the late nineteenth century, the RCT has become the "gold standard" for medical science. Its primary function is examining drugs for use in humans. However, even with constant emphasis on the standardization of medical science in the RCT, and the resulting optimization of pharmaceutical invention and production, there is conflicting evidence regarding the success of the method in terms of safeguarding the public. A meta-analysis published in the *Journal of the American Medical Association* has shown that properly prescribed drugs—meaning that drugs are being used as they were designed and researched through RCTs performed with humans —are the fourth leading cause of death in the United States.[19] Much has been written of the difficulties with the present "high-tech" culture in America, but the most pressing issue seems to be that while Americans continue to express a belief in scientific evidence, they are ignoring hard evidence that there are problems in the system that need to be dealt with, such as pharmaceutical drugs.

The insistence by Americans for proof of cultural "progress" through technology is in keeping with the historical need for medical care that produces proof of effect, whether the demonstrative results of calomel and purgatives in the nineteenth century or the chemotherapeutic agents of today. The belief in progress incorporates an optimistic view of the world that change is inherently for the better, and that which emerges in the present is superior to that which has occurred in the past. This is ever present in countries that often are referred to in the international community as "developed." The international community, including the World Health Organization, internalized the belief that technological progress is a sign of a developed country and persists in categorizing countries as "developed" or "developing." Such dualism can be misleading and has the potential to perpetuate the blocks to health care integration that have been in place for centuries. Dualistic thinking does not allow for the creativity and flexibility needed in addressing the unique concerns of individual nations or the global health care community.

A similar problem in language used in the international science community, including health care, can be found in the use of the word "science" or "scientific" to describe activities that are related to the narrower definition of technology, such as exemplified in modern devices and RCTs. For example, it is commonly stated that the activities of traditional healers are not "science based," when in fact many healing traditions, such as traditional Chinese medicine, Ayurveda, or the work of a bush healer in the rain forest, are highly scientific. Spiritual healers too often are scientific in their exploration of the healing effects of their work. The vernacular use of the word "science" has narrowed in meaning and has become ethnocentric and exclusionary in its use by the dominant culture in America. The research of American folklorists demonstrates that the word "scientific" has come to connote "better" and more "reliable" and is used as an evaluative term.[20] And while the biomedical culture has been the dominant system in America for many years, recent nursing studies have shown that people with chronic illnesses quickly come to realize the limitations of biomedicine, understand medicine as a belief system rather than as a synonym for scientific knowledge, and find that solutions to their daily, chronic health challenges more often come from the implementation of self-care practices and the aid of traditional healers and complementary therapies.[21]

"Traditional healing" is defined by the World Health Organization (WHO) as "the health practices, approaches, knowledge and beliefs incorporating plant, animal and mineral based medicines, spiritual therapies, manual techniques and exercises, applied singularly or in combination, to treat, diagnose and prevent illness or maintain well-being."[22] Resolution WHA44.34 of the 44th World Health Assembly urged members, such as the United States, to "identify activities leading to cooperation between those providing traditional medicine and modern health care, respectively, especially in regards to the use of scientifically proven safe and effective traditional remedies to reduce national drug costs."[23] For years, the WHO, with its Traditional Medicine Programme, has been pursuing the goal of cooperation between traditional and biomedical practitioners primarily in "developing" nations.

Primary health care (PHC) is the foundation for this cooperation. There is an important role for nurses in achieving this vision. In 1985, the WHO executive board concluded that the role of nurses "would move from the hospital to everyday life in the community, that nurses would become resources to people, rather than to physicians, and that nurses would become leaders and managers of PHC teams, including supervising nonprofessional community health workers."[24] This vision is somewhat similar to that of Florence Nightingale and the work in the borderland of some mid-nineteenth-century, and earlier, nurses. For years the international health community has recognized nurses' reestablishment of their health care expertise in the domestic sphere as being vital to the success of health systems. The public has continued to recognize and appreciate the integrative work of nurses. One chronically ill person in a study by Thorne recalled the following:

> I guess I heard about [the Naturopath], it would've been a year, or 2 years before. And it was through a lady in our church, who is an RN, who got into this area of holistic medicine, and naturopathy and she was very much against going to a chiropractor or anything. And so when she got interested in it, I mean, she really researched it. So it was like when she told me about it, it was like, "Well, I can accept this," because here's an RN who knows the medical side, and she's saying this other has validity. I was really skeptical.[25]

As this example demonstrates, the public trusts nurses' rationality. Historically nurses have been entrusted by society to represent the best of both worlds of traditional healing and biomedicine.

Botanical therapies have been identified by the WHO as a key component of the global strategies to provide primary health care for all people. "Traditional medicines play an important part in health care, particularly as regards informed self-medication, in many developed and developing countries."[26] Plant remedies hold the potential for empowered self-care. "They [medicinal plants] offer the local population and others immediate access to safe and effective products for the use in the treatment of illness through self-medication and plants are valuable for modern medicine. For individuals, families, and communities in many countries, the proper use of medicinal plants in therapy is a necessity, not a luxury, one that plays a very important role in self-medication, thereby reducing demands on the precious time of already overtaxed health professionals."[27] Botanical therapies are an essential part of traditional medicine systems in continents such as Asia, Africa, and Latin America, because "traditional medicine is firmly embedded within wider belief systems."[28] Traditional healers are trusted and respected community members who continue the historical practice of serving their communities' health care needs. They often are quite skilled at meeting the common and often chronic illness needs of community members that even orthodox health care practitioners and systems cannot meet.

With 80 percent of the world's populations still engaged in the use of traditional healing methods, it is important that nurses are exhibiting an interest in regaining their connection to traditional healing. One study of health practitioner attitudes toward complementary therapies found that more than 50 percent of American nursing students and faculty wished to acquire training in complementary therapies especially with herbs.[29] The first American textbook on nurse herbalism since the mid-twentieth century was published in 2001,[30] in which nurses were encouraged to explore their history with the use of botanical therapies and ways for integrating their knowledge of biomedical and traditional healing related to herbs to create new research studies and practice models to produce greater care options for the public.

One nurse historian wrote: "The task of recasting nursing and nurses as critical historical actors in and interpreters of the world of science and research is that which now awaits us.[31] Nurses have the opportunity to be active participants in the making of history through the pursuit of the herbal integration process from the level of scholarship and research and community practice. Given nursing history with botanical therapies, American nurses have the potential to make significant national and global contributions to the further exploration of the role of botanical therapies in the promotion of health, the cure of disease, and the resolution of chronic illnesses currently plaguing humanity.

Nurses understand that the use of botanical therapies does not have to be a part of their past or represent a retreat to some out-of-date ideology. Herbalism, like all aspects of culture, has itself progressed. For example, as the materia medica has expanded, plants once used in healing that were either somewhat toxic or caustic, for instance tobacco, have been replaced in common use by other remedies that are just as effective and less risky. Another example of progress is that herbs are available in tea bags for greater convenience. Herbalists weigh the benefits and risks of these kinds of conveniences. They understand that plant material that goes through the packaging process has the potential not only for losing its aroma and flavor but, in the case of medicinal plants, also may lose its potency.

Nurses are uniquely positioned in their role as trusted community health providers to guide patients in evaluating the benefits and risks of any health care option, whether surgical, pharmaceutical, spiritual, or botanical. Modern nurses have the opportunity to carry on the historical tradition of herbal diplomacy in supporting the public's use of herbs in healing while using their knowledge of science to not only produce new botanical options in caregiving, as did the Shakers, Latter-day Saints, and Sisters of Charity, but also to provide botanical safeguards for human and plant populations by researching and experimenting with individual and community botanical programs.

There was no evidence that the nurses of the nineteenth century thought of preserving plant populations, but nurse-herbalists of the twenty-first century, given the significant increase in human population, will need to take into account the protection of plant populations from potential extinction due to overuse and/or misuse. They also may want to consider taking part in the movement to protect the rights of traditional healers and their healing plants as international resources from intellectual and bio-piracy. Nurses, such as Nurse Davis, in their historical roles as herbal diplomats, have developed relationships with knowledgeable plant healers. Today it is important that nurses consider entering into health and botanical policy discussions with a knowledge of transcultural issues and an understanding of the historical and cultural issues involved in the promotion of botanical therapies for long-term use and for large populations.

Nurse scholars have demonstrated decades of expertise in using research designs such as ethnography and epidemiology as well as community health program development and evaluation strategies that are known to be effective in determining the long-term effects of healing modalities. One proposal for the integration of biomedical and traditional healing suggests that public health agendas include "the awareness of social, cultural, and political dimensions and should address values (equity, ethics), sustainability (regulation, financing, knowledge generation, knowledge management, capacity building), and the research environment."[32] Nurses, with their history of supporting integrative community health agendas that are solution focused and open to evaluating all possible contributions to community health such as suggested in this proposal, may want to become involved in designing public health agendas for the integration of biomedical and traditional healing practices, such as the use of botanical therapies.

Nurses use transcultural awareness when dealing with botanical and other traditional healing practices in families and communities. They understand that "many indigenous practices have emerged from historical test and may depend for their effectiveness on an integrated, interacting set of values and beliefs. It may well be that their effective power lies in the family's commitment to them and to their symbolic contribution to family identity. The replacement of some indigenous practices by professional strategies might in some instances offer little or no technical advantage while eroding the integrity of the family's capacity for healing and caring."[33]

As nurses expand their own professional identities and roles to embrace their historical traditions in using herbs, they will need to consider that herbs also are very much a part of the non-health professional culture in the United States. Patients use herbs based on the ways their mothers, fathers, grandfathers, and grandmothers taught them. If nurses seek to integrate botanical therapies as did the mid-nineteenth-century nurses of the borderland, then they will have a very different context with which to contend. Nurses now use and value clinical trial data and other research methodologies and include this evidence when considering the use of an herb in the care of a patient. Patients using herbs may not. Some patients have very personal reasons for their choices in using certain herbs for healing. Plants are a part of the environment and culture. They are a part of people's lives and, therefore, part of their history and identity. Nurses, using therapeutic relationship techniques, can explore and research the cultural and historical botanical evidence revealed by their patients, which can then be added to the collection of scholarship on botanical therapies in nursing practice.

Botanical Nostalgia?

Rather than embracing healing traditions as part of historical progress in health care that may complement biomedicine, some nurses view complementary therapies as a backward step, not only in terms of progress but in terms of professional nursing identity. One nursing scholar, while recognizing nursing's historical connection to healing traditions such as herbs, suggests that nurses' "proud heritage" and identity should be supported by requiring that nurses only begin to implement complementary therapies after "rigorous scientific testing" of the modality has been done. She expresses concern that the integration of healing traditions is representative of nurses' acceptance of "pseudo-science" as "valid," and that nurses must unite against "the misuse of alternative therapies to protect our patients and the credibility of our practice."[34] While many in nursing would not disagree with the basic desires of the author to maintain a proud heritage, there must be concern that the views expressed in this article perpetuate nurses' ethnocentric participation in the conflict between traditional healing and biomedical cultures. The author identifies the risk of using traditional healing and complementary therapies to the profession, but she ignores the risks of biomedicine.

Biomedical ethnocentrism has led to the accusation that nurses, practitioners, and the public who seek traditional forms of healing are nostalgic for the past. Some believe that the desire to use herbs in any form other than as industry-produced, standardized extracts, which many claim are more "effective and safe" because they are industry produced, is perhaps irrational and nostalgic. I once heard a nurse speaker say that nurses who use complementary therapies, such as herbs in their own healing or in helping others, are "nostalgic for the past." Then, in 1996, an editor of a medical journal article, "Medical Nostalgia: Simple Medical Care versus Technology," stated: "I sense nostalgia, a yearning to return to the 'simple' life only found in remote primitive tribes."[35] While medicinal plants are quite complex, it is a myth that their use is simple. Perhaps it is alleged because herbs have historically been called "*simples.*" Is it nostalgic (i.e., unscientific, emotional, and nonprogressive) to want to study and use herbs in nursing practice? Is it nostalgic to suggest that historical evidence may indicate that the future or trajectory of herbal diplomacy, if embraced by willing nurses, could become international in scope, integrative in approach, and ultimately empowering for the profession?

Historian John Tosh defines nostalgia as "backward looking . . . interpreting in one direction only—as change for the worse . . . nostalgia presents the past as an alternative to the present, instead of as a prelude to it . . . nostalgia indulges a desire to escape from it [the present]."[36] The purpose of this history, or any historical work, is not to escape into the past. A look backward into history, not with a sense of nostalgia or escape, can be helpful in creating and supporting personal and professional identity. One purpose of this book was to begin to provide supporting evidence on the use of botanical therapies from the history of nursing so that present and future policy and practice decisions can be informed.

With historical evidence, nurses of the twenty-first century may be better equipped to "immigrate to the borderland, where they can explore and perhaps even embrace health beliefs of both traditional and biomedical health cultures. Immigrants face significant cultural challenges, however, as they seek to integrate and identify with a new culture. The immigrant deals with issues of identity and nostalgia. Nostalgia, from the Greek word meaning "to return," has been defined as a medical condition in people when they were away from home and yearned to return but for some reason could not. Today, with the exponential increase in mobility between cultures, nostalgia is no longer defined only as a psychiatric condition. It also is defined as a "psychological filter employed in establishing and maintaining a sense of personal identity . . . we derive from our nostalgic remembrance the comfort of identifying with ourselves."[37] Ritivoi, in her study of nostalgia in immigrants, found that nostalgia is "genuine *pharmakos,* both medicine and poison: it can express alienation, or it can replenish and rebuttress our sense of identity by consolidating the ties with our history."[38] Nurses may become nostalgic, in the positive sense of replenishing professional identity, in preparation for any integrative work that they attempt. Looking to the past can be both reassuring and comforting.

Nurses understand the importance of comfort in healing. In the nineteenth century, nurses such as Matilda Coskery recognized the importance of familiarity in creating congenial and supportive environments. Patients, when they are diagnosed with disease and are faced with tremendous changes in their lives, seek out their familiar, family healing traditions in an attempt to soothe themselves. They are nostalgic for the trusted remedies of their ancestors. Botanical therapies often are a part of the self-care, self-comforting measures they choose.

Plants are a fundamental part of the human experience. They are everywhere. Most people have a healing connection with at least one plant, even if that connection is the cup of coffee or tea they brew to wake themselves up in the morning. Plants often are associated with memories of home, the environment of origin. The histories of American settlers, immigrants, and those who moved to the Western frontier often include descriptions of the herbal remedies and the receipts for creating them that are brought to a new environment as reminders of home. Even today, herbal and culinary receipt books are not forgotten by the immigrant. Folklorist Janet Theophano, wrote of recipes: "Their existence in writing offers us a kind of permanence that, if and when we want it, is waiting for us to retrieve."[39] Plant remedies often are a stabilizing factor in people's lives.

Healing plants may be conceived of as a metaphor for the integrative spirit of the borderland; they are gentle yet powerful healers that offer an opportunity for integration into any health care culture. Like the mid-nineteenth-century nurses, healing plants are diplomats too. They have been the instrument of peaceful exchange in the pipes of American Indians and the resource for extending women's healing networks, as in the example of the LDS nurse giving asafoetida to the needy woman on the pioneer trail. Botanical therapies are the instruments of the *process*[40] of our ongoing history of healing: they are neither the cause nor the result of our progress; they are neither the cause nor the result of any nostalgia humans may hold.

"Plant-Like Gentleness"

Nineteenth-century women leaders such as Margaret Fuller spoke about the importance of the "feminization of culture." They believed that American culture, the public sphere in particular, was incomplete, and that women held some of the keys to greater balance, peace, and health in society. Their ideals included the image of the reinstatement of "a 'plant-like gentleness,' a harmonic, peaceful rule, and an end to violence in all areas of life."[41] Even though people know that a rose's thorns can prick and that lobelia, when taken in excessive doses, can make one vomit, they still retain the belief in the inherent gentleness of plant remedies. Like some Regulars of the nineteenth century, health practitioners today often puzzle over the continued popular belief that herbal remedies are gentler and safer. But put into context with the aftereffects of all of the other remedies that patients are exposed to in the biomedical culture—the adverse effects of drugs and scars from surgeries—is it really difficult to understand the source of patients' beliefs?

In this fast-paced technological world of rapid transport and a growing sense of the global nature of community, there is a need for integrative solutions that respect diverse beliefs and traditions. We have the opportunity to include not only biomedical values, beliefs, and practices in national health care policies and professional nursing policies but also the indigenous and traditional values, beliefs, and practices of health and healing as represented in the science and art of herbalism. The history of the women nurses of the American Botanical Medical Movement of the mid-nineteenth century—with the stories of the caring traditions of Prudence, Matilda, Mary Ann, Patty, and so many others—is relevant to nurses, herbalists, healers, women and men of the twenty-first century. Their works demonstrate the importance of a tiered system of health care that embraces an integrative approach to health and healing. Their stories can encourage us to seek greater understanding of a feminine way of being that is the potential of every woman and the brethren as well. Their lives inspire us to pursue "plant-like gentleness" in nursing practice, with a greater zest for research into the caring activities so precious and foundational to nursing identity. Nineteenth-century Shakers, Latter-day Saints, and Sisters of Charity nurse-herbalists remind us that healing power is not in the object, technology, or botanical therapy; it is in the spirit of the healer and the one who needs healing. Herbal diplomacy founded upon this understanding of healing has a truly universal potential.

Glossary of Terms

Alkaloid—Substance obtained from plants that reacts with acids to form salts used for medical purposes.*

Anthelmintic—An agent that destroys parasites.

Antimony—A crystalline, metallic element. Compounds of it are used in medicines.*

Arsenic—A metallic element that is quite poisonous. It is found in minute amounts in vegetables and animals.*

Blistering—A medical treatment in which a substance is applied to the skin for the purpose of raising a blister.

Cantharides—Dried insects of the species Cantharis vesicatoria, formerly used externally as a counterirritant. *

Carminative—A substance that relieves flatulence.

Catarrh—Chronic inflammation of the nose and mucous membranes.

Compress—In herbalism, a cloth soaked in an herbal infusion and then applied externally to the body.

Counterirritant—A substance applied to the body to create a local inflammatory response signified by redness and warmth of the skin for the purpose of affecting healing in a part of the body that is adjacent to or beneath the location of the counterirritant, e.g., mustard plaster.

Decoction—A water extraction of the medicinal property of plants in which the plant material, usually barks and roots, is simmered.

Emetic—A substance that causes vomiting.

Heroics—The form of medicine practiced by nineteenth-century orthodox physicians.

Humor—A fluid or semifluid substance in the body. Early medicine was based upon humoral theory. According to this theory, the body was made of four humors, or fluids.

Hydrotherapy—The use of water in various remedies such as baths, steams, and packs (compresses).

Infused oil—An oil extraction of the medicinal components of a plant.

Infusion—A water extraction of the medicinal properties of plants in which the plant material, usually flowers and leaves, is steeped in boiled water.

Inhalation—To breathe in water vapor (hydrotherapy) with or without an herbal infusion added to the water.

Injection—An enema.

Laudanum—A tincture of opium.

Liquid extract—An alcohol extraction of a medicinal plant, with two or five parts alcohol to one part plant.

Materia medica—A book of substances used in preparing medicines.

Mucilage—The sticky or slimy constituent of a plant.

Paregoric—Camphorated tincture of opium. Large doses are poisonous.

Plaster—A topical herbal application of a plant paste to the skin for healing purposes such as producing a counterirritant effect, e.g., mustard plaster.

Poultice—An herbal application of chopped-up plant material applied to the skin in a cloth, e.g., onion poultice.

Purgative—A substance that causes bowel evacuation, e.g., castor oil.

Quinine—A bitter, white crystalline alkaloid derived from cinchona bark and used as medicine.

Receipt—The nineteenth-century term for recipe.

Simple—A healing plant or plant remedy.

Steam—The use of the vapors from boiled water to heal the body through inhalation or absorption through the skin.

Tincture—An alcohol extraction of a medicinal plant, with ten parts alcohol to one part plant.

Tisane—An herbal tea—infusion or decoction.

Tonic—A substance that improves overall general health.

Vapor bath—Another hydrotherapeutic name for a steam.

Wild crafting—To harvest healing plants from their natural habitat.

* Definition adapted from *Taber's Cyclopedic Medical Dictionary*, 14th ed., 1981, Philadelphia: F.A. Davis, Co.

NOTES

CHAPTER 1: INTRODUCTION: HARVESTING A HISTORY OF WOMEN HEALERS

1 Heywood, *Journal of Martha Spence Heywood: Recorded during the years 1850 to 1856.*

2 Saleratus, or *sal aeratus*, is potassium bicarbonate. According to the nineteenth-century text by Felter and Lloyd, *King's American dispensatory*, 1983, p. 1547, *sal aeratus* is an antacid and a diuretic used as a remedy for ailments such as gout, rheumatism, and fever.

3 Buchan, *Domestic medicine, or, The family physician being an attempt to render the medical art more generally useful, by showing people what is in their own power both with respect to the prevention and cure of diseases. Chiefly calculated to recommend a proper attention to regimen and simple medicines*, 1769.

4 "Herbals" are books on plant-based remedies.

5 Risse, *Medicine without doctors: Home health care in American history, 1977;* Rothstein, *American physicians in the nineteenth century: From sects to science*, 1972; Vogel and Rosenberg, *The therapeutic revolution: Essays in the social history of American medicine*, 1979.

6 Berman, *The impact of the nineteenth-century Botanico-Medical Movement on American pharmacy and medicine*, 1954; Berman, *Social roots of the 19th-century botanico-medical movement in the United States*, 1956.

7 Haller, *The people's doctors: Samuel Thomson and the American botanical movement, 1790–1860*, 2000.

8 Berman and Flannery, *America's botanico-medical movement: Vox populi*, 2001.

9 Thomson, *New guide to health, or, Botanic family physician containing a complete system of practice, upon a plan entirely new: with a description of the vegetables made use of, and directions for preparing and administering them to cure disease: to which is prefixed a narrative of the life and medical discoveries of the author*, 1835.

10 Beach, *The family physician, or, The reformed system of medicine on vegetable or botanical principles being a compendium of the "American Practice" designed for all classes*, 1843.

11 Sklar, *Women and power in American history to 1880*, 2002.

12 A. Digby and J. Stewart, "Welfare in Context," in (ed.) A. Digby and J. Stewart, *Gender, health, and welfare*, 1996, p. 14.

13 Donovan, *Feminist theory: The intellectual traditions*, 2000, p. 47.

14 Baker, The domestication of politics: Women and American political society, 1780–1920, 1984, p. 623.

15 Kerber, Separate spheres, female worlds, woman's place: The rhetoric of women's history, 1988, p. 18.

16 Donovan, *Feminist theory: The intellectual traditions*, 2000, p. 47. Contemporary feminist theorists define the nineteenth century as an important period for women, the initiation of cultural feminism.

17 Donovan, *Feminist theory: The intellectual traditions*, 2000, p. 48.

18 Donovan, p. 51.

19 Alcoff, Cultural feminism versus post-structuralism: The identity crisis in feminist theory, 1988, p. 433–435.

20 Tosh, *The pursuit of history: Aims, methods, and new directions in the study of modern history*, 2000, p. 4.

21 Abram, *Send us a lady physician: Women doctors in America, 1835–1920*, 1985.

22 Verbrugge, *Able-bodied womanhood: Personal health and social change in nineteenth-century Boston*, 1988.

23 Silver-Isenstadt, *Shameless: The visionary life of Mary Gove Nichols*, 2002.

24 Thomson, *New guide to health, or, Botanic family physician containing a complete system of practice, upon a plan entirely new: with a description of the vegetables made use of, and directions for preparing and administering them to cure disease: to which is prefixed a narrative of the life and medical discoveries of the author*, 1835.

25 Sharp, Folk medicine practices: Women as keepers and carriers of knowledge, 1986, p. 248.

26 Gartrell, Women healers and domestic remedies in 18th-century America: The recipe book of Elizabeth Coates Paschall, 1987, p. 24.

27 Tannenbaum, *The healer's calling: Women and medicine in early New England*, 2002.

28 Reverby, *Ordered to care: The dilemma of American nursing, 1850–1945*, 1987, p. 3.

29 Christman, Who is a nurse? 1998.

30 Church, Historiography in nursing research, 1987, p. 275.

31 Reverby, *Ordered to care: The dilemma of American nursing, 1850–1945*, 1987.

32 Ashley, *Hospitals, paternalism, and the role of the nurse*, 1976.

33 Melosh, *"The physician's hand": Work, culture, and conflict in American nursing*, 1982.

34 Harmer, *Text-book of the principles and practice of nursing*, 1924; Harmer and Henderson, *Textbook of the principles and practice of nursing*, 1955.

35 The term *materia medica* is defined as a "description of substances used in preparing medicine." This term is still used in clinical herbalism and pharmacy.

36 Throughout this book, plants may be referred to by their common name only or by their botanical name and common name if able to be identified from the source material. When known, the Linnaean system of botanical binomial nomenclature will be used to clarify the plant being discussed. Plants being discussed in general, not in relation to a specific manuscript, will be identified by both their common and botanical names.

37 Harmer and Henderson, *Textbook of the principles and practice of nursing*, 1955, p. 264.

38 Vogel and Rosenberg, *The therapeutic revolution: Essays in the social history of American medicine*, 1979.

39 Kett, *The formation of the American medical profession: The role of institutions, 1780–1860*, 1968.

40 Starr, *The social transformation of American medicine*, 1982.

41 Starr, p. 155.

42 Chamberlain, *Old wives' tales: Their history, remedies and spells*, 1981; Tannenbaum, *The healer's calling: Women and medicine in early New England*, 2002; Ehrenreich and English, *For her own good: 150 years of the experts' advice to women*, 1978, p. 34; Ulrich, *A midwife's tale: The life of Martha Ballard, based on her diary, 1785–1812*, 1990.

43 Schorske, as quoted in Tosh, *The pursuit of history aims, methods, and new directions in the study of modern history*, 2000, p. 96.

44 Marshall and Wall, Religion, gender, and autonomy: A comparison of two religious women's groups in nursing and hospitals in the late nineteenth and early twentieth centuries, 1999; Nelson, *Say little, do much: Nurses, nuns, and hospitals in the nineteenth century*, 2001.

45 *Merriam-Webster's collegiate dictionary*, 1999.

46 Cott in Kerber et al., Beyond roles, beyond spheres: Thinking about gender in the early republic, 1989, p. 567.

47 Baker, The domestication of politics: Women and American political society, 1780–1920, 1984, p. 624.

48 A. Digby, "Victorian values and women in public and private," in (ed.) T. Smout et

al., *Victorian values: A joint symposium of the Royal Society of Edinburgh and the British Academy December 1990*, 1992.

49 Cummings, *Cultural diplomacy and the United States government: A survey*, 2003, p. 1.

50 Farnsworth et al., Medicinal plants in therapy, 1985, p. 965.

51 Farnsworth and Morris, Higher plants—the sleeping giant of drug development, 1976.

52 Mahady et al., *Botanical dietary supplements: Quality, safety, and efficacy*, 2001, p. 1.

53 McFarlin et al., A national survey of herbal preparation use by nurse-midwives for labor stimulation. 1999.

54 Leininger, *Care: The essence of nursing and health*, 1984, p. 9.

CHAPTER 2: MID-NINETEENTH-CENTURY AMERICAN HEALTH CARE

1 Coffin, *A Botanic guide to health and the natural pathology of disease*, 1846, p. vi.

2 Rosenberg, *The cholera years: The United States in 1832, 1849, and 1866*, 1962.

3 Rothstein, *American physicians in the nineteenth century: From sects to science*, 1972, p. 55.

4 Cassedy, *Medicine and American growth, 1800–1860*, 1986, p. 81.

5 Porter, *The greatest benefit to mankind: A medical history of humanity*, 1997, p. 266.

6 Rosenberg, *The cholera years: The United States in 1832, 1849, and 1866*, 1962.

7 Berman and Flannery, *America's botanico-medical movement: Vox populi*, 2001, p. 4.

8 Starr, *The social transformation of American medicine*, 1982, p. 38.

9 Starr, p. 65.

10 Porter, *The greatest benefit to mankind: A medical history of humanity*, 1997, p. 245.

11 *The Holy Bible, — King James Version*, 1972, Genesis 1.

12 Porter, *The greatest benefit to mankind: A medical history of humanity*, 1997, p. 302.

13 Merchant, *The death of nature: Women, ecology, and the scientific revolution*, 1989, p. 190.

14 "Simples" refers to an herbal remedy of one to three herbs commonly used to ease symptoms.

15 Merchant, *The death of nature: Women, ecology, and the scientific revolution*, 1989, p. 8.

16 Rothstein, *American physicians in the nineteenth century: From sects to science*, 1972, p. 43.

17 Rothstein, p. 49.

18 Rothstein, p. 44.

19 Blake, "From Buchan to Fishbein," in (ed.) G. Risse et al., *Medicine without doctors: Home health care in American history*, 1977, p. 16.

20 Vogel & Rosenberg, *The therapeutic revolution: Essays in the social history of American medicine*, 1979, p. 14.

21 R. Morantz, "Nineteenth century health reform and women," in (ed.) G. Risse et al., *Medicine without doctors: Home health care in American history*, 1977, p. 75.

22 Silver-Isenstadt, *Shameless: The visionary life of Mary Gove Nichols*, 2002, insert 12.

23 Silver-Isenstadt, p. 248.

24 R. Morantz, "Nineteenth century health reform and women," in (ed.) G. Risse et al., *Medicine without doctors: Home health care in American history*, 1977, p. 76.

25 Turner & Craven, *The United States, 1830–-1850: The nation and its sections*, 1935, p. 20.

26 Blau, *Social theories of Jacksonian democracy: Representative writings of the period 1825–1850*, 1954, p. xiv.

27 Van Deusen, *The Jacksonian era*, 1959, p. 13.

28 Blau, *Social theories of Jacksonian democracy: Representative writings of the period 1825–1850*, 1954, p. xiv.

29 Van Deusen, *The Jacksonian era*, 1959, p. 13.

30 Gunn, *Domestic medicine or poor man's friend in the hours of affliction, pain, and sickness*, 1830, p. 10.

31 Rothstein, *American physicians in the nineteenth century: From sects to science*, 1972, p. 80.

32 Kett, *The formation of the American medical profession: The role of institutions*, 1780–1860, 1968, p. 30.

33 Rothstein, *American physicians in the nineteenth century: From sects to science*, 1972, p. 78.

34 Rothstein, p. 107.

35 Ekirch, *The idea of progress in America, 1815–1860*, 1951, p. 107.

36 Kett, *The formation of the American medical profession: The role of institutions*, 1780–1860, 1968, p. 31.

37 Jefferson et al., *The life and selected writings of Thomas Jefferson*, 1944, pp. 583–584; Rothstein, *American physicians in the nineteenth century: From sects to science*, 1972, p. 43.

38 Vogel and Rosenberg, *The therapeutic revolution: Essays in the social history of American medicine*, 1979, p. 15.

39 Kett, *The formation of the American medical profession: The role of institutions, 1780–1860*, 1968, p. 97.

40 Kett, p. 97.

41 Porter, *Health for sale: Quackery in England* 1660–1850, 1989, p. 91.

42 Porter, p. 37.

43 Rothstein, *American physicians in the nineteenth century: From sects to science*, 1972, p. 35.

44 Rothstein, p. 35.

45 Thomson, *New guide to health, or, Botanic family physician containing a complete system of practice, upon a plan entirely new: with a description of the vegetables made use of, and directions for preparing and administering them to cure disease: to which is prefixed a narrative of the life and medical discoveries of the author*, 1835, p. 16.

46 Thomson, p. 18.

47 Thomson, p. 19.

48 Thomson, p. 20.

49 Thomson, p. 23.

50 Thomson, p. 23.

51 Thomson, p. 25. Thomson records that the "root doctors" used roots and herbs in practice.

52 Thomson received U.S. patents for his medical system in 1813, 1823, and 1836.

53 Thomson, *New guide to health, or, Botanic family physician containing a complete system of practice, upon a plan entirely new: with a description of the vegetables made use of, and directions for preparing and administering them to cure disease: to which is prefixed a narrative of the life and medical discoveries of the author*, 1835, p. 32.

54 Andrew Jackson served as the seventh president of the United States for two terms, from 1829 to 1837. Jackson was a lawyer and a highly successful major general before becoming a senator and then president. "Old Hickory," as he was called, was viewed as the champion of the "common man" allowing men on horseback to ride into the White House after his inauguration. He became associated with the new Democratic Party that formed in 1828, hence, the term *Jacksonian democracy.* Jackson's democracy was not extended to all Americans. Jackson was renowned for his mistreatment of various Indian tribes, in particular, the forced removal of the Cherokee nation.

55 Haller, *The people's doctors: Samuel Thomson and the American botanical movement,* 1790–1860, 2000, p. 16.

56 Rafinesque, *Medical flora or, Manual of the medical botany of the United States of North America,* 1828, p. 23. "Puking" has been a part of spiritual healing practice in many cultures. In addition to the American Indian tradition, the East Indian Ayurvedic tradition that is thousands of years old includes the notion of therapeutic vomiting induced at the right time for the right patient. It is only administered by a knowledgeable therapist.

57 Thomson, *New guide to health, or, Botanic family physician containing a complete system of practice, upon a plan entirely new: with a description of the vegetables made use of, and directions for preparing and administering them to cure disease: to which is prefixed a narrative of the life and medical discoveries of the author,* 1835, pp. 79–80.

58 Berman, Social roots of the 19th-century botanico-medical movement in the United States, 1956, p. 4.

59 Haller, *Kindly medicine: Physio-medicalism in America,* 1836–1911, 1997, p. 18.

60 *Berman & Flannery, America's botanico-medical movement: Vox populi,* 2001, p. 11.

61 Bigelow, *Discourse on self-limited disease,* 1836.

62 Berman & Flannery, *America's botanico-medical movement: Vox populi,* 2001, p. 11.

63 Haller, *The people's doctors: Samuel Thomson and the American botanical movement,* 1790–1860, 2000, p. 103.

64 Rothstein, *American physicians in the nineteenth century: from sects to science,* 1972, p. 325.

65 As quoted in Rothstein, *American physicians in the nineteenth century: from sects to science,* 1972, p. 325.

66 Berman and Flannery, *America's botanico-medical movement: Vox populi,* 2001, p. 146.

CHAPTER 3: THE MID-NINETEENTH-CENTURY PATIENT: HERBS, ADVICE BOOKS, AND MEDICAL FREEDOM

1 Jefferson & University of Virginia, letter to William C. Jarvis, in *The Writings of Thomas Jefferson*, 1820.

2 Merriam, *The annals of the Merriam family*, 1946.

3 Merriam, p. 52.

4 Merriam, p. 54.

5 Merriam, p. 59.

6 Merriam, p. 60.

7 Merriam, p. 61.

8 Merriam, p. 63.

9 Merriam, p. 87.

10 R. Morantz, "Nineteenth century health reform and women," in (ed.) G. Risse et al., *Medicine without doctors: Home health care in American history*, 1977, p. 77.

11 Morantz, p. 73.

12 Levin et al., *The hidden health care system mediating structures and medicine*, 1981, p. 166.

13 Graham, The Graham system: What is it? 1837. Graham's system was comprised of lifestyle and dietary changes and included instructions in making bread from unbolted wheat (hence today's "graham" crackers). He encouraged a diet of fruits and vegetables in their "natural state,"chewing food thoroughly and slowly, no stimulants of any kind (i.e., tea, coffee, wine, beer, or tobacco), avoiding liquid foods, sleeping seven hours on a hard mattress, daily bathing, and daily walking or horseback riding, to name a few.

14 Starr, *The social transformation of American medicine*, 1982, p. 56.

15 Wesley, Rev. John Wesley, 1838, p. 105.

16 Starr, *The social transformation of American medicine*, 1982, p. 17.

17 R. Morantz, "Nineteenth century health reform and women," in (ed.) G. Risse et al., *Medicine without doctors: Home health care in American history*, 1977, p. 74.

18 Kett, *The formation of the American medical profession: The role of institutions, 1780–1860*, 1968, p. 31.

19 Levin et al., *The hidden health care system: Mediating structures and medicine*, 1981, p. 161.

20 Tannenbaum, *The healer's calling: Women and medicine in early New England*, 2002, p. 24.

21 Fellman & Fellman, *Making sense of self: Medical advice literature in late nineteenth century America*, 1981, p. 5.

22 Jefferson et al., *The life and selected writings of Thomas Jefferson*, 1944, p. 426.

23 Jefferson et al., p. 690.

24 Starr, *The social transformation of American medicine*, 1982, p. 13.

25 Starr, p. 14.

26 University of Virginia Geospatial and Statistical Data Center, *United States Historial Census Data Browser*, Online 1998, University of Virginia.

27 *Note:* Although Thomson often professed his theories to have originated with him, traditional Chinese medicine theory, which is centuries older than Thomsonian theory, also focuses on the importance to health and longevity of maintaining warmth in the "middle burner," the area in the middle of the body, including the stomach and the bowels.

28 Haller, *The people's doctors: Samuel Thomson and the American botanical movement, 1790-1860*, 2000, p. 53.

29 Beach, *The family physician, or, The reformed system of medicine on vegetable or botanical principles being a compendium of the "American Practice" designed for all classes*, 1843.

30 Mott, *The Ladies medical oracle, or, Mrs. Mott's advice to young females, wives, and mothers being a non-medical commentary on the cause, prevention, and cure of diseases of the female frame together with an explanation of her system of European vegetable medicine for the cure of diseases and the patent medicated Champoo baths*, 1834.

31 Walsh, *Doctors wanted: No women need apply*, 1977, p. 22.

32 Mott, *The ladies medical oracle, or, Mrs. Mott's advice to young females, wives, and mothers being a non-medical commentary on the cause, prevention, and cure of diseases of the female frame together with an explanation of her system of European vegetable medicine for the cure of diseases and the patent medicated Champoo baths*, 1834, p. 11. The treatments cited are found in the practice of Thomsonian and Regular physicians.

33 Mott, p. 140. *Note:* European traditional healers often used botanical and

hydrotherapy applications in a similar approach to what is described in Mott's advice book.

34 Mott, p. 198.

35 Silver-Isenstadt, *Shameless: The visionary life of Mary Gove Nichols,* 2002, p. 300.

36 Child, *The American frugal housewife,* 1999, p. 25.

37 Child, p. 25. Child is differentiating between American and English plant species and showing a preference for the English remedy.

38 Child, *The family nurse,* 1997.

39 Karcher, *The first woman in the republic: A cultural biography of Lydia Maria Child,* 1994, p. 149.

40 Buchan, *Domestic medicine, or, The family physician being an attempt to render the medical art more generally useful by shewing people what is in their own power both with respect to the prevention and cure of diseases. Chiefly calculated to recommend a proper attention to regimen and simple medicines,* 1769.

41 Buchan, section XI.

42 Buchan, p. viii.

43 Gunn, *Gunn's domestic medicine or poor man's friend in the hours of affliction, pain, and sickness,* 1830.

44 Gunn, p. 15.

45 Lewis, Clark, & DeVoto, *The journals of Lewis and Clark,* 2002, p. 413.

46 Peck, *Or perish in the attempt: Wilderness medicine in the Lewis and Clark expedition,* 2002, p. 55.

47 University of Virginia Health System, The medical training of Meriwether Lewis, 1998.

48 Lewis, Clark, & DeVoto, *The journals of Lewis and Clark,* 1997, p. 135.

49 Lewis, Clark, & DeVoto, p. 143.

50 Berman & Flannery, *America's botanico-medical movement: Vox populi,* 2001, p. 39.

51 Culpeper, *Culpeper's complete herbal & English physician,* 1990.

52 Child, *The family nurse,* 1997, p. 116.

53 Farnsworth, *Relative safety of herbal medicines,* 1993, p. 36 C–D.

54 Hatfield, *Memory, wisdom, and healing: The history of domestic plant medicine,* 1999, p. 173.

55 J. Cassedy, "Why self-help?" in (ed.) G. Risse et al., *Medicine without doctors: Home health care in American history,* 1977, p. 46.

56 Berman & Flannery, *America's botanico-medical movement: Vox populi,* 2001, p. 77.

57 Berman & Flannery, p. 77.

58 U.S. Patent and Trademark Office, http://www.uspto.gov/web/offices/pac/doc/general/whatis.htm

59 Jefferson et al., *The life and selected writings of Thomas Jefferson,* 1944, pp. 450–451.

60 National Archives Experience, http://www.archives.gov/exhibit_hall/charters_of_freedom/bill_of_rights/amendments_1-10.html

61 The term *physic* was commonly used in the nineteenth century as a noun or an adjective. The adjective form of the word is used here to describe that which is healing, or of health.

62 Wilson, *Pious traders in medicine: A German pharmaceutical network in eighteenth-century North America,* 2000, p. 75.

63 Wilson, p. 101.

64 Wilson, p. 211.

65 Wilson, p. 214.

66 Berman & Flannery, *America's botanico-medical movement: Vox populi,* 2001, p. 44.

CHAPTER 4: THE MID-NINETEENTH-CENTURY NURSE: HOME, HERBS, AND WOMEN'S HEALING NETWORKS

1 Susan Fenimore Cooper, mid-nineteenth-century naturalist, botanical illustrator and author of *Rural hours by a lady* (written mid-nineteenth century), as quoted in Kramer, *Women of flowers: A tribute to Victorian women illustrators,* 1996, p. 89.

2 Libster, *Demonstrating care: The art of integrative nursing,* 2001.

3 Reverby, *Ordered to care: The dilemma of American nursing, 1850–1945,* 1987, p. 11.

4 Reverby, p. 14.

5 Tannenbaum, *The healer's calling: Women and medicine in early New England,* 2002, p. 118.

6 B. Welter, "The cult of true womanhood: 1820–1860," in (ed.) M. Gordon, *The American family in social-historical perspective,* 1983, p. 372.

7 Lewis, *Women and social action in Victorian and Edwardian England,* 1991, p. 6.

8 C. Hall, "Private persons versus public someones," in (ed.) T. Lovell, *British feminist thought,* 1990, p. 53.

9 Sklar, *Catharine Beecher: A study in American domesticity,* 1973, p. 135.

10 Beecher and Stowe, *The American woman's home, or, Principles of domestic science: Being a guide to the formation and maintenance of economical, healthful, beautiful, and Christian homes,* 1869, p. 71.

11 Leighton, *American gardens of the nineteenth century: "For comfort and affluence,"* 1987, p. 93.

12 Leighton, *Early American gardens: "For meate or medicine"* 1986, p. 120.

13 Child, *The American frugal housewife,* 1999.

14 Leighton, *American gardens of the nineteenth century: "For comfort and affluence,"* 1987, p. 321.

15 Degler, *At odds: Women and the family in America from the Revolution to the present,* 1980, p. 367.

16 Degler, p. 368.

17 As quoted in B. Welter, "The cult of true womanhood: 1820–1860," in (ed.) M. Gordon, *The American family in social-historical perspective,* 1983, p. 378.

18 As quoted in B. Welter, p. 378.

19 Degler, *At odds: Women and the family in America from the Revolution to the present,* 1980, p. 299.

20 Beecher and Stowe, *The American woman's home, or, Principles of domestic science: Being a guide to the formation and maintenance of economical, healthful, beautiful, and Christian homes,* 1869, p. 255.

21 Melder, Ladies bountiful: Organized women's benevolence in early nineteenth-century America, 1967, p. 116.

22 Abel, *Hearts of wisdom: American women caring for kin, 1850–1940,* 2000, p. 56.

23 As quoted in Abel, *Hearts of wisdom: American women caring for kin, 1850–1940,* 2000, p. 50.

24 Beecher, *Miss Beecher's domestic receipt-book*, 2001, p. 193.

25 Beecher, p. 213.

26 Beecher, p. 212.

27 Sklar, *Catharine Beecher: A study in American domesticity*, 1973, p. 135.

28 Munroe, A tender wife, 1831, p. 1.

29 Duby et al., *A history of women in the West: Emerging feminism from Revolution to World War*, 1993, p. 334.

30 Webster et al., *An encyclopedia of domestic economy: Comprising such subjects as are most immediately connected with housekeeping; as, the construction of domestic edifices, with the modes of warming, ventilating, and lighting them; a description of the various articles of furniture; a general account of the animal and vegetable substances used in food, and the methods of preserving and preparing them by cooking; making bread; materials employed in dress and toilet; business of the laundry; description of the various wheel-carriages; preservation of health; domestic medicines, &c.*, 1845, pp. 1204–1205. According to *Merriam Webster's Dictionary*, the roots of the word "hysteria" pertain to the womb. The Greeks, as well as nineteenth-century physicians, believed that the cause of hysterics and invalidism originated in the womb as the word "hysteria" suggests.

31 Webster et al., p. 1205.

32 Webster et al., p. 1205.

33 Verbrugge, *Able-bodied womanhood: Personal health and social change in nineteenth-century Boston*, 1988.

34 Verbrugge, p. 43.

35 Delamont & Duffin, *The nineteenth-century woman: Her cultural and physical world*, 1978, p. 26.

36 Digby, *Making a medical living: Doctors and patients in the English market for medicine, 1720–1911*, 1994, ch. 9.

37 Gilman, *The yellow wallpaper*, 1973.

38 Price-Herndl, *Invalid women: Figuring feminine illness in American fiction and culture, 1840–1940*, 1993, p. 1.

39 Theophano, *Eat my words: Reading women's lives through the cookbooks they wrote*, 2002, p. 13.

40 Theophano, p. 49.

41 Viaux family, *Recipe book*, 1814–1816.

42 Often in recipe books, the recipes that either are identical to or closely resemble Samuel Thomson's remedies are referred to as "Thompson" remedies. Discrepancies in the spelling of Thompson's name and the specifics of the remedy are most likely the result of communicating recipes through an oral rather than a written tradition.

43 Coe, *Receipt book,* N.d., p. 2.

44 Gartrell, Women healers and domestic remedies in 18th century America: The recipe book of Elizabeth Coates Paschall, 1987.

45 Porter, Lay medical knowledge in the eighteenth century: The evidence of the gentleman's magazine, 1985.

46 Donovan, *Feminist theory: The intellectual traditions,* 2000, p. 61.

47 C. Morrell, "Octavia Hill and women's networks in housing," in A. Digby and J. Stewart, *Gender, health, and welfare,* 1996, p. 93.

48 Cott, *The bonds of womanhood: "Woman's sphere" in New England,* 1780–1835, 1977, p. 168.

49 Fuller, *Woman in the nineteenth century,* 1843, p. 18.

50 Verbrugge, *Able-bodied womanhood: Personal health and social change in nineteenth-century Boston,* 1988, p. 51.

51 Ladies Physiological Institute, Records of the meeting of the Ladies Physiological Institute of Boston and vicinity, 1850–1851, pp. 53-54.

52 Ladies Physiological Institute, p. 127.

53 Verbrugge, *Able-bodied womanhood: Personal health and social change in nineteenth-century Boston,* 1988, p. 57.

54 Ladies Physiological Institute, Records of the meeting of the Ladies Physiological Institute of Boston and vicinity, 1850–1851, p. 47.

55 James, A case of abortion, 1840, p. 252.

56 P. Watson, "The hidden ones," in (ed.) P. Benes and J. Benes, *Medicine and healing,* 1992, p. 33.

57 Vicinus, *Independent women: Work and community for single women 1850–1920,* 1985.

58 Vicinus, p. 49.

59 Lewis, *Women and social action in Victorian and Edwardian England,* 1991, p. 8.

60 A. Digby, "Victorian values and women in public and private," in (ed.) T. Smout et. al., *Victorian values: A joint symposium of the Royal Society of Edinburgh and the British Academy December 1990*, 1992.

61 A. Digby & J. Stewart, "Welfare in context," in (ed.) A. Digby and J. Stewart, *Gender, health, and welfare*, 1996, p. 10.

62 Ulrich, *A midwife's tale: The life of Martha Ballard, based on her diary, 1785–1812*, 1990.

63 As quoted in Leighton, *Early American gardens: "For meate or medicine,"* 1986, p. 65.

64 As quoted in Leighton, p. 117.

65 Beach, *Improved system of midwifery: Adapted to the reformed practice of medicine*, 1847, pp. 124, 135.

66 Beach, p. 124.

67 Josselyn, The genesis of the American materia medica, 1927.

68 Beach, *Improved system of midwifery: Adapted to the reformed practice of medicine*, 1847, p. 135. The inner bark of slippery elm (most likely *Ulmus fulva*) is soft and is used for a number of health reasons, including moistening tissues such as mucous membranes and in the gastrointestinal tract. While a piece of the bark has been known to be used to stimulate labor by inserting it into the cervical os, it seems from Beach's reference to using the bark for three months that the botanical use was oral.

69 Ulrich, *A midwife's tale: The life of Martha Ballard, based on her diary, 1785–1812*, 1990, p. 62.

70 As quoted in Melosh, *"The physician's hand": Work, culture, and conflict in American nursing*, 1982, p. 17.

71 *Merriam-Webster's collegiate dictionary, 1999*, p. 799.

72 Florance, *Healing and the home: Home medicine in pioneer Utah*, 1980, p. 35.

73 Orem, *Nursing concepts of practice*, 2001, p. 18.

74 Orem, p. 22.

75 Orem, p. 56.

76 Tannenbaum, *The healer's calling: Women and medicine in early New England*, 2002, p. 115.

77 Tannenbaum, p. 118.

78 Sturbridge Village Exhibit, *Hepsibeth Hemenway*, 2002.

79 One unpublished manuscript by Sister Matilda Coskery is described in chapter 7.

80 Griffith & Thomson, *The domestic management of the sickroom necessary, in aid of medical treatment, for the cure of diseases*, 1845, pp. 93–94. And see Smith, *Domestic medicine, surgery, and materia medica with directions for the diet and management of the sickroom*, 1851, p. 342.

81 Ashley, *Hospitals, paternalism, and the role of the nurse*, 1976, p. 2.

82 As quoted in Ashley, *Hospitals, paternalism, and the role of the nurse*, 1976, p. 2.

83 Brown & Ladies' Medical Academy, The capability of women to practice the healing art, 1859, p. 10.

84 D'Antonio, The legacy of domesticity, 1993, p. 242.

85 Smith, *Domestic medicine, surgery, and materia medica with directions for the diet and management of the sickroom*, 1851, pp. 342-343.

86 D'Antonio, The legacy of domesticity, 1993, p. 242.

87 Cleaveland, Nurses, 1852, p. 372.

88 Walsh, *Doctors wanted: No women need apply*, 1977, p. 143.

89 Melosh, *"The physician's hand": Work, culture, and conflict in American nursing*, 1982, p. 19.

90 Melosh, p. 19.

Stage II: Harvesting History — Gathering In

1 Baker, *Cyclone in calico: The story of Mary Ann Bickerdyke*, 1952, p. 142.

2 Baker, p. 191.

3 Ulrich, *A midwife's tale: The life of Martha Ballard, based on her diary, 1785–1812*, 1990.

Chapter 5: Herbs and the Shaker Infirmary and Community Nurses

1 Stein, *The Shaker experience in America: A history of the United Society of Believers*, 1992, p. 13.

2 United Society of Shakers, *The origins of the Shaker Church*, 2000.

3 Blinn, *Historical record of the Society of Believers in Canterbury, N.H., vol. I and II*, 1892, pp. 2–3. The members are referred to here as either "Shakers" or "Believers."

4 Stein, *The Shaker experience in America: A history of the United Society of Believers*, 1992, p. 327.

5 Andorn, Shakerism for today, 1957, p. 8.

6 Evans, *Shakers compendium of the origin, history, principles, rules and regulations, government, and doctrines of the United Society of Believers in Christ's Second Appearing*, 1859, p. 55.

7 Andrews, *The people called Shakers: A search for the perfect society*, 1953, p. 292.

8 Andorn, Shakerism for today, 1957, p. 5.

9 As quoted in Stein, *The Shaker experience in America: A history of the United Society of Believers*, 1992, p. 27.

10 Shakers, *Millennial Laws*, 1781.

11 Madden, *Bodies of life: Shaker literacies and literature*, 1995, p. 28.

12 Thurman, *"O sisters ain't you happy?": Gender, family, and community among the Harvard and Shirley Shakers, 1781–1918*, 2002, p. 8.

13 Andrews, *The people called Shakers: A search for the perfect society*, 1953, p. 26.

14 Andrews, p. 194.

15 Thurman, *"O sisters ain't you happy?": Gender, family, and community among the Harvard and Shirley Shakers, 1781-1918*, 2002, p. 83.

16 Beale & Boswell, *The earth shall blossom: Shaker herbs and gardening*, 1991, p. 118.

17 Hammond, *Day book*, 1820–1826, March 25–27, 1822, entry.

18 Harvard Shakers, *Physicians' journal, or, an account of the sickness at Harvard*, 1843.

19 Harvard Shakers, *Harvard Shaker covenants*, N.d.

20 *Harvard Shakers, Teachings to the children on health*, N.d., pp. 84–86.

21 Barnabas Hinckley (1818–1861) joined the Shakers as a young child and served as a physician beginning in 1837 at age nineteen. He received a medical degree in 1858 and died at age forty-three.

22 Miller, *Shaker herbs: A history and a compendium*, 1976, p. 37.

23 Allard, *Autobiography*: 1885, pp. 48-49.

24 Thurman, *"O sisters ain't you happy?": Gender, family, and community among the Harvard and Shirley Shakers, 1781–1918*, 2002, p. 125.

25 Whitcher, *Mary Whitcher's Shaker house-keeper*, 1882, p. 1.

26 *Blinn, Historical record of the Society of Believers in Canterbury, N.H., vol. I and II,* 1892, p. 143.

27 J. Blake, "From Buchan to Fishbein, in G. Risse et al., *Medicine without doctors: Home health care in American History,* 1977, p. 27.

28 Blinn, *Historical record of the Society of Believers in Canterbury, N.H., vol. I and II,* 1892, p. 144.

29 Blinn, p. 221.

30 Blinn, p. 161.

31 Blinn, *Church record,* 1784-1879, pp. 86, 143.

32 Sabbathday Lake Shakers, *Community records,* N.d.

33 U.S. Department of Commerce, *Historical statistics of the United States: Colonial times to 1970,* 1975. Life expectancy statistics are rare for the mid-nineteenth century. After 1900, U.S. statistics show that the life expectancy for white males was 48.2 years, white females 51.1, black males 32.5, and black females, 35. There are published life expectancy statistics for the state of Massachusetts for 1850, 1855, and 1878–1882. In 1850, life expectancy for white males was 38.3 and females 40.5. In 1855, males 38.7 and females 40.9. In 1878–1882, males 41.7 and females 43.5. The data show that many Shakers did exceed the normal white American life expectancy, often by decades. Accessed March 2003 at http://www.infoplease.com/ipa/A0005140.html.

34 Andrews, *The people called Shakers: A search for the perfect society,* 1953, p. 197.

35 Andrews, p. 197.

36 As documented in Andrews, *The people called Shakers: A search for the perfect society,* 1953, p. 111.

37 Watervliet Shakers, *Membership, birth, death, and statistical records, Watervliet, N.Y. 1797–1913,* 1797–1913.

38 Harvard Shakers, *Physicians' journal, or, an account of the sickness at Harvard,* 1843, recorded April 14, 1834.

39 Harvard Shakers.

40 Harvard Shakers.

41 Harvard Shakers.

42 Mace, *The journal of Sister Aurelia Mace,* 1896, p. 27.

43 Blinn, *Historical notes having reference to the Believers in Enfield, N.H., vol. II,* 1895, p. 109.

44 Harvard Shakers, *Church family day book*, 1828–1838.

45 Shakers, *Millennial Laws*, 1821.

46 Harvard Shakers, *Physicians' journal, or, an account of the sickness at Harvard*, 1843, recorded January 31, 1835.

47 Blinn, *Historical record of the Society of Believers in Canterbury, N.H., vol. I and II*, 1892, p. 139. Note: "Nursing department" was the actual term used by the Shakers.

48 Blinn, p. 159. Tenney was the physician who trained Corbett.

49 Blinn, *Church record*, 1784–1879, p. 143.

50 Harvard Shakers, *Physicians' journal, or, an account of the sickness at Harvard*, 1843, recorded March 23, 1835.

51 Shirley Shakers, *Nurse house book*, N.d.

52 Hammond, *Day book*, 1820–1826.

53 Mace, *The journal of Sister Aurelia Mace*, 1896, p. 30.

54 Mace, p. 47. Debra Pote was one of the original founders of the Sabbathday Lake family in New Gloucester, Maine.

55 Klamkin, *Hands to work: Shaker folk art and industries*, 1972, p. 42.

56 There are two types of "emetics" listed in the Harvard physicians' journal: "Emetic" and "real Emetic." Harvard Shakers, *Physicians' journal, or, an acccount of the sickness at Harvard*, 1843, recorded April 14, 1834. It might be concluded that lobelia seed was the herb used for the "real" emetic, as it is also delineated in the entry on January 30, 1835, "Ziba Winchester took an Emetic. Susan K. M. & Mary Grosvenor gave it to him. He took a teaspoonful of the seed of Lobelia & it had a good effect." A regular emetic probably referred to lobelia leaf or a combination of herbs.

57 The Shakers used adult cradles in caring for the sick. The cradles are on display at the Hancock Shaker Village Museum and Fruitlands Museum in Massachusetts. Harvard Shakers, *Physicians' journal, or, an account of the sickness at Harvard*, 1843, recorded April 22, 1835.

58 Sister Sarah Flint Mace of Sabbathday Lake exemplifies the Shaker home health nurse. "If a Sister anywhere in the village was sick she would often be at their bedside in the night to care for them. Saturday afternoons she would be round with her pail of warm water and towels to wash the aged Sisters' feet and keep them in order. She was a careful chiropodist, and the aged Sisters appreciated her kindness." Mace, The journal of Sister Aurelia Mace, 1896, pp. 62-63.

59 Harvard Shakers, *Physicians' journal, or, an account of the sickness at Harvard*, 1843, recorded July 1-3, 1835.

60 Harvard Shakers.

61 Harvard Shakers, recorded March 23, 1835.

62 Harvard Shakers, recorded January 22, 1834.

63 Harvard Shakers, recorded February 2, 1834.

64 Harvard Shakers, recorded July 6, 1835. Probably Dr. Kittridge, whom the Harvard Shakers saw for lameness and broken bones. The blisters in this case were applied to Brethren Benjamin Kendall's back for complaint of lameness.

65 Canterbury Shaker Nurses, *Infirmary recipe book*, 1841?–1873, p. 10.

66 In the physician's journal from the Harvard infirmary, the names of patients, nurses, and attendants are recorded without a title. On occasion, people are recorded as "Sister," "Brother," "Elder," or "Eldress." Br. Joseph Mayo may have been a Harvard Shaker physician although he lived until age eighty-one, dying in 1852, and is not mentioned further in the infirmary records. He was sixty-four in 1835 when he "ordered" hellebore snuff and may have been referred to as "Brother" out of respect for his age and knowledge.

67 Hellebore is an herb. *King's American Dispensatory*, by Felter and Lloyd, includes two listings under hellebore, *Adonis vernalis* also known as "false hellebore" and *Dracontium foetidum* also known as "skunk cabbage." *Adonis* was used more for cardiac conditions. It is more likely that the snuff suggested here was powdered skunk cabbage. Skunk cabbage in medicinal doses, according to *King's*, was used as an antispasmodic and for its mild narcotic influence, both qualities that would have been helpful in a severe headache. In addition, skunk cabbage is often mentioned in Shaker manuscripts and is included in Harvard Shaker Elisha Myrick's herbarium. The herbarium, housed in the Shaker collection at the Fruitlands Museum in Harvard, Massachusetts, is a rare botanical document. Myrick, a self-taught botanist, created his herbarium in 1854. It contains pressed samples of the community's "Prominent Medicinal Plants" *organized by common name and including the botanical name* most likely based upon the Ammos Eaton system of nomenclature. The Harvard herbarium provides sufficient botanical data to increase the potential for identification accuracy of the herbs mentioned in Harvard infirmary records.

68 Harvard Shakers, *Physicians' journal, or, an account of the sickness at Harvard*, 1843, recorded December 17, 1835.

69 Thurman, *"O sisters ain't you happy?": Gender, family, and community among the Harvard and Shirley Shakers, 1781–1918*, 2002, p. 79.

70 Harvard Shakers, *Physicians' journal, or, an account of the sickness at Harvard,* 1843, emphasis added.

71 Blinn, *Historical record of the Society of Believers in Canterbury, N.H., vol. I and II,* 1892, p. 139.

72 Shirley Shakers, *Nurse house book,* N.d.

73 Shakers, *Receipt book,* N.d.

74 Shakers, *A book of medical recipes,* 1840–1860, pp. 11, 14.

75 Standish, *A collection of medicinal receipts for the use of physicians,* 1860.

76 Felter & Lloyd, *King's American dispensatory,* 1983, p. 1131.

77 Miller, *Shaker herbs: A history and a compendium,* 1976, p. 28.

78 According to *King's American Dispensatory, Lysimachia* is a relative of *Primula officinalis,* or primrose.

79 Blinn, *Church record,* 1784–1879, p. 119.

80 Andrews, *The Community industries of the Shakers,* 1933, p. 107.

81 Hammond, *Day book,* 1820–1826, recorded August 16, 1825; January 2, 1826.

82 Hammond.

83 Blinn, *Historical notes having reference to the Believers in Enfield, N.H., vol. II,* 1895, pp. 219-220.

84 Thurman, *"O sisters ain't you happy?": Gender, family, and community among the Harvard and Shirley Shakers, 1781–1918,* 2002, p. 79.

85 Hammond, *Day book,* 1820—-1826. Thomsonians were commonly referred to as "cayenne pepper doctors."

86 Hancock Shakers, *Recipes and prescriptions from Hancock Shaker Village,* N.d., p. 105.

87 Canterbury Shaker Nurses, *Infirmary recipe book,* 1841?-1873, p. 9.

88 Harvard Shakers, *Physicians' journal, or, an account of the sickness at Harvard,* 1843, January 15, 1836.

89 Shakers, *Millennial Laws,* 1821.

90 Hancock Shakers, *Recipes and prescriptions from Hancock Shaker Village,* N.d., p. 2.

91 Harvard Shakers, *Physicians' journal, or, an account of the sickness at Harvard,* 1843.

92 Both Mary Babbit and Susan Myrick were assigned to the physicians' order, but they also are recorded in the Harvard *Physician's Journal* as having served as nurses.

93 Harvard Shakers, *Physicians' journal, or, an account of the sickness at Harvard*, 1843.

94 Thomson, *New guide to health, or, Botanic family physician containing a complete system of practice, upon a plan entirely new: with a description of the vegetables made use of, and directions for preparing and administering them to cure disease: to which is prefixed a narrative of the life and medical discoveries of the author*, 1835.

95 Standish, *A collection of medicinal receipts for the use of physicians*, 1860.

96 Andrews, *The community industries of the Shakers*, 1933, p. 89.

97 Smith, *The Indian doctor's dispensatory being Father Smith's advice respecting diseases and their cure*, 1813.

98 Rafinesque, *Medical flora, or, Manual of the medical botany of the United States of North America*, 1828.

99 Hancock Shakers, *Recipes and prescriptions from Hancock Shaker Village*, N.d., p. 178.

100 Hancock Shakers, p. 178.

101 Hancock Shakers, p. 261.

102 Canterbury Shaker Nurses, *Infirmary recipe book*, 1841?–1873, p. 12.

103 Morrell, *A choice collection of medical and botanical receipts: Selected from experienced physicians by whom they have been proved and found useful in the various disorders and infirmities for which they are prescribed. To which is prefixed remarks and observations for the consideration of physicians and nurses among Believers*, 1849.

104 Morrell, *Receipts & counsels exclusively for female diseases*, 1854.

105 Morrell, p. 22; Morrell, *A choice collection of medical and botanical receipts: Selected from experienced physicians by whom they have been proved and found useful in the various disorders and infirmities for which they are prescribed. To which is prefixed remarks and observations for the consideration of physicians and nurses among Believers*, 1849, p. 166.

106 Morrell, pp. 7-8.

107 Morrell, *A choice collection of medical and botanical receipts: Selected from experienced physicians by whom they have been proved and found useful in the various disorders and infirmities for which they are prescribed. To which is prefixed remarks and observations for the consideration of physicians and nurses among Believers*, 1849, preface, p. 1.

108 Morrell, preface, p. 1.

[109] Morrell, preface, p. 5.

[110] Morrell, preface p. 2 and p. 166.

[111] Morrell, p. 164.

[112] Hancock Shakers, *Recipes and prescriptions from Hancock Shaker Village*, N.d.

[113] Harvard Shakers, *Physicians' journal, or, an account of the sickness at Harvard*, 1843, January 15, 1836.

[114] Harvard Shakers, February 6–8, 1835. It is most probable that this was a poultice application, since the wormwood was said to have been bruised instead of decocted and applied as a compress with the vinegar.

[115] Canterbury Shakers, *Recipes*, N.d.

[116] Canterbury Shakers.

[117] New Lebanon Shaker Nurses, *Notebook of receipts from the nurses' shop — New Lebanon*, 1815.

[118] Andrews, *The community industries of the Shakers*, 1933, p. 96.

[119] Bullard, Shaker housekeeping, 1906, p. 33.

[120] Klamkin, *Hands to work: Shaker folk art and industries*, 1972, p. 50.

[121] Klamkin, p. 42.

[122] Bullard, Shaker housekeeping, 1906, p. 33.

[123] Shakers, Medicinal objects, N.d.

[124] Piercy, Shaker medicines, 1957, p. 15.

[125] Andorn, Shakerism for today, 1957, p. 7.

[126] Buchanan, *The Shaker herb and garden book*, 1996, p. 20.

[127] Shakers, *Millennial Laws*, 1821, Part III, Section I.

[128] Buchanan, *The Shaker herb and garden book*, 1996, p. 27.

[129] Allard, Autobiography, 1885, pp. 30-31.

[130] Andrews, *The community industries of the Shakers*, 1933, p. 92.

[131] Buchanan, *The Shaker herb and garden book*, 1996, p. 106.

[132] Buchanan, p. 23.

[133] Andrews, *The community industries of the Shakers*, 1933, p. 40.

134 Allard, *Autobiography*, 1885, p. 51.

135 Piercy, Shaker medicines, 1957, p. 19.

136 Miller, *Shaker herbs: A history and a compendium*, 1976, p. 51.

137 Blinn, *Church record*, 1784–1879, p. 77.

138 Blinn, p. 66.

139 Canterbury Shakers, *Recipes*, N.d.

140 Beale & Boswell, *The earth shall blossom: Shaker herbs and gardening*, 1991, p. 139.

141 Miller, *Shaker herbs: A history and a compendium*, 1976, p. 31.

142 Beale & Boswell, *The earth shall blossom: Shaker herbs and gardening*, 1991, p. 210.

143 Berman & Flannery, *America's botanico-medical movement: Vox populi*, 2001, p. 59.

144 Blinn, *Historical record of the Society of Believers in Canterbury, N.H., vol. I and II*, 1892, p. 242.

145 Blinn, p. 245.

146 Shakers, *Millennial Laws*, 1821, Part XVIII.

147 Andrews, *The people called Shakers: A search for the perfect society*, 1953, p. 169.

148 Evans, *New England witchcraft and spiritualism*, 1881, pp. 3-4. Elder Evans uses the term "anti-Christians" to refer to those whom in his belief are not true Christians.

149 Blinn, *Church record*, 1784—1879, p. 184.

150 Blinn, *Historical record of the Society of Believers in Canterbury, N.H., vol. I and II*, 1892, p. 184.

151 Blinn, p. 143.

152 Blinn, *Church record*, 1784–1879, p. 30.

153 Andrews, *The people called Shakers: A search for the perfect society*, 1953, p. 170.

154 Andrews, *The community industries of the Shakers*, 1933, pp. 164-165.

155 Myrick, *Daybook*, 1850, June 25, 1850, entry.

156 New Lebanon Shaker Nurses, *Notebook of receipts from the nurses' shop — New Lebanon*, 1815, p. 53.

157 Hancock Shakers, *Recipes and prescriptions from Hancock Shaker Village*, N.d., p. 140.

158 Hancock Shakers, p. 8.

159 "Wabanaki" or "Wobanaki" has been transformed into the Indian tribe "Abenaki."

160 Allard, *Autobiography*, 1885, pp. 34-36.

161 Hoffman, Mt. Lebanon medicine makers—the Shakers, 1920, p. 197.

162 Elkins, *Fifteen years in the Senior Order of Shakers*, 1853, p. 60.

163 Blinn, *Historical notes having reference to the Believers in Enfield, N.H., vol. II*, 1895, p. 117.

CHAPTER 6: HERBS AND THE PIONEER NURSES AND MIDWIVES OF THE CHURCH OF JESUS CHRIST OF LATTER-DAY SAINTS

1 Derr et al., *Women of covenant: The story of Relief Society*, 1992, p. 129. As quoted from the *Woman's Exponent 28* (April 15 and May 1, 1900); 121. This was the description of LDS woman leader Zina Young, Thomsonian, nurse-midwife, Relief Society president, and wife to Brigham Young, LDS church leader who succeeded Joseph Smith. Zina Young was one of the women trained as a nurse by Willard Richards and Susannah Lippincott in 1848.

2 Arrington & Bitton, *The Mormon experience: A history of the Latter-day Saints*, 1979, p. xiii.

3 Arrington & Bitton, p. xvi.

4 Church of Jesus Christ of Latter-day Saints, *The Book of Mormon: The doctrine and covenants of the Church of Jesus Christ of Latter-day Saints. The pearl of great price*, 1981.

5 Arrington & Bitton, *The Mormon experience: A history of the Latter-day Saints*, 1979, p. 22.

6 Church of Jesus Christ of Latter-day Saints, *The Book of Mormon: The doctrine and covenants of the Church of Jesus Christ of Latter-day Saints. The pearl of great price*, 1981, *Moroni* 10:9 – 10:11.

7 Church of Jesus Christ of Latter-day Saints.

8 Church of Jesus Christ of Latter-day Saints, *D&C* 89:2.

9 Church of Jesus Christ of Latter-day Saints, *Deseret News*, January 25, 1851.

10 Sorensen, For Zion's sake: The emergence of Mormon nursing, 1998, p. 52.

11 Church members referred to themselves as "Saints."

12 Church of Jesus Christ of Latter-day Saints, *The Book of Mormon: The doctrine and covenants of the Church of Jesus Christ of Latter-day Saints. The pearl of great price*, 1981, *D&C* 89:6 – 11.

13 Church of Jesus Christ of Latter-day Saints, *D&C* 89:18 – 21.

14 Levi Richards was a Thomsonian physician and personal physician to Smith. He also was the brother of Willard Richards.

15 Richards, *Journal*, 1836–1849, p. 85.

16 R. Daines, "Heros and horse doctors: Medicine in Cache Valey, 1857–1900," in (ed.) D. Alder, *Cache Valley: Essays on her past and people*, N.d., p. 67.

17 Church of Jesus Christ of Latter-day Saints, *Deseret News*, July 19, 1852.

18 Church of Jesus Christ of Latter-Day Saints.

19 Church of Jesus Christ of Latter-day Saints, *Times and Seasons*, 1843, p. 325, emphasis added. The article is signed "P——S". It is quite possible that the article was written by prominent LDS midwife Patty Sessions, since she was present in the Nauvoo community at the time of publication and the article acknowledges the importance of "good nursing" in addition to "herbs and mild foods."

20 Church of Jesus Christ of Latter-day Saints, p. 325.

21 Church of Jesus Christ of Latter-day Saints, p. 325, emphasis added.

22 Church of Jesus Christ of Latter-day Saints, p. 326.

23 Beecher & Stowe, *The American woman's home, or, Principles of domestic science: Being a guide to the formation and maintenance of economical, healthful, beautiful, and Christian homes*, 1869, p. 104.

24 Young, & Church of Jesus Christ of Latter-day Saints, *Journal of discourses*, 1956, July 1, 1869, v. 13, p. 142.

25 Alder, *Cache Valley: Essays on her past and people*, N.d., p. 66.

26 Young, & Church of Jesus Christ of Latter-day Saints, *Journal of discourses*, 1956, February 17, 1861, v. 9, p. 125.

27 Young, & Church of Jesus Christ of Latter-day Saints, p. 125.

28 Young, & Church of Jesus Christ of Latter-day Saints, October 9, 1872, p. 225.

29 Young, & Church of Jesus Christ of Latter-day Saints, p. 225.

30 Young, & Church of Jesus Christ of Latter-day Saints, July 1, 1869, p. 143.

31 Carter, *Pioneer medicines*, 1945, p. 211.

32 Young & Church of Jesus Christ of Latter-day Saints, *Journal of discourses*, October 9, 1872, p. 225.

33 Young & Church of Jesus Christ of Latter-day Saints, August 31, 1875, p. 71.

34 Carter, *Pioneer medicines*, 1945, p. 190.

35 This is not the same person as Shaker Mother Ann Lee.

36 Carter, *Pioneer medicines*, 1945, p. 201.

37 Derr et al., *Women of covenant: The story of Relief Society*, 1992, p. 71.

38 Derr et al., p. 70.

39 Derr et al., p. 1.

40 Derr et al., p. vii.

41 Noall, *Intimate disciple: A portrait of Willard Richards*, 1957, p. 549.

42 Derr et al., *Women of covenant: The story of Relief Society* 1992, p. 131.

43 Lyman, *Journal*, 1860-1879, March 7, 1879.

44 Sessions & Smart, *Mormon midwife: The 1846–1888 diaries of Patty Bartlett Sessions*, 1997, p. 57.

45 Church of Jesus Christ of Latter-day Saints, *Deseret News*, 1850, May 15, 1852.

46 Church of Jesus Christ of Latter-day Saints, May 15, 1852.

47 Lyman, *Journal*, 1860–1879, Recorded August 26, 1860. "Girls" refers to girls who were offered by their families to sit with a sick neighbor and perform basic comfort measures and household tasks.

48 Richards, *Diary*, 1846–1848, Recorded July 25–26, 1846.

49 Richards, *Diary*, 1846–1848, Recorded August 4, & 22, 1846.

50 As quoted in Derr et al., *Women of covenant: The story of Relief Society*, 1992, p. 131.

51 Divett, *Medicine and the Mormons*, 1981, p. 123.

52 Carter, *Pioneer medicines*, 1945, pp. 191–193.

53 According to *King's Dispensatory*, asafoetida, produced in Afghanistan and Persia, was imported as gum resin primarily from Bombay, India.

54 Carter, *Pioneer medicines*, 1945, p. 199.

55 Mills & Bone, *Principles and practice of phytotherapy: Modern herbal medicine*, 2000, p. 166.

56 Carter, *Pioneer medicines*, 1945, p. 192; Mills & Bone, *Principles and practice of phytotherapy: Modern herbal medicine*, 2000, p. 433.

57 Felter & Lloyd, *King's American dispensatory*, 1983,

58 Church of Jesus Christ of Latter-day Saints, *Deseret News.*

59 Church of Jesus Christ of Latter-day Saints, April 3, 1852.

60 Carter, *Pioneer medicines*, 1945, p. 193. Carter writes that she collected numerous oral histories of the curative value of lobelia (see Color Index). Her writings describe the curing action of lobelia as being related to the destruction of "poison" and acting "like intelligence." Many herbs, such as lobelia, are known today as "thinking herbs." For example, ginseng can affect blood pressure, either by lowering it or raising it, depending upon patient. This "thinking" action has been described scientifically as an amphoteric or adaptogen action and is currently under investigation. Lobelia has a history of traditional use in the United States, taken orally as a tea or tincture for threatening miscarriage. Dr. John Christopher, a twentieth- century herbalist, described numerous experiences of giving the herb to women in need. According to *Every woman's herbal*, by Christopher, page 47, the herb seems to help stop uterine bleeding if the fetus is viable and "direct" the miscarriage if the fetus is dead.

61 Church of Jesus Christ of Latter-day Saints, *Deseret News*, 1850.

62 Smith, Why are Mormons so susceptible to medical and nutritional quackery?, 1983. Note: Herbs continue to be part of Utah's culture. Nature's Way, one of America's largest herbal supplement manufacturers, and John Christopher's Original Formulas, started in 1945, are both located in Springville, Utah.

63 Smith, p. 34.

64 Smith, p. 30.

65 Smith, p. 33, emphasis not added.

66 Farnsworth, Relative safety of herbal medicines, 1993, p. 36C-D.

67 O'Connor, *Healing traditions: Alternative medicine and the health professions*, 1995, pp. 28,31, emphasis not added.

68 Smith, Why are Mormons so susceptible to medical and nutritional quackery? 1983, p. 38.

69 Richards, *Diary*, 1836–1840.

70 Winters, *Mothers in Israel: Mary Ann Stearns Winters' narrative (1833–1912)*, 1969, p. 3. It is noteworthy that Winters recalls Sister Young as being "a strong convert" to Thomsonianism. Mrs. Young may have been a strong influence on her husband in deciding to strongly support the LDS members' use of Thomsonian botanical therapies.

71 Richards, *Journal*, 1836–1849. Recorded October 6, 1842.

72 Richards.

73 Richards. Recorded October 11 and 13, 1842.

74 Richards.

75 Richards, Recorded May 11, 1844.

76 Richards, p. 106.

77 Meeks, *Reminiscences (Journal)*, 1879, p. 4.

78 Meeks, p. 5.

79 Meeks, p. 10.

80 Meeks, p. 61

81 Meeks, p. 61. This organization became known as the "Council of Health."

82 Meeks, p. 62.

83 Winters, *Mothers in Israel: Mary Ann Stearns Winters' narrative (1833–1912)*, 1969, p. 3.

84 Carter, *Our pioneer heritage: And they were healed*, 1959. The accounts of Margaret Cooper West's botanical nursing practice were dictated by Mary Riggs West to Kate Carter, who compiled family stories of Utah Pioneer men and women. The dictations appear in quotations in Carter's book. Many of Carter's original notes are housed at the Daughters of the Utah Pioneers (DUP) Museum in Salt Lake City. The DUP Archivist, Edith Menna, notes that in preparing her manuscript, Carter sent word out to the Utah community requesting family records and stories of pioneer healers. She received "volumes" of data, including primary journal and diary accounts. While it is possible that the stories may be embellished by family members, many historical facts in the oral histories are corroborated by social history. For example, in 1833, Samuel Thomson's movement had been established in Midwestern states such as Ohio and Tennessee. Therefore, the idea that a man would sell a copy of Thomson's book to Margaret Cooper West in her home in Tennessee is very plausible.

85 Carter, p. 74.

86 Carter, p. 75.

87 Tannenbaum, *The healer's calling: Women and medicine in early New England*, 2002, p. 114.

88 Carter, *Our pioneer heritage: And they were healed*, 1959, p. 78. This passage does not appear in quotes in Carter's book and may be a summary of Carter's understanding

of Thomsonian nursing practice based upon the West family history as well as other histories she was given.

89 Carter, p. 78.

90 Carter, p. 78. Though not clearly specified in Carter's book, the detailed accounts of the remedies outlined by Kate Carter may have been given to her by Mary Riggs West, as they appear in the section on Margaret Cooper West. Margaret passed her botanical remedies to her children and grandchildren, in particular, Nancy Marie Babbitt Riggs who, according to Carter, continued her work as a nurse and practitioner of Margaret's remedies.

91 Carter, p. 79.

92 Winters, *Mothers in Israel: Mary Ann Stearns Winters' narrative (1833–1912)*, 1969, p. 29.

93 Winters, p. 30.

94 Winters, pp. 30-31.

95 Winters, pp. 33–34.

96 Winters, p. 2.

97 Winters, p. 13.

98 Sessions & Smart, *Mormon midwife: The 1846-1888 diaries of Patty Bartlett Sessions*, 1997, p. 299.

99 Sessions & Smart, p. 8.

100 Sessions & Smart, p. 7.

101 Sessions & Smart, p. 7.

102 Sessions & Smart, p. 394. A picture of Sessions's copy of Beach's book is published with her diaries.

103 Beach, *The family physician, or, The reformed system of medicine on vegetable or botanic principles being a compendium of the "American Practice" designed for all classes, 1843.*

104 Sessions & Smart, p. 104

105 Sessions & Smart, p. 19.

106 Sessions & Smart, p. 28.

107 Derr et al., *Women of covenant: The story of Relief Society*, 1992, p. 71.

108 Sessions & Smart, *Mormon midwife: The 1846–1888 diaries of Patty Bartlett Sessions*, 1997, p. 176.

109 Sessions & Smart, pp. 148, 150.

110 Sessions & Smart, p. 184.

111 Sessions & Smart, p. 75.

112 Sessions & Smart, p. 77.

113 Sessions & Smart, p. 135.

114 Sessions & Smart, p. 135.

115 Sessions & Smart, p. 59.

116 Sessions & Smart, p. 66.

117 Sessions & Smart, p. 76.

118 Sessions & Smart, p. 124.

119 Sessions & Smart, p. 259.

120 Ulrich, *A midwife's tale: The life of Martha Ballard, based on her diary, 1785-1812*, 1990.

121 Sessions & Smart, *Mormon midwife: The 1846–1888 diaries of Patty Bartlett Sessions*, 1997, p. 219.

122 Sessions & Smart, p. 238. Possibly referring to the plant known as Joe Pye weed or gravel root (*Eupatorium maculatum*) of the Asteraceae family. The name "Joe Pye" supposedly came from an Indian who cured typhus with the plant by encouraging sweating.

123 Sessions & Smart, p. 246.

124 Sessions & Smart, p. 211.

125 Sessions & Smart, p. 213.

126 Sessions & Smart, p. 179.

127 Sessions & Smart, p. 180.

128 Sessions & Smart, p. 183.

129 Sessions & Smart, p. 216.

130 Sessions & Smart, p. 220.

131 Church of Jesus Christ of Latter-day Saints, *Deseret News*, April 11, 1855.

132 Church of Jesus Christ of Latter-day Saints, April 11, 1855.

133 Cassedy, *Medicine and American growth, 1800–1860*, 1986, p. 176.

134 Walsh, *Doctors wanted: No women need apply*, 1977, p. 7.

135 Abram, *Send us a lady physician: Women doctors in America, 1835–1920*, 1985, pp. 82-83. For example, Dr. Marie Zakrzewska had been a chief midwife and professor of midwifery in Germany before moving to the United States, where she ultimately attended medical school and received her degree in 1856. She then practiced with Elizabeth Blackwell.

136 Derr et al., *Women of covenant: The story of Relief Society*, 1992, p. 398.

137 Bishop, *Sketch of Ann Green Dutson Carling*, N.d., p. 2.

138 Bishop, p. 4.

139 Nielson & Flack, *The Dutson family history*, 1957, p. 7.

140 Lyman, *Journal*, 1860–1879, Entry: March 7, 1879.

141 Nielson & Flack, *The Dutson family history*, 1957, p. 6.

142 Nielson, *And they were healed — Ann Carling*, N.d., p. 2.

143 Nielson & Flack, *The Dutson family history*, 1957, p. 8.

144 Nielson, *And they were healed — Ann Carling*, N.d., p. 2.

145 Arrington and Bitton, The Mormon experience: A history of the Latter-day Saints, 1979, p. 145.

146 Arrington and Bitton, p. 14.

147 Arrington and Bitton, p. 145.

148 Richards, *Diary*, 1846–1848.

149 Richards.

150 Winters, *Mothers in Israel: Mary Ann Stearns Winters' narrative (1833–1912)*, 1969, pp. 31, 33, 35.

151 Winters, p. 24.

152 Sessions & Smart, *Mormon midwife: The 1846–1888 diaries of Patty Bartlett Sessions*, 1997, p. 28.

153 Derr et al., *Women of covenant: The story of Relief Society*, 1992, p. 77.

154 Rose, *History of medicine in Utah*, 1939, p. 33.

155 Derr et al., *Women of covenant: The story of Relief Society*, 1992, p. 76.

156 Derr et al., p. 77; "J. H. M.," Iron County — Parowan: To Bro. Geo. A. Smith, 1855.

157 Kay, *Healing with plants in the American and Mexican West*, 1996, p. 142.

158 Chinese ephedra contains the constituent ephedrine from which the stimulant drug is derived. Morman tea, according to pharmacognosist, Varro Tyler, Ph.D., does not contain the alkaloid ephedrine or its derivatives.

159 Carter, *Pioneer medicines*, 1945, p. 191.

160 Moerman, *Native American ethnobotany*, 1998.

161 Atkin, *Thomas Atkin diary (1833--1919)*, 1919, p. 15.

162 Libster, *Delmar's integrative herb guide for nurses*, 2002, p. 103.

163 Fowler, *Diaries*, 1899–1900.

164 Brigham Young University School of Nursing. http://www.byui.edu/catalog/2001-2002/Nursing.htm.

165 Derr et al., *Women of covenant: The story of Relief Society*, 1992, p. 73.

166 Derr et al., p. 75.

Chapter 7: Herbs and the Sisters of Charity and Early American Hospitals

1 Sullivan, *Spiritual writings of Louise de Marillac: Correspondence and thoughts*, 1991, p. 711.

2 The Sisters of Charity of St. Joseph's of Emmitsburg, Maryland, formally joined the Daughters of Charity in Paris in 1850 when the sisters made their vows in keeping with the manner of the DOC in Paris. The Americans would continue to be referred to as "Sisters of Charity," not "Daughters of Charity," until 1850, after the merger with the French DOC. They will be referred to only as Sisters of Charity here.

3 McNeil, *The Vincentian family tree*, 1996, p. 168.

4 McNeil, p. xv.

5 McNeil, p. xvii.

6 Coste, *Saint Vincent de Paul: Correspondance, Entretiens, Documents*, 1924, vol. 13, pp. 809–810. A hotel *dieu*, in addition to functioning as a hospital, frequently houses the poor, those considered socially deviant, and the mentally ill.

7 Kramer & Sprenger, *Malleus maleficarum*, 1971, p. 156.

8 Guazzo & Summers, *Compendium maleficarum: The Montague Summers edition*, 1988, p. 90.

9 Kramer & Sprenger, *Malleus maleficarum*, 1971, p. 87.

10 Kramer & Sprenger, p. 66.

11 Nelson, *Say little, do much: Nurses, nuns, and hospitals in the nineteenth century*, 2001, p. 3.

12 Nelson, p. 23.

13 Ryan & Rybolt, *Vincent de Paul and Louise de Marillac: Rules, conferences, and writings*, 1995, p. 168.

14 Cummings, *History of the hospital work and the development of the schools of nursing of the Sisters of Charity in the Eastern Province (1860-1900)*, 1948, p. 49.

15 Cummings, p. 48.

16 Sullivan, *Spiritual writings of Louise de Marillac: Correspondence and thoughts*, 1991.

17 Sullivan, p. 640.

18 Sullivan, p. 47.

19 Felter & Lloyd, *King's American dispensatory*, 1983, p. 1675.

20 Sullivan, *Spiritual writings of Louise de Marillac: Correspondence and thoughts*, 1991, p. 743.

21 Sullivan, p. 256. In addition to being used as a coffee substitute, chicory root is used as a diuretic and laxative.

22 Sullivan, p. 624.

23 Sullivan, p. 615.

24 Sullivan.

25 Jones, Sisters of Charity and the ailing poor, 1989, p. 346.

26 Arnault de Nobleville, *Le Manuel des Dames de Charite, ou Formules de Medicamens Faciles a Preparer*, 1765, pp. v-vi.

27 Sullivan, *Spiritual writings of Louise de Marillac: Correspondence and thoughts*, 1991, p. 213.

28 Sullivan, p. 214.

29 Sullivan, p. 266.

30 Sullivan, p. 284.

31 Sullivan, p. 607.

32 Sullivan, p. 750.

33 Sullivan, p. 286.

34 Sullivan, p. 752.

35 Sullivan, p. 809.

36 Sullivan, p. 763.

37 Sullivan, p. 726.

38 Seton et al., *Collected writings*, vol. 3. In press. Also, manuscript can be found at the Archives of St. Joseph's Provincial House 1-3-3-5:7(6).

39 Sullivan, *Spiritual writings of Louise de Marillac: Correspondence and thoughts*, 1991, p. 763.

40 Sullivan, p. 189.

41 Sullivan, pp. 291, 517, 763.

42 Dirvin, *Mrs. Seton, foundress of the American Sisters of Charity*, 1993, p. 194.

43 Melville, *Elizabeth Bayley Seton, 1774–1821*, 1951, p. 161.

44 Melville, p. 164.

45 Melville, p. 162, emphasis added.

46 Melville, p. 165.

47 Melville, p. 163.

48 Melville, pp. 163–164.

49 McNamara, *Sisters in arms: Catholic nuns through two millennia*, 1996, p. 607.

50 Daughters of Charity, *Mother Rose White*, 1936, p. 45.

51 Daughters of Charity, *Mother Augustine and Mother Xavier*, 1938, p. 134.

52 Armiger, *The history of the hospital work of the Daughters of Charity of St. Vincent de Paul in the Eastern Province of the United States 1823–1860*, 1947, p. 107.

53 Armiger, p. 106.

54 Armiger, p. 22.

55 Dirvin, *Mrs. Seton, foundress of the American Sisters of Charity*, 1993, p. 49.

56 Dirvin, p. 51.

57 Bramucci, *Medical care in the city of Baltimore*, 2001.

58 Babb, *French refugees from Saint-Domingue to the Southern United States: 1791–1810*, p. 54. Accessed June 2003 at http://freepages.genealogy.rootsweb.com/~saintdomingue/Babb%20Index.htm.

59 Personal communication, Father Albert Ledoux, Bruté scholar, Mt. St. Mary's College, Emmitsburg, Maryland, June 16, 2002.

60 Godecker, *Simon Bruté de Remur*, 1931, p. 66.

61 Jameson, *The American domestick medicine, or Medical admonisher*, 1817, p. 612.

62 Jameson, p. 644.

63 Hannefin, *Daughters of the church: A popular history of the Daughters of Charity in the United States 1809–1987*, 1989, p. 34.

64 Daughters of Charity, *Lives of the deceased sisters*, 1870, p. 13. This quote most likely refers to spiritual education.

65 Daughters of Charity, p. 21.

66 Daughters of Charity, p. 22.

67 Daughters of Charity.

68 Coskery, *Advices concerning the sick*, N.d., p. 31.

69 Rothstein, *American physicians in the nineteenth century: From sects to science*, 1972, p. 183.

70 Coskery, *Advices concerning the sick*, N.d.

71 Coskery, pp. 6-7, emphasis in original.

72 Coskery, p. 12, emphasis in original.

73 Coskery, p. 24.

74 Daughters of Charity, *The Seton Institute . . . a century of progress*, 1949, p. 4.

75 Daughters of Charity, pp. 4-5.

76 Stokes, *The Ninth Annual Report of the Mount Hope Institution, near Baltimore for the year 1851*, 1852, p. 15. Dr. Stokes accepted his position as attending physician at Mt. Hope in 1842 after his trip abroad, during which he visited reputable institutions for the mentally ill. He served with the SOC for fifty years.

77 Daughters of Charity, *Lives of the deceased sisters*, 1870, p. 12.

78 Coskery, *Advices concerning the sick*, N.d., p. 11.

79 Coskery, p. 17, emphasis in original.

80 Armiger, *The history of the hospital work of the Daughters of Charity of St. Vincent de Paul in the Eastern Province of the United States 1823–1860*, 1947, p. 59.

81 Digby, *Madness, morality, and medicine: A study of the York Retreat, 1796–1914*, 1985, pp. 34, 36.

82 Armiger, *The history of the hospital work of the Daughters of Charity of St. Vincent de Paul in the Eastern Province of the United States 1823–1860*, 1947, p. 58.

83 From the archives of the Seton Institute, as recorded in Armiger, *The history of the hospital work of the Daughters of Charity of St. Vincent de Paul in the Eastern Province of the United States 1823–1860*, 1947, p. 56. This would have been Sister Matilda Coskery.

84 Armiger, *The history of the hospital work of the Daughters of Charity of St. Vincent de Paul in the Eastern Province of the United States 1823–1860*, 1947, p. 56.

85 Armiger, p. 57.

86 Coskery, *Advices concerning the sick*, N.d., p. 17.

87 Grob, *Mental illness and American society, 1875–1940*, 1983, p. 258.

88 Clark, *Instruction on the care of the sick*, 1846, p. 65.

89 Clark.

90 Clark, p. 73.

91 Clark, pp. 75–78.

92 Clark, pp. 41–42.

93 Clark, p. 45.

94 Daughters of Charity, *Lives of the deceased sisters, Mother Xavier Clark*, 1870, p. 135.

95 Clark, *Instruction on the care of the sick*, 1846, p. 50.

96 *Merriam-Webster's collegiate dictionary*, 1999, p. 1237.

97 de Paul, *The conferences of St. Vincent de Paul to the Daughters of Charity*, 1938–1940.

98 de Paul, p. 57.

99 Ryan & Rybolt, *Vincent de Paul and Louise de Marillac: Rules, conferences, and writings*, 1995, p. 181.

100 Coskery, *Advices concerning the sick*, N.d., pp. 6-7.

101 de Paul, *The conferences of St. Vincent de Paul to the Daughters of Charity*, 1938–1940, pp. 58–59.

102 Sullivan, *Spiritual writings of Louise de Marillac: Correspondence and thoughts*, 1991, p. 495.

103 Clark, *Instruction on the care of the sick*, 1846, p. 61.

104 Ryan & Rybolt, *Vincent de Paul and Louise de Marillac: Rules, conferences, and writings*, 1995, p. 169.

105 Ryan & Rybolt, pp. 168–169.

106 de Paul, *The conferences of St. Vincent de Paul to the Daughters of Charity*, 1938–1940, p. 65.

107 de Paul, p. 62.

108 Daughters of Charity, *The Rule of 1812: Regulations for the Society of Sisters of Charity in the United States of America*, 1812, Chapter II, Article III, "On Obedience," emphasis added.

109 Byrne, *History of the Seton Institute, Baltimore, Maryland, and its affiliate School of Nursing conducted by the Daughters of Charity of St. Vincent de Paul in the Eastern Province of the United States*, 1950, p. 7.

110 Byrne, p. 8, emphasis in original.

111 Hannefin, *Daughters of the church: A popular history of the Daughters of Charity in the United States 1809–1987*, 1989, p. 69.

112 Daughters of Charity, *Letter of William Stewart, mayor of Baltimore—Extract from the chronicles of Baltimore*, 1832.

113 Armiger, Two sister-nurses claimed by cholera, 1964.

114 Beecher & Stowe, *The American woman's home, or, Principles of domestic science: Being a guide to the formation and maintenance of economical, healthful, beautiful, and Christian homes*, 2002, p. 254, emphasis in original.

115 Maher, *To bind up the wounds: Catholic sister nurses in the U.S. Civil War*, 1989, p. 126.

116 James et al., *Notable American women, 1607–1950: A biographical dictionary*, 1971, p. 486.

117 James et al., p. 487.

118 Dix, *Memorial of Miss D. L. Dix to the Hon. The General Assembly in behalf of the insane of Maryland*, 1852, p. 1505.

119 James et al., *Notable American women, 1607–1950: A biographical dictionary*, 1971, p. 488.

120 Nelson, *Say little, do much: Nurses, nuns, and hospitals in the nineteenth century*, 2001, p. 30.

121 Livermore, *My story of the war: A woman's narrative of four year's personal experience as nurse in the Union Army, and in relief work at home, in hospitals, camps, and at the front during the war of the rebellion. With anecdotes, pathetic incidents, and thrilling reminiscences portraying the lights and shadows of hospital life and the sanitary service of the war*, 1889, p. 224.

122 Seton et al., *Collected writings*, January 9, 1810, in press.

123 Berman & Flannery, *America's botanico-medical movement: Vox populi*, 2001, p. 82.

124 Armiger, *The history of the hospital work of the Daughters of Charity of St. Vincent de Paul in the Eastern Province of the United States 1823–1860*, 1947, p. 75, emphasis added.

125 Stepsis & Liptak, *Pioneer healers: The history of women religious in American health care*, 1989, p. 27, emphasis added.

126 Daughters of Charity, *Civil War notes 7-5-1*, 1860, p. 48.

127 Armiger, *The history of the hospital work of the Daughters of Charity of St. Vincent de Paul in the Eastern Province of the United States 1823–1860*, 1947, p. 25, emphasis in original.

128 Ryan & Rybolt, *Vincent de Paul and Louise de Marillac: Rules, conferences, and writings*, 1995, p. 185.

129 Stepsis & Liptak, *Pioneer healers: The history of women religious in American health care*, 1989, p. 25.

130 Ryan & Rybolt, *Vincent de Paul and Louise de Marillac: Rules, conferences, and writings*, 1995, p. 173.

131 McNamara, *Sisters in arms: Catholic nuns through two millennia*, 1996, p. 592.

132 Stepsis & Liptak, *Pioneer healers: The history of women religious in American health care*, 1989, p. 30.

133 Daughters of Charity, *Civil War notes 7-5-1*, 1860, pp. 241-242.

134 Daughters of Charity, *Mont St. Vincent—Cradle of Mount Hope (Book) 11-2-39*, 1852, p. 17.

135 Coskery, *Advices concerning the sick*, N.d., p. 36.

136 Coskery, p. 37.

137 Sullivan, *Spiritual writings of Louise de Marillac: Correspondence and thoughts*, 1991, p. 468.

138 Coskery, *Advices concerning the sick*, N.d., p. 22, emphasis in original.

STAGE III: HARVESTING HISTORY — PROCESSING

1 N. Rogers, "Women and sectarian medicine," in R. Apple, ed., *Women, health, and medicine in America: A historical handbook*, 1990, p. 284.

2 Mack, "Something wicked this way comes"—Herbs even witches should avoid, 1998, On the front page of the article about herbs is a picture of three old crones dressed in robes with warts on their noses and big eyes. They are stirring a large round vat of bubbling liquid and one is holding a sprig of a plant over the pot.

3 N. Rogers, "Women and sectarian medicine," in R. Apple, ed., *Women, health, and medicine in America: A historical handbook*, 1990, p. 282.

4 N. Rogers, p. 282.

CHAPTER 8: THE INTEGRATION OF THE SPHERES

1 Donovan, *Feminist theory: The intellectual traditions*, 2000, p. 57. Matilda Gage was a nineteenth-century suffragist leader. She collaborated with Elizabeth Cady Stanton and Susan B. Anthony on the *History of Woman Suffrage.* Gage believed that the lost memory of the divine attribute of the feminine, when back in its rightful place in culture, would restore "the lost power," the special gift of women, intuition. She even went so far as to call for the reinstatement of prayer to a feminine deity and overcoming the particularly Christian belief of women being inferior and polluted.

2 As quoted in Berman, *The impact of the nineteenth-century botanico-medical movement on American pharmacy and medicine*, 1954, p. 30.

3 Benner, *From novice to expert: Excellence and power in clinical nursing practice*, 2001, pp. 33–34.

4 Coskery, *Advices concerning the sick*, N.d., p. 12.

5 Rothstein, *American physicians in the nineteenth century: From sects to science*, 1972, p. 33.

6 O'Connor, *Healing traditions: Alternative medicine and the health professions*, 1995.

7 Löwy, Ludwik Fleck on the social construction of medical knowledge, 1988, p. 135.

8 Löwy, p. 135.

9 Löwy, p. 147.

10 Löwy, p. 147.

11 Barnett, *The idea of higher education*, 1990, p. 110.

12 Belenky, *Women's ways of knowing: The development of self, voice, and mind*, 1997, p. 134.

13 Pill & Stott, Choice or chance: Further evidence on ideas of illness and responsibility for health, 1985, p. 983.

14 Pill & Stott, p. 983.

15 Nightingale et al., *Suggestions for thought*, 1994, p. 113.

16 Rothstein, *American physicians in the nineteenth century: From sects to science*, 1972, p. 33.

17 O'Malley, *Florence Nightingale 1820–1856: A study of her life down to the end of the Crimean War*, 1931, p. 189.

18 Orem, *Nursing concepts of practice*, 2001, p. 43.

19 Eisenberg et al., Trends in alternative medicine use in the United States, 1990–1997: Results of a follow-up national survey, 1998; O'Connor, *Healing traditions: Alternative medicine and the health professions*, 1995, p. 26.

20 Bushy, Cultural considerations for primary health care: Where do self-care and folk medicine fit? 1992, p. 11.

21 Levin et al., *The hidden health care system: Mediating structures and medicine*, 1981.

22 Levin et al., p. 66.

23 Leavitt, *Brought to bed: Childbearing in America, 1750 to 1950*, 1986, p. 211.

24 Merchant, *The death of nature: Women, ecology, and the scientific revolution*, 1989, p. 155.

25 Ehrenreich & English, *For her own good: 150 years of the experts' advice to women*, 1978, p. 66.

26 Taylor et al., Biobehavioral responses to stress in females: Tend-and-befriend, not fight-or-flight, 2000.

27 Taylor et al., p. 411.

28 One excellent book on Indian-white relations from the Indian perspective is by Peter Nabokov, *Native American testimony*. The book does not specifically include the relations between Indian and white women of the mid-nineteenth century.

29 Cooper, *The American democrat, or, Hints on the social and civic relations of the United States of America*, 1956, p. 161.

30 Riley, *Women and Indians on the frontier, 1825–1915*, 1984, p. 155.

31 Mayhew, *Narratives of the lives of pious Indian women who lived on Martha's Vineyard more than one hundred years since. Carefully revised from the London edition, originally printed for Samuel Gerrish, bookseller in Boston, New England, 1727*, 1830, pp. 19, 21.

32 Mayhew, p. 50.

33 Riley, *Women and Indians on the frontier, 1825–1915*, 1984, p. 169.

34 Riley, p. 174.

35 Riley, p. 162.

36 Perrone et al., *Medicine women, curanderas, and women doctors*, 1989, p. 59.

37 A. Digby, "Victorian values and women in public and private," in Smout et al., eds., *Victorian values: A joint symposium of the Royal Society of Edinburgh and the British Academy December 1990*, 1992, p. 198.

38 Marshall & Wall, Religion, gender, and autonomy: A comparison of two religious women's groups in nursing and hospitals in the late nineteenth and early twentieth centuries, 1999, p. 12.

39 Marshall & Wall, p. 7.

40 A. Digby, Victorian values and women in public and private, in Smout et al., eds., *Victorian values: A joint symposium of the Royal Society of Edinburgh and the British Academy December 1990*, 1992, p. 214.

41 Nightingale et al., *Ever yours: Florence Nightingale selected letters*, 1990, p. 59.

42 Woodham Smith, *Florence Nightingale, 1820–1910*, 1951, p. 64.

43 Cope, *Florence Nightingale and the doctors*, 1958, p. 122.

44 Cope, p. 121.

45 Seymer, *The selected writings of Florence Nightingale*, 1954, p. 317.

46 As quoted in R. Morantz, "Nineteenth century health reform and women," in G. Risse et al., eds., *Medicine without doctors: Home health care in American history*, 1977, p. 82.

CHAPTER 9: CONCLUSION - THE FUTURE OF HERBAL DIPLOMACY

1 Leininger, *Care: The essence of nursing and health*, 1984, p. 6.

2 Leininger.

3 A. Digby, "Victorian values and women in public and private," in (ed.) T. Smout et al., *Victorian values: A joint symposium of the Royal Society of Edinburgh and the British Academy December 1990*, 1992.

4 Libster, Integrative care—product and process: Considering the three T's of timing, type, and tuning, 2003, p. 3.

5 Perrone et al., *Medicine women, curanderas, and women doctors*, 1989, p. 75.

6 Landy, *Culture, disease, and healing: Studies in medical anthropology*, 1977, p. 470.

7 A. Digby & H. Sweet, "Western and indigenous medicine: Nurses as culture brokers in twentieth century South Africa," in (ed.) W. Ernst, *Plural Medicine: Tradition and modernity*, 1800–2000, 2002.

8 Balick & Cox, *Plants, people, and culture. The science of ethnobotany*, 1996, p. 36.

9 Vogel, *American Indian medicine*, 1970, p. 101.

10 Vogel, p. 123.

11 Examples include *Bowker, The Indian vegetable family instructor: Containing the names and descriptions of all the most useful herbs and plants that grow in this country, with their medicinal qualities annexed. Also a treatise on many of the lingering diseases to which mankind are subject, with new and plain arguments respecting the management of the same, with a large list of recipes, which have been carefully selected from Indian prescriptions and from those very persons who were cured by the same after every other remedy had failed*, 1836; Coffin, *A Botanic guide to health and the natural pathology of disease*, 1846; Smith, *The Indian doctor's dispensatory being Father Smith's advice respecting diseases and their cure*, 1813.

12 Libster, Integrative care—product and process: Considering the three T's of timing, type, and tuning, 2003.

13 The term *botanical therapies*, as it is used here, does not include the botanical supplements produced by pharmaceutical companies that are often as equally expensive as drugs.

14 *Merriam-Webster's collegiate dictionary*, 1999, p. 932.

15 *Merriam-Webster's collegiate dictionary*, 1999, p. 1210.

16 Sandelowski, *"Devices and desires: Gender, technology, and American nursing*, 2000, p. 24.

17 Sandelowski, p. 22.

18 Leonard, *Women, technology, and the myth of progress*, 2003, p. 176.

19 Lazarou et al., Incidence of adverse drug reactions in hospitalized patients: A meta-analysis of prospective studies, 1998.

20 O'Connor, *Healing traditions: Alternative medicine and the health professions*, 1995, p. 14.

21 Thorne, *Negotiating health care: The social context of chronic illness*, 1993, pp. 179–182.

22 World Health Organization, *Fact Sheet No. 134: Traditional Medicine*, 2003, p. 1.

23 Baba et al., Natural resources and human health—Plants of medicinal and nutritional value. Proceedings of the 1st WHO symposium on plants and health for all: Scientific advancement, Kobe, Japan, August 1991, 1992, p. 65.

24 Barnes et al., Primary health care and primary care: A confusion of philosophies, 1995, p. 8.

25 Thorne, *Negotiating health care: The social context of chronic illness*, 1993, p. 176.

26 Akerele, Nature's medicinal bounty: Don't throw it away, 1993, p. 392. Dr. Akerele was programme manager of the Traditional Medicine Programme, World Health Organization, until just before he wrote this article in 1993.

27 Akerele, Summary of WHO guidelines for the assessment of herbal medicines, 1993, p. 13.

28 World Health Organization Traditional Medicine Programme, *WHO Traditional Medicine Strategy 2002–2005*, 2002, p. 2.

29 Kreitzer et al., Attitudes toward CAM among medical, nursing, and pharmacy faculty and students: A comparative analysis, 2002, p. 50.

30 Libster, *Delmar's integrative herb guide for nurses*, 2001.

31 D'Antonio, Toward a history of research in nursing, 1997, p. 109.

32 Bodeker & Kronenberg, A public health agenda for traditional, complementary, and alternative medicine, 2002, p. 1588.

33 Levin et al., *The hidden health care system mediating structures and medicine*, 1981, p. 66.

34 Moylan, Alternative treatment modalities: The need for a rational response by the nursing profession, 2000 , p. 261.

35 Bleck, Medical nostalgia: "Simple" medical care versus technology, 1996, p. 1.

36 Tosh, *The pursuit of history: Aims, methods, and new directions in the study of modern history*, 2000, p. 12.

37 Ritivoi, *Yesterday's self nostalgia and the immigrant identity*, 2002, p. 30.

38 Ritivoi, 2002, p. 39.

39 Theophano, *Eat my words: Reading women's lives through the cookbooks they wrote*, 2002, p. 51.

40 Tosh, *The pursuit of history: Aims, methods, and new directions in the study of modern history*, 2000, p. 14.

41 Donovan, *Feminist theory: The intellectual traditions*, 2000, p. 51.

Botanical Color Inserts

1 Felter and Lloyd, *King's American dispensatory*, 1983, p. 1200.

2 Felter and Lloyd, *King's American dispensatory*, 1983, p. 1200; Moerman, *Native American ethnobotany*, 1998, p. 312. American Samuel Thomson claimed to have "discovered" *Lobelia inflata*, however, most ethnobotanists agree that the plant was used by Indians and early settlers before Thomson and others popularized its use.

3 Felter and Lloyd, *King's American dispensatory*, 1983, p. 1202.

4 Felter and Lloyd, *King's American dispensatory*, 1983, p. 1204.

5 Standish, *A collection of medicinal receipts for the use of physicians*, 1860, Sarah A. Standish is identified in the Mount Lebanon Church Family Record as a soap, hat and brush maker. The title page of the receipt book states that she "compiled" the collection.

6 Berman and Flannery, *America's botanico-medical movement: Vox populi*, 2001, p. 76. Haller, *The people's doctors Samuel Thomson and the American botanical movement, 1790-1860*, 2000, p. 86. For example, Samuel Thomson was charged in 1809 with having killed a patient with lobelia. Botanist Manasseh Cutler testified in Thomson's defense that the plant used was marsh rosemary and Thomson was acquitted. And according to Alva Curtis, a follower of Thomson, Regulars used the death of John Gray, supposedly due to lobelia, as an excuse to warn the public against the use of the herb as an emetic.

7 Moerman, *Native American ethnobotany*, 1998, p. 81.

8 Beach, *The family physician, or, The reformed system of medicine on vegetable or botanic principles being a compendium of the "American Practice" designed for all classes*, 1843, p. 674.

9 Rafinesque, *Medical flora or, Manual of the medical botany of the United States of North America*, 1828, p. 55.

10 Smilax, *Sarsaparilla and Sarsaparilla so-called: A popular analysis of a popular medicine*, 1854, p. 26.

11 Felter and Lloyd, *King's American dispensatory*, 1983, p. 284-286. Apparently, asafoetida does not have an American counterpart. It is not listed in Moerman's *Native American ethnobotany* or Erichsen-Brown's *Medicinal and other uses of North American plants.* It is most likely that asafoetida was an imported herb introduced by the European-Americans. According to the *Yoga of Herbs*, by Lad and Frawley, in Ayurvedic (traditional East Indian) medicine, asafoetida is commonly used as a spice in cooking lentils and other legumes. It is primarily used as a digestive aid and to treat roundworm infestation. Asafoetida has been used like cayenne or black pepper.

12 Tantaquidgeon, *Folk medicine of the Delaware and related Algonkian Indians*, 1972, p. 72.

13 Moerman, *Native American ethnobotany*, 1998, p. 196.

14 Moerman, 1998, p. 196.

15 Moerman, 1998, p. 196.

16 Blumenthal et al, *Herbal medicine expanded commission E monographs*, 2000, p. 52.

17 Libster, *Delmar's integrative herb guide for nurses*, 2001, p. 611.

18 Libster, p. 611.

19 Felter and Lloyd, *King's American dispensatory*, 1983, p. 436.

20 Moerman, *Native American ethnobotany*, 1998, p. 136.

21 Libster, *Delmar's integrative herb guide for nurses*, 2001, p. 610.

22 Libster, 2001, p. 612.

23 Kloss, *Back to Eden: A human interest story of health and restoration to be found in herb, root, and bark*, 1983, p. 221.

24 Kloss, p. 226.

25 Jensen, *Promise to the land: Essays on rural women*, 1991, p. 98.

26 Jensen, 1991, p. 101.

27 Jensen, 1991, p. 99.

28 Libster, *Delmar's integrative herb guide for nurses*, 2001, p. 414.

29 Felter and Lloyd, *King's American dispensatory*, 1983, p. 999.

30 Libster, *Delmar's integrative herb guide for nurses*, 2002, p. 414.

Bibliograpy

Chapter 1: Introduction: Harvesting a History of Women Healers

Abram, R. J. (1985). *Send us a lady physician: Women doctors in America, 1835–1920.* New York: Norton.

Alcoff, L. (1988). Cultural feminism versus post-structuralism: The identity crisis in feminist theory. *Signs, 13*, 405–436.

Ashley, J. A. (1976). *Hospitals, paternalism, and the role of the nurse.* New York: Teachers College Press.

Baker, P. (1984). The domestication of politics: Women and American political society, 1780–1920. *American Historical Review 89* (3); 620–647.

Beach, W. (1843). *The family physician, or, The reformed system of medicine on vegetable or botanical principles being a compendium of the "American Practice" designed for all classes* (4th ed). New York: Author. Lloyd Library, Cincinnati, Ohio.

Berman, A. (1954). *The impact of the nineteenth-century botanico-medical movement on American pharmacy and medicine.* Unpublished doctoral dissertation, University of Wisconsin.

Berman, A. (1956). Social roots of the 19th-century botanico-medical movement in the United States. In *Actes du VIII Congres International D'Histoire des Sciences—Florence* (pp. 561–565).

Berman, A., & Flannery, M. A. (2001). *America's botanico-medical movement: Vox populi.* New York: Pharmaceutical Products Press.

Buchan, W. (1769). *Domestic medicine, or, The family physician being an attempt to render the medical art more generally useful, by shewing people what is in their own power both with respect to the prevention and cure of diseases. Chiefly calculated to recommend a proper attention to regimen and simple medicines.* Edinburgh, Scotland: Balfour, Auld, and Smellie. Wellcome Trust Library, London.

Chamberlain, M. (1981). *Old wives' tales: Their history, remedies, and spells.* London: Virago.

Christman, L. (1998). Who is a nurse? *Image: Journal of Nursing Scholarship 30* (3), 211–214.

Church, O. M. (1987). Historiography in nursing research. *Western Journal of Nursing Research 9* (2), 275–279.

Cummings, M. (2003). Cultural diplomacy and the United States government: A survey. *Center for Arts and Culture: Cultural Diplomacy Research Series.* Baltimore: Johns Hopkins University Press.

Digby, A., & Stewart, J. (1996). *Gender, health, and welfare.* Routledge: London.

Donovan, J. (2000). *Feminist theory: The intellectual traditions* (3rd ed.) New York: Continuum.

Ehrenreich, B., & English, D. (1978). *For her own good: 150 years of the experts' advice to women.* Garden City, N.: Anchor Press.

Farnsworth, N., Akerele, O., Bingel, A., Soejarto, D., & Guo, Z. (1985). Medicinal plants in therapy. *Bulletin of the World Health Organization 63* (6), 965–981.

Farnsworth, N. R., & Morris, R. W. (1976). Higher plants—the sleeping giant of drug development. *American Journal of Pharmaceutical Science and Support in Public Health 148* (2), 46–52.

Felter, H. W., & Lloyd, J. U. (1983, originally published 1898). *King's American dispensatory.* (18th ed., 3rd rev. ed.). Sandy, OR: Eclectic Medical Publications.

Gartrell, E. (1987, January). Women healers and domestic remedies in 18th century America: The recipe book of Elizabeth Coates Paschall. *New York Journal of Medicine,* 23–29.

Haller, J. S. (2000). *The people's doctors: Samuel Thomson and the American botanical movement, 1790–1860.* Carbondale, IL: Southern Illinois University Press.

Harmer, B. (1924). *Text-book of the principles and practice of nursing.* New York: Macmillan.

Harmer, B., & Henderson, V. (1955). *Textbook of the Principles and Practice of Nursing.* New York: Macmillan.

Heywood, M. S., *Journal of Martha Spence Heywood: Recorded during the years 1850 to 1856.* Salt Lake City: University of Utah Library, Special Collections #MS 160.

Kerber, L. (1988). Separate spheres, female worlds, woman's place: The rhetoric of women's history. *Journal of American History 75* (1), 9–39.

Kerber, L., Cott, N., Gross, R., Hunt, L., Smith-Rosenberg, C., & Stansell, C. (1989). Beyond roles, beyond spheres: Thinking about gender in the early republic. *The William and Mary Quarterly 46* (3), 565–585.

Kett, J. F. (1968). *The formation of the American medical profession: The role of institutions, 1780–1860.* New Haven, CT: Yale University Press.

Leininger, M. (1984). *Care: The essence of nursing and health.* Detroit, MI: Wayne State University Press.

Mahady, G., Fong, H., & Farnsworth, N. (2001). *Botanical dietary supplements: Quality, safety, and efficacy*. Steenwijk, Netherlands: Swets & Zeitlinger.

Marshall, E. S., & Wall, B. (1999). Religion, gender, and autonomy: A comparison of two religious women's groups in nursing and hospitals in the late nineteenth and early twentieth centuries. *ANS: Advances in Nursing Science 22* (1), 1–22.

McFarlin, B., Gibson, M., O'Rear, J., & Harman, P. (1999). A national survey of herbal preparation use by nurse-midwives for labor stimulation. *Journal of Nurse-Midwifery 44* (3), 205–216.

Melosh, B. (1982). *"The physician's hand": Work, culture, and conflict in American nursing.* Philadelphia: Temple University Press.

Merriam-Webster's collegiate dictionary (1999). (10th ed.) Springfield, MA: Merriam-Webster.

Nelson, S. (2001). *Say little, do much: Nurses, nuns, and hospitals in the nineteenth century*. Philadelphia: University of Pennsylvania Press.

Reverby, S. (1987). *Ordered to care: The dilemma of American nursing, 1850–1945.* Cambridge and New York: Cambridge University Press.

Risse, G. (Ed.). (1977). *Medicine without doctors: Home health care in American history.* New York: Science History Publications.

Rothstein, W. (1972). *American physicians in the nineteenth century: From sects to science.* Baltimore: Johns Hopkins University Press.

Sessions, P. B., & Smart, D. J. (1997). *Mormon midwife: The 1846–1888 diaries of Patty Bartlett Sessions*. Logan: Utah State University Press.

Sharp, S. (1986). Folk medicine practices: Women as keepers and carriers of knowledge. *Women's Studies International Forum 9* (3), 243–249.

Silver-Isenstadt, J. (2002). *Shameless: The visionary life of Mary Gove Nichols*. Baltimore: Johns Hopkins University Press.

Sklar, K. (2002). *Women and power in American history to 1880.* (2nd ed.) Englewood Cliffs, NJ: Pearson Education.

Smout, T. C., Royal Society of Edinburgh, & British Academy. (1992). *Victorian values: A joint symposium of the Royal Society of Edinburgh and the British Academy December 1990. Proceedings of the British Academy.* Oxford: Oxford University Press for the British Academy.

Starr, P. (1982). *The social transformation of American medicine.* New York: Basic Books.

Tannenbaum, R. (2002). *The healer's calling: Women and medicine in early New England.* Ithaca, NY: Cornell University Press.

Thomson, S. (1835). *New guide to health, or, Botanic family physician containing a complete system of practice, upon a plan entirely new: with a description of the vegetables made use of, and directions for preparing and administering them to cure disease: to which is prefixed a narrative of the life and medical discoveries of the author*. Boston: J. Q. Adams, Lloyd Library, Cincinnati, Ohio.

Thomson, S. (1840). On the health of females. *The Boston Thomsonian Manual and Lady's Companion* 6 (16), 241-242. Lloyd Library, Cincinnati, Ohio.

Tosh, J. (2000). *The pursuit of history aims, methods, and new directions in the study of modern history* (3rd ed.) Harlow, England: Longman.

Ulrich, L. (1990). *A midwife's tale: The life of Martha Ballard, based on her diary, 1785–1812.* New York: Knopf. Distributed by Random House.

Verbrugge, M. (1988). *Able-bodied womanhood: Personal health and social change in nineteenth-century Boston.* New York: Oxford University Press.

Vogel, M. J., & Rosenberg, C. E. (1979). *The therapeutic revolution: Essays in the social history of American medicine.* Philadelphia: University of Pennsylvania Press.

Chapter 2: Mid-Nineteenth-Century American Health Care

Berman, A. (1956). Social roots of the 19th-century botanico-medical movement in the United States. In *Actes du VIII Congres International D'Histoire des Sciences—Florence,* (pp. 561–565).

Berman, A., & Flannery, M. A. (2001). *America's botanico-medical movement: Vox populi.* New York: Pharmaceutical Products Press.

Bigelow, J. (1836). *Discourse on self-limited disease.* Medical Communications of the Massachusetts Medical Society. Boston: Massachusetts Medical Society. Lloyd Library, Cincinnati, Ohio.

Blau, J. (1954). *Social theories of Jacksonian democracy: Representative writings of the period 1825–1850.* New York: Liberal Arts Press.

Cassedy, J. (1986). *Medicine and American growth, 1800–1860.* Madison: University of Wisconsin Press.

Coffin, A. I. (1846). *A Botanic guide to health and the natural pathology of disease.* (3rd ed.). Manchester, England: Wm. Irwin. Lloyd Library, Cincinnati, Ohio.

Ekirch, A. (1951). *The idea of progress in America, 1815–1860.* New York: P. Smith.

Gunn, J. C. (1830). *Domestic medicine or poor man's friend: In the hours of affliction, pain, and sickness.* Knoxville, printed under the immediate superintendence of the author: Countway Library, Harvard University, Massachusetts.

Haller, J. S. (1997). *Kindly medicine: Physio-medicalism in America, 1836–1911.* Kent, OH: Kent State University Press.

Haller, J. S. (2000). *The people's doctors: Samuel Thomson and the American botanical movement, 1790–1860.* Carbondale: Southern Illinois University Press.

Jefferson, T., Koch, A., Peden, W. H., & Jefferson, T. (1944). *The life and selected writings of Thomas Jefferson.* New York: Yale University Press.

Kett, J. F. (1968). *The formation of the American medical profession: The role of institutions, 1780–1860.* New Haven, CT: The Modern Library.

Merchant, C. (1989). *The death of nature: Women, ecology, and the scientific revolution.* New York: Harper & Row.

Porter, R. (1989). *Health for sale: Quackery in England 1660–1850.* Manchester: . Manchester University Press.

Porter, R. (1997). *The greatest benefit to mankind: A medical history of humanity.* (1st American ed.) New York: W. W. Norton.

Rafinesque, C. S. (1828). *Medical flora, or, Manual of the medical botany of the United States of North America.* Philadelphia: Atkinson & Alexander. Lloyd Library, Cincinnati, Ohio.

Risse, G. (Ed.) (1977). *Medicine without doctors: Home health care in American history.* New York: Science History Publications.

Rosenberg, C. E. (1962). *The cholera years: the United States in 1832, 1849, and 1866.* Chicago: University of Chicago Press.

Rothstein, W. G. (1972). *American physicians in the nineteenth century: From sects to science.* Baltimore: Johns Hopkins University Press.

Silver-Isenstadt, J. L. (2002). *Shameless: The visionary life of Mary Gove Nichols.* Baltimore: Johns Hopkins University Press.

Starr, P. (1982). *The social transformation of American medicine.* New York: Basic Books.

The Holy Bible—King James Version. (1972). Nashville, TN: Thomas Nelson.

Thomson, S. (1835). *New guide to health, or, Botanic family physician containing a complete system of practice, upon a plan entirely new: with a description of the vegetables made use of, and directions for preparing and administering them to cure disease: to which is prefixed a narrative of the life and medical discoveries of the author.* Boston: J.Q. Adams. Lloyd Library, Cincinnati, Ohio.

Turner, F. J., & Craven, A. O. (1935). *The United States, 1830–1850 : The nation and its sections.* New York: H. Holt and Company.

Van Deusen, G. (1959). *The Jacksonian Era.* New York: Harper & Brothers.

Vogel, M. J., & Rosenberg, C. E. (1979). *The therapeutic revolution: Essays in the social history of American medicine.* Philadelphia: University of Pennsylvania Press.

Chapter 3: The Mid-Nineteenth-Century Patient: Herbs, Advice Books, and Medical Freedom

Beach, W. (1843). *The family physician, or, The reformed system of medicine on vegetable or botanical principles being a compendium of the "American Practice" designed for all classes.* (4th ed.). New York: Author. Lloyd Library, Cincinnati, Ohio.

Berman, A., & Flannery, M. A. (2001). *America's botanico-medical movement: Vox populi.* New York: Pharmaceutical Products Press.

Buchan, W. (1769). *Domestic medicine, or, The family physician being an attempt to render the medical art more generally useful by shewing people what is in their own power both with respect to the prevention and cure of diseases. Chiefly calculated to recommend a proper attention to regimen and simple medicines.* Edinburgh, Scotland: Balfour, Auld, and Smellie. Wellcome Trust Library, London.

Child, L. M. (1997, originally published 1837). *The family nurse.* Bedford, MA: Applewood Books.

Child, L. M. (1999, originally published 1844). *The American frugal housewife.* Mineola, NY: Dover Publications.

Culpeper, N. (1990). *Culpeper's complete herbal & English physician.* Glenwood, IL: Meyerbooks.

Farnsworth, N. (1993). Relative safety of herbal medicines. *Herbalgram 29,* 36A–H.

Fellman, A., & Fellman, M. (1981). *Making sense of self: Medical advice literature in late nineteenth century America.* Philadelphia: University of Pennsylvania Press.

Graham, S. (1837). The Graham system: What is it? *The Graham Journal of Health and Longevity 1* (1), 17–18. Lloyd Library, Cincinnati, Ohio.

Gunn, J. C. (1830). *Domestic medicine or poor man's friend: In the hours of affliction, pain, and sickness.* Knoxville, printed under the immediate superintendence of the author: Countway Library, Harvard University, Massachusetts.

Haller, J. S. (2000). *The people's doctors: Samuel Thomson and the American botanical movement, 1790–1860.* Carbondale: Southern Illinois University Press.

Hatfield, G. (1999). *Memory, wisdom, and healing: The history of domestic plant medicine.* Gloucestershire, UK: Sutton.

Jefferson, T., Koch, A., Peden, W. H., & Jefferson, T. (1944). *The life and selected writings of Thomas Jefferson.* New York: The Modern library.

Jefferson, T., & University of Virginia. (1820). *Letter to William C. Jarvis, September 28, 1820. The Writings of Thomas Jefferson* (Memorial Edition 1903; v. 15: 278). Accessed September 2003 at http://etext.lib.virginia.edu/jefferson/quotations/jeff0350.htm.

Karcher, C. L. (1994). *The first woman in the republic: A cultural biography of Lydia Maria Child.* Durham, NC: Duke University Press.

Kett, J. F. (1968). *The formation of the American medical profession: The role of institutions, 1780–1860.* New Haven, CT: Yale University Press.

Levin, L. S., Idler, E. L., & the American Enterprise Institute for Public Policy Research. (1981). *The hidden health care system: Mediating structures and medicine.* Cambridge, MA: Ballinger.

Lewis, M., Clark, W., Brandt, A., & Viola, H. (2002). *The journals of Lewis and Clark.* Washington, DC: National Geographic Adventure Classics.

Lewis, M., Clark, W., & De Voto, B. A. (1997). *The journals of Lewis and Clark.* Boston: Houghton Mifflin.

Merriam, H. (1946). *The annals of the Merriam family.* Sturbridge, MA: Olde Sturbridge Village Library.

Mott, E. (1834). *The ladies medical oracle, or, Mrs. Mott's advice to young females, wives, and mothers being a non-medical commentary on the cause, prevention, and cure of diseases of the female frame together with an explanation of her system of European vegetable medicine for the cure of diseases and the patent medicated Champoo baths.* Boston: Samuel N. Dickinson. Schlessinger Library, Radcliffe Institute for Advanced Study, Massachusetts.

Peck, D. (2002). *Or perish in the attempt: Wilderness medicine in the Lewis and Clark expedition.* Helena, MT: Farcountry Press.

Risse, G. (Ed.) (1977). *Medicine without doctors: Home health care in American history.* New York: Science History Publications.

Silver-Isenstadt, J. L. (2002). *Shameless: The visionary life of Mary Gove Nichols.* Baltimore: Johns Hopkins University Press.

Starr, P. (1982). *The social transformation of American medicine.* New York: Basic Books.

Tannenbaum, R. (2002). *The healer's calling: Women and medicine in early New England.* Ithaca, NY: Cornell University Press.

University of Virginia Geospatial and Statistical Data Center. United States Historical Census Data Browser. ONLINE 1998. University of Virginia. Accessed June 2003 at http://fisher.lib.virginia.edu/collections/stats/histcensus/

University of Virginia Health System. (1998). The medical training of Meriwether Lewis. Accessed May 2003 at http://hsc.virginia.edu/hs-library/historical/lewis_clark/panel5.html.

Walsh, M. R. (1977). *Doctors wanted: No women need apply.* New Haven, CT: Yale University Press.

Wesley, J. (November 6, 1838). Rev. John Wesley. *Lobelia Advocate and Thomsonian Medical Recorder 1* (7), 105. Lloyd Library, Cincinnati, Ohio.

Wilson, R. (2000). *Pious traders in medicine: A German pharmaceutical network in eighteenth-century North America.* University Park: Pennsylvania State University Press.

Chapter 4: The Mid-Nineteenth-Century Nurse: Home, Herbs, and Women's Healing Networks

Abel, E. K. (2000). *Hearts of wisdom: American women caring for kin, 1850–1940.* Cambridge, MA: Harvard University Press.

Ashley, J. A. (1976). *Hospitals, paternalism, and the role of the nurse.* New York: Teachers College Press.

Baker, N. B. (1952). *Cyclone in calico: The story of Mary Ann Bickerdyke.* Boston: Little, Brown.

Beach, W. (1847). *Improved system of midwifery: Adapted to the reformed practice of medicine.* New York: J. McAlister. Lloyd Library, Cincinnati, Ohio.

Beecher, C. E. (1977, originally published 1841). *A treatise on domestic economy (studies in the life of women).* New York: Schocken Books.

Beecher, C. E. (2001, originally published 1858). *Miss Beecher's domestic receipt-book* . Mineola, NY: Dover Publications.

Beecher, C. E., & Stowe, H. B. (2002, originally published 1869). *The American woman's home, or, Principles of domestic science: Being a guide to the formation and maintenance of economical, healthful, beautiful, and Christian homes.* Piscataway, NJ: Rutgers University Press.

Brown, W. S., & Ladies' Medical Academy (1859). The capability of women to practice the healing art. In *Ladies Medical Academy*. Schlesinger Library, Radcliffe Institute for Advanced Study, Massachusetts.

Child, L. M. (1999, originally published 1844). *The American frugal housewife.* Mineola, NY: Dover Publications.

Cleaveland, C. (1852). Nurses. *The Eclectic Medical Journal 4* (8), 371–373. Lloyd Library, Cincinnati, Ohio.

Coe, S. (n.d.). *Receipt book.* Sophie Coe Collection, Schlesinger Library, Radcliffe Institute for Advanced Study, Massachusetts.

Cott, N. F. (1977). *The bonds of womanhood: "Woman's sphere" in New England, 1780-1835.* New Haven, CT: Yale University Press.

D'Antonio, P. (1993). The legacy of domesticity. *Nursing History Review 1*, 229–246.

Degler, C. N. (1980). *At odds: Women and the family in America from the Revolution to the present.* New York: Oxford University Press.

Delamont, S., & Duffin, L. (1978). *The nineteenth-century woman: Her cultural and physical world.* London and New York: Barnes & Noble.

Digby, A. (1994). *Making a medical living: Doctors and patients in the English market for medicine, 1720–1911.* Cambridge and New York: Cambridge University Press.

Digby, A., & Stewart, J. (Ed.). (1996). *Gender, health, and welfare.* London, Routledge.

Donovan, J. (2000). *Feminist theory: The intellectual traditions.* (3rd ed.). New York: Continuum.

Benes, P., & Benes, J. M. (1992). *Medicine and healing.* Dublin Seminar for New England Folklife Annual proceedings. Boston: Dublin Seminar for New England Folklife, Boston University.

Duby, G., Fraisse, G. E., Klapisch-Zuber, C., Perrot, M., Pantel, P. S., & Thébaud, F. (1993). *A history of women in the West: Emerging feminism from Revolution to World War.* Cambridge, MA: Belknap Press of Harvard University Press.

Florance, V. (1980). *Healing and the home: Home medicine in pioneer Utah.* Unpublished master's thesis. University of Utah.

Fuller, M. (1843). *Woman in the nineteenth century.* American Transcendentalism Web. Accessed February 2003 at http://www.vcu.edu/engweb/transcendentalism/authors/fuller/woman

Gartrell, E. (1987, January). Women healers and domestic remedies in 18th century America: The recipe book of Elizabeth Coates Paschall. *New York Journal of Medicine*, 23–29.

Gilman, C. P. (1973, originally published 1892). *The Yellow wallpaper.* (1st ed.) New York. Feminist Press.

Gordon, M. (Ed.) (1983). *The American family in social-historical perspective.* (3rd ed.) New York: St. Martin's Press.

Griffith, R. E., & Thomson, A. T. (1845). *The domestic management of the sickroom necessary, in aid of medical treatment, for the cure of diseases.* (1st American from the second London ed.) Philadelphia: Lea and Blanchard. Countway Library, Harvard University, Massachusetts.

James, T. (1840). A case of abortion. *Boston Thomsonian manual and lady's companion 6* (16), 252. Lloyd Library, Cincinnati, Ohio.

Josselyn, J. (1927). The genesis of the American materia medica. *Bulletin of the Lloyd Library of Botany, Pharmacy & Materia Medica 26* (Reproduction series no. 8), 3–64. Lloyd Library, Cincinnati, Ohio.

Kramer, J. (1996). *Women of flowers: A tribute to Victorian women illustrators.* New York: Lea and Blanchard.

Ladies Physiological Institute (1850–1851). Records of the meeting of the Ladies Physiological Institute of Boston and vicinity. Schlesinger Library, Radcliffe Institute for Advanced Study, Massachusetts.

Leighton, A. (1986) *Early American gardens:"For meate or medicine."* Amherst: University of Massachusetts Press.

Leighton, A. (1987). *American gardens of the nineteenth century: "For comfort and affluence."* Amherst: University of Massachusetts Press.

Lewis, J. (1991). *Women and social action in Victorian and Edwardian England.* Stanford, CA, Stanford University Press.

Libster, M. (2001). *Demonstrating care: The art of integrative nursing.* Clifton Park, NY: Delmar Thomson Learning.

Lovell, T. (1990). *British feminist thought.* Oxford: Basil Blackwell.

Mather, C., and Jones, G. (eds.) (1972 originally publishes 1722). *Angel of Bethesda.* Barre, MA: American Antiquarian Society and Banc Publishers.

Melder, K. (1967). Ladies bountiful: Organized women's benevolence in early nineteenth-century America. *New York History 48*, 101–123.

Melosh, B. (1982). *"The physician's hand": Work, culture, and conflict in American nursing.* Philadelphia: Temple University Press.

Merriam-Webster's collegiate dictionary. (1999). (10th ed.). Springfield, MA: Merriam-Webster.

Munroe, T. (1831, July) A tender wife. *Godey's Lady's Book*, 1. Colorado: University of Denver.

Nightingale, F. (1980, first published 1859). *Notes on nursing.* Edinburgh, Scotland: Churchill Livingston.

Orem, D. (2001). *Nursing concepts of practice.* (6th ed.) St. Louis, MO: Mosby.

Porter, R. (1985). Lay medical knowledge in the eighteenth century: The evidence of the gentleman's magazine. *Medical History 29*, 138–168.

Price-Herndl, D. (1993). *Invalid women: Figuring feminine illness in American fiction and culture, 1840–1940.* Chapel Hill: University of North Carolina Press.

Reverby, S. (1987). *Ordered to care: The dilemma of American nursing, 1850–1945.* Cambridge and New York: Cambridge University Press.

Sklar, K. K. (1973). *Catharine Beecher: A study in American domesticity.* New Haven, CT: Yale University Press.

Smith, F. G. (1851). *Domestic medicine, surgery, and materia medica with directions for the diet and management of the sickroom.* Philadelphia: Lindsay and Blakiston. Countway Library, Harvard University, Massachusetts.

Smout, T. C., Royal Society of Edinburgh, and British Academy (Ed.). (1992). *Victorian values: A joint symposium of the Royal Society of Edinburgh and the British Academy December 1990.* Proceedings of the British Academy. Oxford: Oxford University Press for the British Academy.

Sturbridge Village Exhibit. (Summer 2002). *Hepsibeth Hemenway.* Special exhibition of portrait from the Worcester Historical Society. Olde Sturbridge Village, Sturbridge, Massachusetts.

Tannenbaum, R. J. (2002). *The healer's calling: Women and medicine in early New England.* Ithaca, NY: Cornell University Press.

Theophano, J. (2002). *Eat my words: Reading women's lives through the cookbooks they wrote.* New York: Palgrave.

Ulrich, L. (1990). *A midwife's tale: The life of Martha Ballard, based on her diary, 1785–1812.* New York: Knopf: Distributed by Random House.

Verbrugge, M. H. (1988). *Able-bodied womanhood: Personal health and social change in nineteenth-century Boston.* New York: Oxford University Press.

Viaux family (1814-1816). *Recipe book.* In Viaux Family Collection, Schlesinger Library, Radcliffe Institute for Advanced Study, Massachusetts.

Vicinus, M. (1985). *Independent women: Work and community for single women 1850-1920.* Chicago: University of Chicago Press.

Walsh, M. R. (1977). *Doctors wanted: No women need apply.* New Haven, CT: Yale University Press.

Webster, T., Parkes, M., & Reese, D. M. (1845). *An encyclopedia of domestic economy: comprising such subjects as are most immediately connected with housekeeping; as, the construction of domestic edifices, with the modes of warming, ventilating, and lighting them; a description of the various articles of furniture; a general account of the animal and vegetable substances used in food, and the methods of preserving and preparing them by cooking; making bread; materials employed in dress and toilet; business of the laundry; description of the various wheel-carriages; preservation of health; domestic medicines, &c.* New York: Harper & Brothers. Old Sturbridge Village Library, Sturbridge, Massachusetts.

STAGE II: HARVESTING HISTORY — GATHERING IN

Baker, N.B. (1952). *Cyclone in calico: The story of Mary Ann Bickerdyke.* Boston: Little, Brown.

Ulrich, L. (1990). *A midwife's tale: The life of Martha Ballard, based on her diary, 1785–1812.* New York: Knopf: Distributed by Random House.

CHAPTER 5: HERBS AND THE SHAKER INFIRMARY AND COMMUNITY NURSES

Allard, E. (1885). *Autobiography.* Old Chatham Shaker Museum and Library, Shaker Manuscripts, Old Chatham, New York.

Andorn, M. (1957). Shakerism for today. In *Selected Papers*, pp. 1–10. Cleveland, OH: The Shaker Historical Society.

Andrews, E. D. (1933). *The community industries of the Shakers.* Charlestown, MA: Emporium Publications.

Andrews, E. D. (1953). *The people called Shakers: A search for the perfect society.* New York: Oxford University Press.

Beale, G., & Boswell, M. R. (1991). *The earth shall blossom: Shaker herbs and gardening.* Woodstock, VT: Countryman Press.

Berman, A., & Flannery, M. A. (2001). *America's botanico-medical movement: Vox populi.* New York: Pharmaceutical Products Press.

Blinn, H. C. (1784–1879). *Church record.* Canterbury Shaker Village, Canterbury, New Hampshire.

Blinn, H. C. (1892). *Historical record of the Society of Believers in Canterbury, N.H., vol. I and II.* Canterbury Shaker Village Collection, Canterbury, New Hampshire.

Blinn, H. C. (1895). *Historical notes having reference to the Believers in Enfield, N.H., vol. II.* Canterbury Shaker Village Collection. Canterbury, New Hampshire.

Buchanan, R. (1996). *The Shaker herb and garden book.* Boston: Houghton Mifflin Company.

Bullard, M. (1906, July). Shaker housekeeping. *Good Housekeeping 43,* 33–37.

Canterbury Shaker Nurses (1841?–1873). *Infirmary recipe book.* Sabbathday Lake Shaker Manuscripts, New Gloucester, Maine.

Canterbury Shakers (N.d.). *Recipes.* Canterbury Shaker Village Collection. Canterbury, New Hampshire. CSV #782, Box 64, Folder 2, and #168, Box 64, Folder 3.

Elkins, J. H. (1853). *Fifteen years in the Senior Order of Shakers.* Hanover, NH: Dartmouth Press. Old Chatham Shaker Village, Old Chatham, New York.

Evans, F. W. (1859). *Shakers compendium of the origin, history, principles, rules and regulations, government, and doctrines of the United Society of Believers in Christ's Second Appearing.* New York: D. Appleton & Co. Old Chatham Shaker Village, Old Chatham, New York.

Evans, F. W. (1881). *New England witchcraft and spiritualism.* Old Chatham Shaker Village, Old Chatham, New York.

Felter, H. W., & Lloyd, J. U. (1983, originally published 1898). *King's American dispensatory.* (18th ed., 3rd rev. ed.). Sandy, OR: Eclectic Medical Publications.

Hammond, J. (1820–1826). *Day book.* Fruitlands Museum Shaker Manuscripts, Harvard, Massachusetts.

Hancock Shakers. (N.d.). *Recipes and prescriptions from Hancock Shaker Village.* Western Reserve Historical Society. Shaker Manuscripts, # XI, B 5, Cleveland, Ohio.

Harvard Shakers. (18281838). *Church family day book.* Fruitlands Museum Shaker Manuscripts, Harvard, Massachusetts.

Harvard Shakers. (1843). *Physicians' journal, or, An account of the sickness at Harvard.* Western Reserve Historical Society. Shaker Manuscripts, # V, B 41, Cleveland, Ohio.

Harvard Shakers. (N.d.) *Harvard Shaker covenants.* Fruitlands Museum Shaker Manuscripts. Microfilm Reel 1.8, Harvard, Massachusetts.

Harvard Shakers (N.d.). *Teachings to the children on health.* Fruitlands Museum Shaker Manuscripts. Reel #19.1, Harvard, Massachusetts.

Hoffman, G. N. (1920). Mt. Lebanon medicine makers—the Shakers. *The Pharmaceutical Era 53* (7), 197–198. Lloyd Library, Cincinnati, Ohio.

Klamkin, M. (1972). *Hands to work: Shaker folk art and industries.* New York: Dodd, Mead.

Mace, A. (1896). *The journal of Sister Aurelia Mace.* Sabbathday Lake Shaker Manuscripts, New Gloucester, Maine.

Madden, E. (1995) *Bodies of life: Shaker literacies and literature.* Unpublished dissertation. University of New Hampshire.

Miller, A. (1976). *Shaker herbs: A history and a compendium.* New York: C.N. Potter. Distributed by Crown Publishers.

Morrell, P. (1849). *A choice collection of medical and botanical receipts: Selected from experienced physicians by whom they have been proved and found useful in the various disorders and infirmities for which they are prescribed. To which is prefixed remarks and observations for the consideration of physicians and nurses among Believers.* Winterthur Library Shaker Manuscripts, Winterthur, Delaware.

Morrell, P. (1854). *Receipts & counsels exclusively for female diseases.* Winterthur Library Shaker Manuscripts, Winterthur, Delaware.

Myrick, E. (1850). *Daybook.* Hancock Shaker Village Library, Harvard Shaker Manuscripts, Hancock, Massachusetts.

New Lebanon Shaker Nurses (1815). *Notebook of receipts from the nurses' shop—New Lebanon.* Hancock Shaker Village Library, Hancock, Massachusetts.

Nichols, M.G. (1842). *Lectures to ladies on anatomy and physiology.* Boston: Saxton & Pierce.

Piercy, H. (1957). Shaker medicines. In *Selected Papers,* pp. 11–32. Cleveland: The Shaker Historical Society.

Rafinesque, C. S. (1828). *Medical flora, or, Manual of the medical botany of the United States of North America.* Philadelphia: Atkinson & Alexander. Lloyd Library, Cincinnati, Ohio.

Risse, G. (Ed.). (1977). *Medicine without doctors: Home health care in American history.* New York: Science History Publications.

Sabbathday Lake Shakers (N.d.). *Community records.* Sabbathday Lake Shaker Manuscripts, New Gloucester, Maine.

Shakers. (1781). *Millennial Laws.* Western Reserve Historical Society, Shaker Collection, Cleveland, Ohio.

Shakers (1821). *Millennial Laws.* Western Reserve Historical Society, Shaker Collection, Cleveland, Ohio.

Shakers. (1840–1860). *A book of medical recipes.* Old Chatham Shaker Village, Old Chatham, New York.

Shakers. (N.d). *Medicinal objects.* Hancock Shaker Village, Shaker Collection, Hancock, Massachusetts.

Shakers. (N.d.). *Receipt book.* Fruitlands Museum Shaker Manuscripts. Reel # 1.3, Harvard, Massachusetts.

Shirley Shakers. (N.d.), *Nurse house book*. Fruitlands Museum, Shaker Manuscripts. Reel # 8.5, Harvard, Massachusetts.

Smith, P. (1813). *The Indian doctor's dispensatory being Father Smith's advice respecting diseases and their cure*. Cincinnati: Browne and Looker. Lloyd Library, Cincinnati, Ohio.

Standish, S. A. (1860). *A collection of medicinal receipts for the use of physicians*. Old Chatham Shaker Village, Old Chatham, New York.

Stein, S. J. (1992). *The Shaker experience in America: A history of the United Society of Believers*. New Haven, CT: Yale University Press.

Thomson, S. (1835). *New guide to health, or, Botanic family physician containing a complete system of practice, upon a plan entirely new: with a description of the vegetables made use of, and directions for preparing and administering them to cure disease: to which is prefixed a narrative of the life and medical discoveries of the author*. Boston: J. Q. Adams. Lloyd Library, Cincinnati, Ohio.

Thurman, S. R. (2002). *"O sisters ain't you happy?": Gender, family, and community among the Harvard and Shirley Shakers, 1781-1918*. Syracuse, NY: Syracuse University Press.

United Society of Shakers. (2000). *The origins of the Shaker Church*. Edited by the United Society of Shakers, Inc. New Gloucester, ME: Author.

U.S. Department of Commerce (1975). *Historical statistics of the United States: Colonial times to 1970*. Edited by U.S. Department of Commerce, Washington, DC: Author, U.S. Bureau of the Census. Accessed June 2003 at http://fisher.lib.virginia.edu/collections/stats/histcensus/

Watervliet Shakers. (1797–1913). *Membership, birth, death, and statistical records Watervliet, NY, 1797–1913*. Western Reserve Historical Society, # 3:A 14. Shaker Manuscripts, Cleveland, Ohio.

Whitcher, M. (1882). *Mary Whitcher's Shaker house-keeper*. Boston: Weeks & Potter. Old Chatham Shaker Village, Old Chatham, New York.

CHAPTER 6: HERBS AND THE PIONEER NURSES AND MIDWIVES OF THE CHURCH OF JESUS CHRIST OF LATTER-DAY SAINTS

Abram, R. J. (1985). *Send us a lady physician: Women doctors in America, 1835–1920*. New York: Norton.

Alder, D. (Ed.). (N.d.). *Cache Valley: Essays on her past and people*. Logan: Utah State University Press.

Arrington, L. J., & Bitton, D. (1979). *The Mormon experience: A history of the Latter-day Saints*. New York: Knopf. Distributed by Random House.

Atkin, T. M. (1919). *Thomas Atkin diary (1833–1919).* Salt Lake City: Utah Historical Society.

Beach, W. (1843). *The family physician, or, The reformed system of medicine on vegetable or botanic principles being a compendium of the "American Practice" designed for all classes.* (4th ed.). New York: Author. Lloyd Library, Cincinnati, Ohio.

Beecher, C. E., & Stowe, H. B. (1869). *The American woman's home, or, Principles of domestic science: Being a guide to the formation and maintenance of economical, healthful, beautiful, and Christian homes.* New York: J. B. Ford.

Bishop, A. M. (N.d.). *Sketch of Ann Green Dutson Carling.* Salt Lake City: Daughters of the Utah Pioneers Collection.

Carter, K. (1945). *Pioneer medicines.* Salt Lake City: Daughters of the Utah Pioneers Collection.

Carter, K. (1959). *Our pioneer heritage: And they were healed.* Salt Lake City: Daughters of the Utah Pioneers Collection.

Cassedy, J. H. (1986). *Medicine and American growth, 1800–1860.* Madison: University of Wisconsin Press.

Christopher, J., & Gileadi, C. (1978). *Every woman's herbal.* Springville, UT: Christopher Publications.

Church of Jesus Christ of Latter-day Saints. (1843). *Times and Seasons 4* (21). Salt Lake City, UT: Archives of the CJCLDS.

Church of Jesus Christ of Latter-day Saints. (1843). *Deseret News.* Salt Lake City, UT: Archives of the CJCLDS.

Church of Jesus Christ of Latter-day Saints. (1981). *The Book of Mormon: The doctrine and covenants of the Church of Jesus Christ of Latter-day Saints. The pearl of great price.* Salt Lake City, UT: Archives of the CJCLDS.

Derr, J. M., Cannon, J. R., & Beecher, M. U. (1992). *Women of covenant: The story of Relief Society.* Salt Lake City, UT: Deseret Book Co.

Divett, R. (1981). *Medicine and the Mormons.* Bountiful, UT: Horizon Publishers & Distributors.

Farnsworth, N. (1993). Relative safety of herbal medicines. *Herbalgram 29,* 36A–H.

Felter, H. W., & Lloyd, J. U. (1983). *King's American dispensatory.* (18th ed., 3rd rev. ed.) Sandy, OR: Eclectic Medical Publications.

Fowler, M. (1899–1900) *Diaries.* Salt Lake City: University of Utah Special Collections.

"J. H. M." (1855). Iron County—Parowan: To Bro. Geo. A. Smith. *Deseret News 5* (144). Salt Lake City, UT: Archives of the CJCLDS.

Kay, M. A. (1996). *Healing with plants in the American and Mexican West.* Tucson: University of Arizona Press.

Libster, M. (2002). *Delmar's integrative herb guide for nurses.* Clifton Park, NY: Delmar Thomson Learning.

Lyman, E. (1860–1879). *Journal.* Salt Lake City, UT: University of Utah Special Collections.

Meeks, P. (1879). *Reminiscences (Journal).* Salt Lake City: Archives of the CJCLDS.

Mills, S,. & Bone, K. (2000). *Principles and practice of phytotherapy: Modern herbal medicine.* Edinburgh, Scotland: Churchill Livingstone.

Moerman, D. E. (1998). *Native American ethnobotany.* Portland, OR: Timber Press.

Nielson, L. (N.d.). *And they were healed—Ann Carling.* Salt Lake City: Daughters of the Utah Pioneers Collection.

Nielson, L., & Flack, D. D. (1957). *The Dutson family history.* Salt Lake City: Daughters of the Utah Pioneers Collection.

Noall, C. (1957). *Intimate disciple: A portrait of Willard Richards.* Salt Lake City: University of Utah Press.

O'Connor, B. B. (1995). *Healing traditions: Alternative medicine and the health professions.* Philadelphia: University of Pennsylvania Press.

Richards, L. (1836–1849). *Journal.* Salt Lake City, UT: Archives of the CJCLDS.

Richards, M. H. P. (1846–1848). *Diary.* Salt Lake City: University of Utah Special Collections.

Richards, W. (1836–1840). *Diary.* Salt Lake City, UT: Archives of the CJCLDS.

Rose, B. (1939). *History of medicine in Utah.* Salt Lake City: University of Utah Press.

Sessions, P. B., & Smart, D. T. (1997). *Mormon midwife: The 1846–1888 diaries of Patty Bartlett Sessions.* Logan, UT: Utah State University Press.

Smith, N. (1983). Why are Mormons so susceptible to medical and nutritional quackery? *Journal of Collegium Aesculapium 1* (1), 29–44.

Sorensen, E. (1998). For Zion's sake: The emergence of Mormon nursing. *Nursing History Review 6*, 51–69.

Tannenbaum, R. (2002). *The healer's calling: Women and medicine in early New England.* Ithaca, NY: Cornell University Press.

Ulrich, L. (1990). *A midwife's tale: The life of Martha Ballard, based on her diary, 1785–1812.* New York: Knopf: Distributed by Random House.

Walsh, M. R. (1977). *Doctors wanted: No women need apply.* New Haven, CT: Yale University Press.

Winters, M. A. S. (1969). *Mothers in Israel: Mary Ann Stearns Winters' Narrative (1833–1912).* Salt Lake City: Daughters of the Utah Pioneers Collection.

Young, B., & Church of Jesus Christ of Latter-day Saints. (1956). *Journal of discourses.* Los Angeles: Gartner Printing and Litho.

Chapter 7: Herbs and the Sisters of Charity and Early American Hospitals

Armiger, B. (1947). *The history of the hospital work of the Daughters of Charity of St. Vincent de Paul in the Eastern Province of the United States 1823–1860.* Unpublished dissertation. Catholic University, Washington, DC.

Armiger, B. (1964). Two sister-nurses claimed by cholera. *Nursing Outlook 12.*

Arnault de Nobleville, L. D. (1765). *Le Manuel des Dames de Charite, ou Formules de Medicamens Faciles a Preparer.* (5th ed.). Paris: Debure. Author's Personal Collection.

Arnault de Nobleville, L. D. (1767). *Description Abrege des Plantes Usuelles. A vecleurs vertus, leursufages & leurs proprietes. Par l'Auteur du manuel de Dames de Charite & pour server de suite au même Ouvrage.* Paris: Debure. Old Cathedral Library, Vincennes, Indiana.

Babb, W. (1954) *French refugees from Saint-Domingue to the Southern United States: 1791–1810.* University of Virginia. Unpublished dissertation. Accessed June 2003 at http://freepages.genealogy.rootsweb.com/~saintdomingue/Babb%20Index.htm.

Beecher, C. E., & Stowe, H. B. (2002, originally published 1869). *The American woman's home, or, Principles of domestic science: Being a guide to the formation and maintenance of economical, healthful, beautiful, and Christian homes.* Piscataway, NJ: Rutgers University Press.

Berman, A., & Flannery, M. A. (2001). *America's botanico-medical movement: Vox populi.* New York: Pharmaceutical Products Press.

Bramucci, N. (2001). *Medical care in the city of Baltimore.* Accessed August 2003 at http://www.mdhistoryonline.net/mdmedicine/cfm/quinan.cfm?id=794

Byrne, S. A. (1950). *History of the Seton Institute, Baltimore, Maryland, and its affiliate School of Nursing conducted by the Daughters of Charity of St. Vincent de Paul in the Eastern Province of the United States.* Unpublished dissertation. Washington, DC: Catholic University of America.

Clark, M. M. X. (1846). *Instruction on the care of the sick.* St. Louis, MO: Archives of Daughters of Charity of St. Vincent de Paul.

Coskery, M. (N.d.), *Advices concerning the sick*. Emmitsburg, MD: Archives of Daughters of Charity, St. Joseph's Provincial House.

Coste, P. (1924). *Saint Vincent de Paul: Correspondance, entretiens, documents.* Paris: Lecoffre and Gabaldo. Emmitsburg, MD: Archives of Daughters of Charity, St. Joseph's Provincial House.

Cummings, C. (1948). *History of the hospital work and the development of the schools of nursing of the Sisters of Charity in the Eastern province (1860–1900).* Unpublished dissertation. Washington, DC: Catholic University of America.

Daughters of Charity. (1812). *The Rule of 1812: Regulations for the Society of Sisters of Charity in the United States of America.* Emmitsburg, MD: Archives of Daughters of Charity, St. Joseph's Provincial House.

Daughters of Charity (1832). *Letter of William Stewart, mayor of Baltimore—Extract from the chronicles of Baltimore.* Emmitsburg, MD: Archives of Daughters of Charity, St. Joseph's Provincial House—Cholera Box 7-7-1-1.

Daughters of Charity. (1852). *Mt. St. Vincent—Cradle of Mt. Hope (Book) 11-2-39.* Emmitsburg, MD: Archives of Daughters of Charity, St. Joseph's Provincial House.

Daughters of Charity (1860). *Civil War notes 7-5-1.* Emmitsburg, MD: Archives of Daughters of Charity, St. Joseph's Provincial House.

Daughters of Charity (1870). *Lives of the deceased sisters.* Emmitsburg, MD: Archives of Daughters of Charity, St. Joseph's Provincial House.

Daughters of Charity (1870). *Lives of the deceased sisters - Mother Xavier Clark.* Emmitsburg, MD: Archives of Daughters of Charity, St. Joseph's Provincial House.

Daughters of Charity. (1936). *Mother Rose White.* Emmitsburg, MD: Archives of Daughters of Charity, St. Joseph's Provincial House.

Daughters of Charity. (1938). *Mother Augustine and Mother Xavier.* Emmitsburg, MD: Archives of Daughters of Charity, St. Joseph's Provincial House.

Daughters of Charity (1949). *The Seton Institute . . . a Century of Progress.* Emmitsburg, MD: Archives of Daughters of Charity, St. Joseph's Provincial House. Seton Institute Collection, Box 11-2-39-1.

de Paul, V. (1938–1940). *The conferences of St. Vincent de Paul to the Daughters of Charity.* London: Burns, Oates & Washbourne. Archives of Archives of Daughters of Charity, St. Joseph's Provincial House.

Digby, A. (1985). *Madness, morality, and medicine: A study of the York Retreat, 1796–1914.* Cambridge and New York: Cambridge University Press.

Dirvin, J. I. (1993). *Mrs. Seton, foundress of the American Sisters of Charity*. Emmitsburg, MD: Basilica of the National Shrine of St. Elizabeth Ann Seton.

Dix, D. (1852). *Memorial of Miss D. L. Dix to the Hon. The General Assembly in behalf of the insane of Maryland*, Archives of the State of Maryland, March 5, 1852.

Felter, H. W., & Lloyd, J. U. (1983). *King's American dispensatory*. (18th ed., 3d rev. ed.) Sandy, OR: Eclectic Medical Publications.

Godecker, M. S. (1931). *Simon Bruté de Remur*, St. Meinrad Historical Essays, St. Meinrad, Indiana. Emmitsburg, MD: Archives of Daughters of Charity, St. Joseph's Provincial House.

Grob, G. N. (1983). *Mental illness and American society, 1875–1940*. Princeton, NJ: Princeton University Press.

Guazzo, F. M., & Summers, M. (1988). *Compendium maleficarum: The Montague Summers edition*. New York: Dover Publications.

Hannefin, D. (1989). *Daughters of the church: A popular history of the Daughters of Charity in the United States 1809–1987*. Brooklyn, NY: New City Press.

James, E. T., James, J. W., Boyer, P. S., & Radcliffe College. (1971). *Notable American women, 1607–1950: A biographical dictionary*. Cambridge, MA: Belknap Press of Harvard University Press.

Jameson, H. G. (1817). *The American domestick medicine, or, Medical admonisher*. Baltimore: F. Lucas. Old Cathedral Library, Vincennes, Indiana.

Jones, C. (1989). Sisters of Charity and the ailing poor. *Social History of Medicine 2* (3), 339–348.

Kramer, H., & Sprenger, J. (1971). *Malleus maleficarum*. New York: Dover Publications.

Livermore, M. A. R. (1889). *My story of the war: A woman's narrative of four years' personal experience as nurse in the Union Army, and in relief work at home, in hospitals, camps, and at the front during the war of the rebellion. With anecdotes, pathetic incidents, and thrilling reminiscences portraying the lights and shadows of hospital life and the sanitary service of the war*. Hartford, CT: A. D. Worthington and Company. Author's personal collection.

Maher, M. D. (1989). *To bind up the wounds: Catholic sister nurses in the U.S. Civil War*. New York: Greenwood Press.

McNamara, J. A. (1996). *Sisters in arms: Catholic nuns through two millennia*. Cambridge, MA: Harvard University Press.

McNeil, B. A. (1996). *The Vincentian family tree*. Chicago: Vincentian Studies Institute.

Melville, A. M. (1951). *Elizabeth Bayley Seton, 1774–1821*. New York: Scribner.

Merriam-Webster's collegiate dictionary. (1999) (10th ed.) Springfield, MA: Merriam-Webster.

Nelson, S. (2001). *Say little, do much: Nurses, nuns, and hospitals in the nineteenth century*. Philadelphia: University of Pennsylvania Press.

Rothstein, W. G. (1972). *American physicians in the nineteenth century: From sects to science*. Baltimore: Johns Hopkins University Press.

Ryan, F., & Rybolt, J. (1995). *Vincent de Paul and Louise de Marillac: Rules, conferences, and writings*. Mahwah, NJ: Paulist Press.

Seton, E. A., Bechtle, R. M., & Metz, J. (in press). *Collected writings*. (vol. 3) Hyde Park, NY: New City Press.

Stepsis, M. U., & Liptak, D. A. (1989). *Pioneer healers: The history of women religious in American health care*. New York: Crossroad.

Stokes, W. (1852). *The Ninth Annual Report of the Mount Hope Institution, near Baltimore for the year 1851*. Baltimore: M. John Murphy and Company. Emmitsburg, MD: Archives of Daughters of Charity, St. Joseph's Provincial House.

Sullivan, L. (1991). *Spiritual writings of Louise de Marillac: Correspondence and thoughts*. Brooklyn, NY: New City Press.

Stage II: Harvesting History — Gathering In

Apple, R. (1990). *Women, health, and medicine in America: A historical handbook*. New Brunswick, NJ: Rutgers University Press.

Mack, R. (1998). "Something wicked this way comes"—Herbs even witches should avoid. *Contemporary Pediatrics 15* (6), 49–64.

Chapter 8: The Integration of the Spheres

Apple, R. (1990). *Women, health, and medicine in America: A historical handbook*. New Brunswick, NJ: Rutgers University Press.

Barnett, R. A. (1990). *The idea of higher education*. Oxford: Society for Research into Higher Education and Open University Press.

Belenky, M. F. (1997). *Women's ways of knowing: The development of self, voice, and mind*. (10th ed.) New York: Basic Books.

Benner, P. (2001). *From novice to expert: Excellence and power in clinical nursing practice.* Upper Saddle River, NJ: Prentice-Hall.

Berman, A. (1954). *The impact of the nineteenth-century botanico-medical movement on American pharmacy and medicine.* Unpublished doctoral dissertation. University of Wisconsin.

Bushy, A. (1992). Cultural considerations for primary health care: Where do self-care and folk medicine fit? *Holistic Nursing Practice 6* (3), 10–18.

Cooper, J. F. (1956, originally published 1838). *The American democrat, or, Hints on the social and civic relations of the United States of America.* New York: Vintage Books.

Cope, Z. (1958). *Florence Nightingale and the doctors.* London: Museum Press.

Coskery, M. (N.d.). *Advices concerning the sick.* Emmitsburg, MD: Archives of Daughters of Charity, St. Joseph's Provincial House,

Donovan, J. (2000). *Feminist theory: The intellectual traditions.* (3rd ed.) New York: Continuum.

Ehrenreich, B., & English, D. (1978). *For her own good: 150 years of the experts' advice to women.* Garden City, NY: Anchor Press.

Eisenberg, D. M., Davis, R. B., Ettner, S. L., Appel, S., Wilkey, S., Van Rompay, M., & Kessler, R. C. (1998). Trends in alternative medicine use in the United States, 1990–1997: Results of a follow-up national survey. *JAMA 280* (18), 1569–1575.

Leavitt, J. W. (1986). *Brought to bed: Childbearing in America, 1750 to 1950.* New York: Oxford University Press.

Levin, L. S., Idler, E. L., & American Enterprise Institute for Public Policy Research (1981). *The hidden health care system: Mediating structures and medicine.* Cambridge, MA: Ballinger.

Löwy, I. (1988). Ludwik Fleck on the social construction of medical knowledge. *Sociology of Health and Illness 10* (2), 133–155.

Mack, R. (1998). "Something wicked this way comes"—Herbs even witches should avoid. *Contemporary Pediatrics* 15 (6), 49–64.

Marshall, E. S., & Wall, B. (1999). Religion, gender, and autonomy: A comparison of two religious women's groups in nursing and hospitals in the late nineteenth and early twentieth centuries. *ANS: Advances in Nursing Science 22* (1), 1–22.

Mayhew, E. E. (1830). *Narratives of the lives of pious Indian women who lived on Martha's Vineyard more than one hundred years since. Carefully revised from the London edition, originally printed for Samuel Gerrish, bookseller in Boston, New-England, 1727.* Boston: James Loring. Worcester, MA: American Antiquarian Society.

Merchant, C. (1989). *The death of nature: Women, ecology, and the scientific revolution.* New York: Harper & Row.

Nabokov, P. (1999). Native American testimony: A chronicle of Indian-white relations from prophecy to present, 1492–200. New York: Penguin Books.

Nightingale, F., Calabria, M. D., & Macrae, J. (1994). *Suggestions for thought.* Philadelphia: University of Pennsylvania Press.

Nightingale, F., Vicinus, M., & Nergaard, B. (1990). *Ever yours: Florence Nightingale selected letters.* Cambridge, MA: Harvard University Press.

O'Connor, B. B. (1995). *Healing traditions: Alternative medicine and the health professions.* Philadelphia: University of Pennsylvania Press.

O'Malley, I. B. (1931). *Florence Nightingale 1820–1856: A study of her life down to the end of the Crimean War.* London: Thornton Butterworth. The University of Colorado Library.

Orem, D. (2001). *Nursing concepts of practice.* (6th ed.) St. Louis, MO: Mosby.

Perrone, B., Stockel, H. H., & Krueger, V. (1989). *Medicine women, curanderas, and women doctors.* Norman: University of Oklahoma Press.

Pill, R., & Stott, N. (1985). Choice or chance: Further evidence on ideas of illness and responsibility for health. *Sociology of Science in Medicine 20* (10), 981–991.

Riley, G. (1984). *Women and Indians on the frontier, 1825–1915.* Albuquerque: University of New Mexico Press.

Risse, G., Number, R., Lewitt, J. (Eds.). (1977). *Medicine without doctors: Home health care in American history.* New York: Science History Publications.

Rothstein, W. G. (1972). *American physicians in the nineteenth century: From sects to science.* Baltimore: Johns Hopkins University Press.

Seymer, L. (1954). *The selected writings of Florence Nightingale.* New York: Macmillan. The University of Colorado Library.

Smout, T. C., Royal Society of Edinburgh, & British Academy (Ed.). (1992). *Victorian values: A joint symposium of the Royal Society of Edinburgh and the British Academy, December 1990.* Proceedings of the British Academy. Oxford: Oxford University.

Taylor, S. E., Klein, L. C., Lewis, B. P., Gruenewald, T. L., Gurung, R. A., & Updegraff, J. A. (2000). Biobehavioral responses to stress in females: Tend-and-befriend, not fight-or-flight. *Psychological Review 107* (3), 411–429.

Woodham Smith, C. (1951). *Florence Nightingale, 1820–1910.* New York: McGraw-Hill. The University of Colorado Library.

CHAPTER 9: CONCLUSION - THE FUTURE OF HERBAL DIPLOMACY

Akerele, O. (1993). Summary of WHO guidelines for the assessment of herbal medicines. *Herbalgram 28*, 13–20.

Akerele, O. (1993). Nature's medicinal bounty: Don't throw it away. *World Health Forum* 14, 390–395.

Baba, S., Akerele, O., & Kawaguchi, Y. (1992). Natural resources and human health—Plants of medicinal and nutritional value. Proceedings of the 1st WHO symposium on plants and health for all: Scientific advancement, Kobe, Japan. August 1991. Amsterdam: Elsevier.

Balick, M. J., & Cox, P. A. (1996). *Plants, people, and culture: The science of ethnobotany.* New York: Scientific American Library.

Barnes, D., Eribes, C., Juarbe, T., Nelson, M., Proctor, S., Sawyer, L., Shaul, M., & Meleis, A. I. (1995). Primary health care and primary care: A confusion of philosophies. *Nursing Outlook 43* (1), 7–16.

Bleck, E. (1996). Medical nostalgia: "Simple" medical care versus technology. *Developmental Medicine and Child Neurology 38* (1), 1–2.

Bodeker, G., & Kronenberg, F. (2002). A public health agenda for traditional, complementary, and alternative medicine. *American Journal of Public Health 92* (10), 1582–1591.

Bowker, P. (1836). *The Indian vegetable family instructor: Containing the names and descriptions of all the most useful herbs and plants that grow in this country, with their medicinal qualities annexed. Also a treatise on many of the lingering diseases to which mankind are subject, with new and plain arguments respecting the management of the same, with a large list of recipes, which have been carefully selected from Indian prescriptions and from those very persons who were cured by the same after every other remedy had failed.* Boston: Pierpont Bowker. Lloyd Library, Cincinnati, Ohio.

Coffin, A. I. (1846). *A Botanic guide to health and the natural pathology of disease.* (3rd ed.). Manchester, England: Wm. Irwin. Lloyd Library, Cincinnati, Ohio.

D'Antonio, P. (1997). Toward a history of research in nursing. *Nursing Research 46* (2), 105–109.

Donovan, J. (2000). *Feminist theory: The intellectual traditions.* (3rd ed.) New York: Continuum.

Ernst, W. (2002). *Plural medicine: Tradition and modernity, 1800–2000.* London: Routledge.

Kreitzer, M., Mitten, D., Harris, I., & Shandeling, J. (2002). Attitudes toward CAM among medical, nursing, and pharmacy faculty and students: A comparative analysis. *Alternative Therapies in Health and Medicine 8* (6), 4447, 50–53.

Landy, D. (1977). *Culture, disease, and healing: Studies in medical anthropology*. New York: Macmillan.

Lazarou, J., Pomeranz, B., & Corey, P. (1998). Incidence of adverse drug reactions in hospitalized patients: A meta-analysis of prospective studies. *JAMA: Journal of the American Medical Association 279* (15), 1200–1205.

Leininger, M. (1984). *Care: The essence of nursing and health.* Detroit: Wayne State University Press.

Leonard, E. B. (2003). *Women, technology, and the myth of progress.* Upper Saddle River, NJ: Prentice-Hall.

Levin, L. S., Idler, E. L., & American Enterprise Institute for Public Policy Research (1981). *The hidden health care system mediating structures and medicine.* Cambridge, MA: Ballinger..

Libster, M. (2002). *Delmar's integrative herb guide for nurses.* Clifton Park, NY: Delmar Thomson Learning.

Libster, M. (2003). Integrative care—product and process: Considering the three T's of timing, type, and tuning. *Complementary Therapies in Nursing and Midwifery,* 9 (1), 1–4.

Merriam-Webster's collegiate dictionary. (1999). (10th ed.) Springfield, MA: Merriam-Webster.

Moylan, L. (2000). Alternative treatment modalities: The need for a rational response by the nursing profession. *Nursing Outlook. 48* (6), 259–261.

O'Connor, B. B. (1995). *Healing traditions: Alternative medicine and the health professions.* Philadelphia: University of Pennsylvania Press.

Perrone, B., Stockel, H. H., & Krueger, V. (1989). *Medicine women, curanderas, and women doctors.* Norman: University of Oklahoma Press.

Ritivoi, A. D. (2002). *Yesterday's self nostalgia and the immigrant identity.* Lanham, MD: Rowman & Littlefield.

Sandelowski, M. (2000). *Devices and desires: Gender, technology, and American nursing.* Chapel Hill: University of North Carolina Press.

Smith, P. (1813). *The Indian doctor's dispensatory being Father Smith's advice respecting diseases and their cure.* Cincinnati: Browne and Looker. Lloyd Library, Cincinnati, Ohio.

Smout, T. C., Royal Society of Edinburgh, & British Academy (Ed.). (1992). *Victorian values: A joint symposium of the Royal Society of Edinburgh and the British Academy,December 1990.* Proceedings of the British Academy. Oxford: Oxford University Press for the British Academy.

Theophano, J. (2002). *Eat my words: Reading women's lives through the cookbooks they wrote*. New York: Palgrave.

Thorne, S. E. (1993). *Negotiating health care: The social context of chronic illness.* Newbury Park, CA: Sage Publications.

Tosh, J. (2000). *The pursuit of history: Aims, methods, and new directions in the study of modern history*. (3rd ed.) Harlow, England: Longman.

Vogel, V. J. (1970). *American Indian medicine.* Norman: University of Oklahoma Press.

World Health Organization. (2003, May). *Fact Sheet No. 134: Traditional Medicine.* Geneva, Switzerland: World Health Organization.

World Health Organization Traditional Medicine Programme. (2002). *WHO Traditional Medicine Strategy 2002–2005.* Geneva, Switzerland: World Health Organization.

BOTANICAL COLOR INSERTS

Beach, W. (1843). *The family physician, or, The reformed system of medicine on vegetable or botanic principles being a compendium of the "American Practice" designed for all classes.* (4th ed.). New York: Author. Lloyd Library, Cincinnati, Ohio.

Berman, A., & Flannery, M. A. (2001). *America's botanico-medical movement: Vox populi.* New York: Pharmaceutical Products Press.

Blumenthal, M., Bundesinstitut für Arzneimittel und Medizinprodukte (Germany), & Commission E. (2000) *Herbal medicine expanded commission E monographs.* Newton, MA: Integrative Medicine Communications.

Erichsen-Brown, C. (1979). *Medicinal and other uses of North Amerian plants: A historical survey with special references to the Eastern Indian tribes.* New York: Dover Publications.

Felter, H. W., & Lloyd, J. U. (1983). *King's American dispensatory.* (18th ed., 3rd rev. ed.) Sandy, OR: Eclectic Medical Publications.

Grieve, M. 1981 *A modern herbal.* New York: Dover Publications.

Haller, J. S. (2000). *The people's doctors: Samuel Thomson and the American botanical movement, 1790–1860.* Carbondale: Southern Illinois University Press.

Jensen, J. M. (1991). *Promise to the land: Essays on rural women.* Albuquerque: University of New Mexico Press.

Kloss, J. (1983). *Back to Eden: A human interest story of health and restoration to be found in herb, root, and bark.* Santa Barbara, CA: Woodbridge Press.

Lad, V., & Frowley, D. (1986). The yoga of herbs. Santa Fe, NM: Lotus Press.

Libster, M. (2002). *Delmar's integrative herb guide for nurses.* Clifton Park, NY: Delmar Thomson Learning.

Moerman, D. E. (1998). *Native American ethnobotany*. Portland, OR: Timber Press.

Rafinesque, C. S. (1828). *Medical flora, or, Manual of the medical botany of the United States of North America.* Philadelphia: Atkinson & Alexander. Lloyd Library, Cincinnati, Ohio.

Smilax, L. (1854). *Sarsaparilla and sarsaparilla so-called: A popular analysis of a popular medicine.* London: Aylott & Co. Lloyd Library, Cincinnati, Ohio.

Standish, S. A. (1860). *A collection of medicinal receipts for the use of physicians.* Old Chatham, NY: Old Chatham Shaker Village Library.

Tantaquidgeon, G. (1972). *Folk medicine of the Delaware and related Algonkian Indians.* Harrisburg: Pennsylvania Historical and Museum Commission.

Index

Page references in italics refer to tables or color inserts.

About the Author

Dr. Martha Libster is recognized as an expert on the historical and contemporary integration of botanical therapies and nursing care. She is the author of *The Integrative Herb Guide for Nurses* (book and CD-ROM) and *Demonstrating Care: The Art of Integrative Nursing*. She is an international speaker for health professionals and the public on topics including botanical therapies, integrative care, and healing traditions. Dr. Libster is Creative Director of Golden Apple Healing Arts, LLC, a holistic health resource and education network supporting public self-care, nurse-herbalism, and integrative healthcare. She has over 15 years of experience in the integration of conventional nursing and complementary therapies and has practiced in a wide variety of healthcare settings including six years in a holistic health facility where she was the Director of herb programs and emergency response. She is a practitioner and consultant in traditional Chinese and western herbal therapies. Dr. Libster holds a doctorate degree in humanities–health care history from Oxford Brookes University, Oxford, England, a Master's degree in psychiatric nursing from the University of Colorado with a specialty in infant–parent psychotherapy, and Bachelor degrees in dance education/movement therapy from New York University and in nursing from Mount St. Mary's College, Los Angeles, California. She is presently associate professor of nursing and associate director of the Center for Nursing History, Ethics and Human Rights at Purdue University. Dr. Libster can be reached at martha@goldenapplehealingarts.com or by FAX at 765-583-4498.